Then Life Took Control

'The personal nature makes it easy to relate to. The experiences are easy to empathise with and understand why you reacted in ways that you did. It's well written, honest and very gripping.'
Miss Clare French, PhD Student,
University College London

'I simply couldn't put it down, and I'm sure it will be compelling reading for fellow sufferers and healthcare professionals.'
Joan Deitch, Editor

This read is honest and open. It discusses a range of difficulties with Life in a refreshing way. I found it very inspiring.'
Carole Barclay, former Student,
Middlesex University

'The diaries are blunt and honest. They tell it like it happened in a 'no frills' way that I think a lot of people with long-term health conditions and carers will appreciate and respond to.'
Ben Hibberd, Mental Health Lead, City and
Hackney Carers Centre

Then Life Took Control

A Journal:
From Sickness to Wellbeing

SAM SHAKES

Nature Inspired Books

First Published in Great Britain in 2010

Nature Inspired Books
P.O. Box 66230
London E2 2BD

samshakes@thenlifetookcontrol.co.uk

www.thenlifetookcontrol.co.uk

A catalogue record for this book is available from the British Library.

ISBN: 978-0-9566378-0-2

Illustrations by Sam Shakes.

.

Printed and bound in Great Britain by
CPI Antony Rowe, Chippenham and Eastbourne.

Episodes

1998

Diagnoses – Confusion	9
The Loss and Gain of Living	28
Surgery: The Ruthless Remedy	44
An Unrecognisable Me	56

1999

A Strange and Chaotic Existence	69
Dilemmas, Changes, Realisations	98
Upheaval of Ideas – Distress of Changes	129
Déjà vu?	153

2000

Managing 'Madness'?	187
Changing 'Bad' Behaviour	226
Then Life Took Control	259
A Sense Of Freedom	309

Afterword	331
Acknowledgements	332
Inspirational Books	335

'We are made up of the stories of others,
And we all have a story to tell…
Here's part of mine…
And yours.'

1998

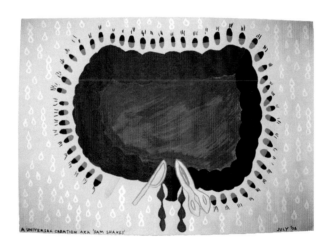

A UNIVERSAL CREATION AKA 'SAM SHAKES'   JULY '08

Diagnosis: Confusion

Sun 4th Jan '98

Gosh – back at University tomorrow! It's still sinking in that I'm a full-time student! Gave up work to commit myself solely to study (no in between with me – it's either, or!) would have found it too stressful to do both.

* * *

Mon 5th Jan '98

Attended a revision lecture, and wrote down everything. I'm so nervous about these exams, they'll be the first ones I've taken since school – ten years ago!

* * *

Tue 6th Jan '98

Feeling under pressure and stressed. Deadline for two essays is this Friday and I've got an exam next Wednesday!

I'm doing so much studying that I'm forgetting to eat and my stomach has been bloated, and very windy. I must start eating properly. Strange but when my stomach feels like this, I lose my appetite and eating sometimes makes me feel worse.

* * *

Thu 8th Jan '98

I've been eating more regularly, yet I'm still experiencing bloatedness, and wind in my stomach. I passed a brown slimy discharge that really stunk. Not a normal poohy odour, but a stench with an oxide smell. I must have 'cold' in my stomach.

* * *

Mon 12th Jan '98

I've noticed that I'm going from one extreme to the next – I've either got constipation or diarrhoea. Wonder if this is to do with stress and me

9

feeling under pressure (exam on Wednesday)?

* * *

Wed 14th Jan '98

Not sure how well I did, in the exam. My stomach was really bloated. Thankfully I didn't need to go to the toilet during the exam but I felt very sickly (and still do).

* * *

Fri 16th Jan '98

The diarrhoea is getting on my nerves. I've been about four times today, and it's making me feel very tired and miserable...

Thank goodness essays and exams are over.

* * *

Sat 17th Jan '98

The diarrhoea is becoming a problem. I'm finding it hard to relax when having sex with Barry (Boyfriend) – I'm scared that I'll pooh myself. So for the last week and a half, we haven't had sex.

I can't tell him about my fear of incontinence during the activity. He's asked a few times 'what's the matter?' And knows I'm having 'stomach problems', but doesn't relate them to me not wanting sex.

* * *

Mon 19th Jan '98

Tried having sex, but was too tense. I lied and told Barry that I didn't feel in the mood – that I was too tired. But the truth was that I was scared of poohing myself. He asked if me not wanting sex had 'something to do with him'.

* * *

Wed 21st Jan '98

Barry's getting on my nerves. Now he's accusing me of sleeping with someone else! I told him to 'stop being stupid', and still couldn't tell him that I was scared of poohing myself. I wish I could. And I wish he would leave me alone.

* * *

Thu 22nd Jan '98

Went out for a comedy evening and had to use the toilet a couple of times. I expelled a brown slimy discharge, with a lot of wind, and an oxide smell. When I passed this discharge, I made a sloppy farty noise (so embarrassing – the noise, as well as the smell). I tried to stop it, because I didn't want anyone outside, or next-door to hear. But I had 'no control'.

* * *

Fri 23rd Jan '98

Went shopping with Barry to Lakeside. I needed to use the toilet with urgency! My stomach was really bloated and it's so hard to control my bowels. As soon as I sat on the toilet my back passage exploded. Loads of that brown slimy discharge and oxide smell – and loads of noise. This is getting on my nerves.

* * *

Sat 24th Jan '98

Celebrated my Birthday in a Wine Bar. Drank a lot, which increased the wind in my stomach, and caused severe bloatedness. I expelled loads of that brown slimy discharge and now I'm getting cramping pains when I go. Wonder why this is happening?

* * *

Mon 9th Feb '98

New semester, and feeling very nervous at starting studying again.

* * *

Wed 11th Feb '98

I'm finding it difficult to manage study and relationships at the moment. Any spare time from sourcing books, reading or writing, is taken up sleeping. I feel so tired all the time.

I fell asleep in the library today for about two and a half hours! Usually, I can't sleep anywhere, but in bed. When I woke up, there was a woman sitting opposite me, smiling. I asked her if I'd been snoring, she said I had. I felt so embarrassed and joked, 'I don't know why I'm so tired.' She laughed and added 'it's these bloody books – I think they're a form of sedative!'

I told Barry that it would be a good idea if we had a break, just for a week. We've been arguing constantly, and most of the time it's to do with my short-temper (I feel so irritable most of the time).

Stomach has started feeling bloated, and I've expelled that brown slimy discharge, with cramping pain (again).

* * *

Sun 15th Feb '98

I must start eating a healthier diet. My bloated stomach is making me feel sick, and the cramping pains are more painful. I think the weird oxide smell, and brown slimy discharge is a result of my 'poor diet'.

I've been constipated for a couple of days, and I've been forcing – trying to expel, and now I've got piles (trust me to have similar genes to Mum)! Must get some Preparation H (ointment) for them. I've had piles for two weeks now, and it's very painful when I open my bowels. Bum must be very sore, because I saw 'blood around my stool' today.

* * *

Mon 16th Feb '98

Got exam results today. All my marks fell within the 2:2 classification! Not bad for the first set of results. The study and stress over the last six weeks was worth it. I've been studying a lot and have been worried about what results I'd get – now I can relax.

* * *

Tue 17th Feb '98

Met with Barry and never realised how much I'd missed him (haven't seen him for a week)! We ate at my favourite Indian restaurant, but eating spicy food proved to be a bad decision. I experienced burning in my stomach, followed by bloatedness, and dashed to the toilet to expel the familiar brown slimy discharge and lots of wind. I felt so ill – we had to leave early.

When we arrived home I rushed to the toilet again. I felt exhausted, irritable, and desperate to sleep. We tried having sex, but yet again, I couldn't relax. I thought that brown slimy discharge would explode out of my bum if I relaxed, and Barry pressing down on my bloated stomach, made me feel worse.

Leaving the restaurant early, and not being able to have sex, ruined our reunion. I was disappointed – Barry was disappointed. We ended up arguing. I told him we needed another break.

* * *

Fri 20th Feb '98

For the last few days I've been rubbing Preparation H on my bum (day and night), but it doesn't seem to be helping. I complained to Mum, telling her that 'the Preparation H doesn't work!' She said it's because I'm not inserting it into my bum. 'You need to insert the ointment into your bum,' she stressed. So I squatted in the bathroom, and inserted the tube in what felt like a pinhole to the passage of my anus. At first

I couldn't feel where to insert it – and it seemed impossible. I started sweating, my hands were shaking, and I began to feel sick, but I persevered – I had to do something to get rid of these piles. Eventually, I managed to insert the long white tube into my bum, and squeezed some ointment in. But five minutes later – I was on the toilet! After spending nearly twenty minutes trying to get the Preparation H in – it was out! I felt like crying. I wanted to insert more, but the thought of going through that pain again was unbearable. So I applied some ointment on my anus, and went to bed. Feeling miserable (inside and out).

* * *

Tue 24th Feb '98

Met with Barry after another weeks break. Yet again, I was feeling so irritable – I didn't even want him to cuddle me. I don't know why I agreed to met with him – I knew we'd end up arguing. 'You're so miserable and moany,' he shouted. 'I know,' I screamed back at him and asked him to leave.

Why am I feeling so bloody moody? I cried myself to sleep.

* * *

Thu 26th Feb '98

Now opening my bowels about four times a day, and what's coming out most of the time, isn't 'stool', but that weird oxide smell, and brown slimy discharge, with blood. I think the brown slimy discharge can be remedied by a healthier diet. And the expelling of blood will stop – just need to get rid of the piles.

* * *

Fri 13th Mar '98

Barry called and left a message on the ansaphone. I didn't call back, because I didn't have the energy to argue, and I'm feeling too sensitive to deal with any form of criticism.

* * *

Sat 14th Mar '98

5.30pm: expelled and there was so much blood. The water in the toilet bowl was tainted with it, and there were splashes on the sides. I think something is seriously wrong?...

I rang Sharaz (a friend) and asked her to come to Accident and Emergency (A&E) with me. At the A&E reception I gave a history of my symptoms. The nurse suggested that the bleeding from my back passage must be 'internal piles'. I felt so relieved. I didn't 'really' think there was 'something seriously wrong'. I left the hospital with no examination.

* * *

Sun 15th Mar '98

Neither my health nor mood is improving.

I've been thinking about Barry almost constantly, since Friday when he left a message. It's unfair to treat him the way I have, so I'm going to tell him it's better if we split.

* * *

Mon 16th Mar '98

Met with Barry, and told him the 'bad news'. He was shocked at my suggestion of splitting up. 'It's nothing to do with you, and I'm unsure why I'm being so miserable, but I think it might be something to do with me feeling so unwell,' I explained. He shouted, 'Well go to the fucking doctor's – instead of splitting up with me!' But I stuck to my decision. We split up today.

I thought about what Barry said, 'Go to the fucking doctor's'. But it was only two days ago that a nurse suggested I had 'internal piles'. I'm not going to the doctor's for 'internal piles' – 'severe cramps in my stomach' – and 'bleeding'.

* * *

Tue 17th Mar '98

Unable to go to University – too fatigued.

9.30am: decided to go to the doctor's, because although the piles have virtually gone, I'm still experiencing cramping pains in my stomach and passing a lot of blood from my back passage.

'When did you first notice blood in your stool?' the doctor asked. 'Not sure. About a week,' I told her. However, when I recalled the time it was actually over three weeks! She prodded my abdomen and carried out a finger examined in my anus. 'Ummm. I'm going to send a referral to hospital for further examination,' she informed. Sounded serious. 'Hospital'? 'Further examination'? I thought she'd simply give me a prescription – prescribe some medication to 'settle my stomach', and stop the 'bleeding', but she said she'd 'send a referral to hospital for further examination'. 'How long will I have to wait for an appointment?' I asked. 'Could take up to three to four weeks,' she informed. 'Three to four weeks' – I doubt I can carry on like this for 'three to four weeks'. Still, I'm glad she doesn't think it's anything too serious? She can't, otherwise she would have prescribed medication, or referred me urgently, I guess?

* * *

Wed 18th Mar '98

Now opening my bowels about six times a day, and getting severe colicky pain, and there's an increase in the amount of blood when I open. Sometimes I just pass blood, which drips from my bum – bright red. I'm beginning to wonder if 'internal piles' can get this sore? There is sooo much pain – and sooo much blood. Actually, I think 'something is seriously wrong'. But then the doctor would know, wouldn't she?

I felt shattered, but I still managed to go to University.

* * *

Thu 19th Mar '98

I must stop fooling myself. I'm going to the toilet six times a day, with blood – wind – mucus – pain, and now I'm vomiting. I brought up yellow bile this morning, vomited some soup and have just puked some water! I can't even keep water down?! I think 'something is seriously wrong'. This 'is' more than internal piles? Surely they can't make you feel like this? If these symptoms continue – I'll go back to the doctor's 'tomorrow'.

* * *

Fri 20th Mar '98

Had a restless night, experiencing fever and was woken this morning at 7am with the urgency to go to the toilet. More blood – wind – mucus – pain. I'm feeling fatigued and very, very ill. 'Something is seriously wrong'.

Made an emergency appointment. Met a doctor who I told of my history and of the 'new symptom of vomiting'. She told me there was 'nothing she could do, or suggest!' I left the surgery feeling angry. 'Something is seriously wrong' – and I'm not being listened to.

* * *

Mon 23rd Mar '98

Planned to go to University, but there was no way I could. Too tired – too sick. I need to sort this illness out – and I need to study!

I rang the doctor's and made an appointment for 'tomorrow'.

* * *

Tue 24th Mar '98

8am: Feeling too weak to go to the doctor's, so had to cancel the appointment. I stayed in bed hoping rest would remedy me.

5pm: resting has not helped – I'm feeling worse. Lots of – blood – wind – mucus – pain, and vomiting. Fuck! I need help! 'Something is seriously wrong'. But I haven't got the energy to find out – I'm so exhausted – mentally and physically. I'm crying as I write this.

* * *

Wed 25th Mar '98

Been up most of the night. And, blood – wind – mucus – pain, and vomiting almost constantly today.

7.05pm: I struggled to call Mum from bed, and when she entered my room I whispered, pitifully and crying, 'I can't take this anymore. I've got to go to A&E.'

11.05pm: returned from A&E. Professionals examined me with a Sigmoidoscope (an examination of the colon with the use of a light) and took biopsies. They suggested that I might have something called 'Colitis' (I think), but I was in too much pain, and too tired to be sure what they said. I have no idea what 'Colitis' is, and at the moment I don't care. I just want my bowels to stop opening and to get some sleep. They gave me tablets (Mesalazine), and told me that 'they were an anti-inflammatory drug, that should help'. I hate taking tablets, but I'll take these – 'for now'.

* * *

Mon 30th Mar '98

The tablets have helped, and this recovery came just in time because, I had to go to University today – I've got two essays that are due in on Friday – and I need to attend the rest of the week.

* * *

Thu 2nd Apr '98

2.45pm: Out-Patient's appointment at Lank's Hospital. The Consultant introduced himself as 'Mr. Bows'. He then confirmed diagnoses – I had 'Ulcerative Colitis (UC)'. When he said it, I snapped back 'Ulcerative WHAT?!' And he slowly repeated 'Ulcerative Colitis.' He said the 'Nurse Specialist (Toni Helpful) would explain what it was. Toni explained that UC was an 'incurable bowel disease'. I was dumbstruck. She gave me a prescription for more Mesalazine (two tablets to be taken three times a day – 'indefinitely') and Colifoam (a steroid enema – to be inserted day and night for the next seven days, to reduce the inflammation).

She said I 'might have to 'take tablets for the rest of my life'. There's no way I'm 'taking tablets for the rest of my life' – I'm only twenty-six. 'UC' – sounds serious. I knew 'something was seriously wrong'. But an 'incurable bowel disease?!' The appointment came to an end. Toni said I could contact her anytime by air-call (leaving a message at reception and be called immediately), but I doubt I'll be that desperate or in need. I'll soon be better – just a matter of finding out what's causing this upset, eating healthier foods, and resting. She handed me a leaflet. On the front it read: *Ulcerative Colitis and Crohn's Disease: The British Digestive Foundation.* How embarrassing! I tucked it deep in my bag – I didn't want anyone outside to see it.

Sharaz and Petrinella (friends) were waiting outside for me. They asked what the Consultant had said. I told them he diagnosed me as having some 'bowel disease' (too scared to say 'incurable'), and that it was suggested that I might have 'take tablets for the rest of my life!' They looked shocked – I was in shock, but laughed and said, 'that's what they say, but I'm not going to 'take tablets for the rest of my life'.

We went to the Indian restaurant as planned. I left doubled up in pain, and tried to laugh it off with the waiter, who assumed that the dish was too spicy for me!

When I got home, I rushed straight to the toilet where my bowels exploded – blood – wind – mucus – pain. I sat on the toilet and silently repeated in my mind, 'an incurable bowel disease – Ulcerative Colitis?' I felt like crying and a lump came to my throat, but I forced it down. What would crying do? Crying wouldn't take away the blood – wind – mucus – pain. Crying wouldn't rid me of 'an incurable bowel disease'.

I went to my room, and plucked out two of the hard burgundy synthetic tablets – and read silently Mesalazine. I really didn't want to take them, but the pain was so severe. I retched as I reluctantly swallowed the tablets. And, grudgingly went to bed.

* * *

Fri 3rd Apr '98

Woke up thinking about reading the leaflet that Toni had given me, but I really don't want to know anything about this 'so-called incurable bowel disease' they say I have. 'Disease?' I don't feel that ill. I'm sure they 'must be wrong'.

* * *

Sat 4th Apr '98

Having taken those dreaded tablets religiously for two days (twelve tablets in total!) I no longer have blood – wind – mucus – pain. Now my bowels aren't moving! I've decided to give my body a break from the pills. So I've stopped taking them. It can't be 'right' that my bowels aren't working – at all!

* * *

Wed 8th Apr '98

I was sorting out my handbag, and came across the leaflet Toni gave me. I read: *Ulcerative Colitis and Crohn's Disease*, then tossed it on the floor.

* * *

Fri 10th Apr '98

Must start looking for 'alternative remedies'. I'm sure a healthier diet and certain herbs can cure this so-called 'incurable bowel disease'. I can't rely on anti-inflammatory tablets and steroid enemas. They won't cure – merely suppress.

* * *

Thu 16th Apr '98

Haven't taken any of the prescribed medication for nearly two weeks, but today I've started to get that windy pain in my stomach. Shit! Wish I'd found out what alternative remedies are recommended for 'bowel problems' because now I'll have to use what they've prescribed (I can't bare to let my bowels get sick again). But I'm not going to take the tablets. I'll insert the Colifoam enema instead, that's better than taking tablets?

* * *

Sun 19th Apr '98

Been using the Colifoam enemas for the last four days, because I'm desperate, but the blood – wind – mucus – pain, is back. I'm going to start taking those awful tablets again, because I don't want this flare-up to get too rageful. But I'm going to take half the dosage (I'm sure I don't need as many as they say). I hate taking tablets.

Must recover in four days time, because I've an Out-Patient's appointment, and I want to be 'well', so they can 'leave me alone'.

* * *

Thu 23rd Apr '98

Attended the Out-Patient's appointment today and 'won!' Mr. Bows asked how I was, I told him 'fine'. He examined me and said that everything felt okay! He looked pleased with himself, glad that his prescribed medication had worked! He instructed that I continue taking Mesalazine three times a day (as I had been!), and that I needn't insert the Colifoam enemas twice a day anymore! Now I'm sure I don't have this so-called 'incurable bowel disease' they suggest I have. If so, why has it cleared up without continuous medication and with half the recommended dosage?

I think 'something is seriously wrong'. But I don't have an 'incurable bowel disease' (I think it's something less serious than that). I'm sure they've misdiagnosed. Now I've got to start remedying myself – naturally.

* * *

Fri 24th Apr '98

Decided to read the leaflet Toni gave me titled, *Ulcerative Colitis and Crohn's Disease*. The list of symptoms were constipation, diarrhoea, mucus, blood in stool, fever, loss of appetite, severe abdominal cramps and fatigue. I'd experienced all of these. I think they're right. I think I've got 'Ulcerative Colitis'.

* * *

Mon 27th Apr '98

Been numb for most of the weekend – in shock, and unable to write in journal. I spent most of Saturday and Sunday in bed. Can't believe I've got an 'incurable bowel disease' – well, I still don't think its 'incurable', but I am seriously ill.

I need to seek alternative remedies – 'I'm not going to take tablets for the rest of my life'.

* * *

Tue 28th Apr '98

Went to Health shop, and the library to research alternative therapies, and UC. I was pleasantly surprised when I read that UC is a 'civilised disease', and that the contributing factors are, 'a refined diet', 'sedentary lifestyle', and 'stress'. I can change all of these! All I need to do is eat a healthier diet, exercise and practice relaxing. These will cure me.

* * *

Wed 29th Apr '98

Purchased a book titled *Back to Eden* which is dedicated to curing ailments via herbs, roots, and barks. The author suggested that some of the causes of UC could be infectious organisms, improper mixtures of food that irritate the stomach and bowels, too much cane sugar, grease, white flour, eating too hastily, very soft foods, stress, and food cooked in aluminium utensils. The treatments suggested were herbal enemas, liquid diets, and homemade herbal teas six to eight times a day.

I've got a lot to change, my diet – eating habits – and cooking preparations. I feel under pressure.

* * *

Fri 1st May '98

Started drinking Aloe Vera juice. It's got a very bitter taste (I heaved as I swallowed it), but I'll drink it – if it's going to help. I've read that it's great for inflammation, which is all UC is – inflammation of the colon.

* * *

Sun 3rd May '98

Managed to drink some Aloe Vera this evening, but missed yesterdays, and this mornings dosage. I 'must' start taking it properly, if I want it to remedy me. Still, some is better than none at all.

* * *

Tue 5th May '98

Whilst speaking to Aunty Bernice (a few days ago) I mentioned that one of the suggested causes of UC was 'improper mixtures of food that irritate the stomach and bowels'. She said she would loan me a book titled, *Food Combining for Health: Don't mix foods that fight,* by Doris Grant and Jean Joice. They suggested that:

1. *Starches and sugars should not be eaten with proteins and acid fruits at the same meal.*
2. *Vegetables, salads and fruits should form the major part of the diet.*
3. *Proteins, starches and fats should be eaten in small quantities.*
4. *Only whole grain and unprocessed starches should be used, and all refined processed foods should be taboo – in particular, white flour and sugar and all foods made with them, and highly processed fats such as margarine.*
5. *An interval of at least four to four and a half hours should elapse between meals of different character.*

I've been cruel to my bowels.

* * *

Sat 9th May '98

Travelled 'all the way' to South London from East London to buy the recommended herbs to combat UC. I purchased Golden Seal, Yellow Dock Root, Burdock, and Periwinkle. Felt like a farmer coming from harvest, as I left the shop with my bags of 'bush!' Hope these will work.

* * *

Mon 11th May '98

Purchased a Douche Can which is equipment used to administer liquid enemas. I never knew such apparatus existed until speaking with an assistant in a herbal shop. And, I never knew people were carrying out such activities in todays 'civilised' society. A natural way to cleanse the colon.

* * *

Thu 14th May '98

Made up the recommended herbal enema and poured it into the Douche Can that was hanging from the shower rail via a hanger. It was recommended that you lie down to administer, roll from side to side, and retain it for as long as possible. I lay on my side in the empty bath and inserted the white plastic tube into my sore anus. I then turn the tap to allow the liquid in. It felt strange as the fluid entered my anus (my anus is a 'one way street' – 'exits' only!) and it felt cooling – and very refreshing. I held it in for about three minutes and had to dash out of the bath straight onto the loo – where my anus exploded the enema and lose stool out – with a vengeance! It felt so cleansing. I think these natural enemas are going to help.

* * *

Sat 23rd May '98

Stomach is feeling bloated! I'm pissed off with this, but I've only myself to blame. I haven't been drinking the herbal drinks, using the enema, maintaining a healthy diet, or managing my stress. I'm finding it hard to adopt these new habits. That's why UC has prevailed. The herbal drinks take so much time to prepare (and taste awful). I'm finding it hard to adopt a healthier diet. The University menu hasn't got healthy options and when I arrive home – I'm too tired to prepare food and so snack on what's available (which usually isn't healthy). And as for stress – there is always so much to do – and so little time (I can't 'laze' around relaxing). Actually, trying to change my lifestyle is causing me dis-tress.

* * *

Tue 26th May '98

I only take the prescribed medication in 'an emergency' – when my stomach feels like it's going to get upset. An 'emergency' emerged a couple of days ago (loads of blood – wind – mucus – pain), so I started taking those awful tablets. But I think I left it too late to recover in time for my next Out-Patients appointment (in two days time). Still, I'll go on full dosage and hope for the best.

* * *

Wed 27th May '98

Booked flight to Jamaica! I'll be there for three and half months. Despite having UC, I'm still going away. Not going to allow this so called 'incurable bowel disease' to put me off doing anything I want to.

* * *

Thu 28th May '98

Just returned from an Out-Patients visit – this time I 'lost'. Toni asked if I'd been taking the prescribed medication, and if everything was 'okay' – I lied and answered 'yes' to both questions. Then to my shock and horror she asked if she could feel my abdomen! I didn't want her to (because I was experiencing a flare up, and knew an examination would reveal this), but then I couldn't say 'no'. She prodded and pushed my abdomen and said, 'Your tummy feel's quite tender. Can I examine your back passage?' I thought, 'Shit – all will be revealed now!' Yet again I couldn't say 'no'. So, I said 'yes' and reluctantly, took the familiar position of laying on my side, with knees up, and buttocks out. 'Contact blood' on finger examination (revealing the flare-up)! Toni then asked if I'd been taking the prescribed medication regularly. I thought about lying again, but didn't want to, so I told her the truth – that I hadn't. I felt guilty and sad as I admitted the truth. I felt guilty that I'd lied – and very sad that I needed to pretend that I was 'okay'. Who was I trying to fool? Toni knew different – and unfortunately, somewhere, so did I.

* * *

Fri 29th May '98

Back on flipping medication! I've only got myself to blame. I haven't been drinking the herbal remedies, or been practicing relaxation. I must start.

* * *

Mon 1st Jun '98

Collected 'repeat prescription', which had been altered by Toni. She said she'd 'prescribed extra', since I was going away. When I gave the pharmacist the prescription, he sighed and informed, 'I haven't got the full amount, you'll have to come back.' Yet he handed me a carrier bag full of medication?! I thought, 'surely this is more than enough?' But,

I asked what the remaining amount was and he informed that I only had half the quantity prescribed! I thought 'my luggage will definitely be overweight with all this medication!' Must get rid of this illness – it's very inconvenient.

* * *

Mon 8th Jun '98

Today is departure day! Leaving to spend three and a half months in Jamaica and hoping the break from the stress of studying, London life and eating fresh food will be revitalising – and liberate me of UC.

* * *

TRAVEL JOURNAL

Mon 8th Jun '98

10pm: local time! I've arrived safely – in Kingston – Jamaica!

Opened bowels twice (blood – wind – mucus – pain).

* * *

Tue 9th Jun '98

9am: had a good night's sleep. The air is fresh and the temperature right – hot! For breakfast I had two juicy mangoes, and a sweet banana. These fresh fruits will cleanse my system – and boot out UC!

Opened bowels four times today.

* * *

Thu 11th Jun '98

Been in Jamaica for three days and I feel great! My bowels are more settled no symptoms of blood – wind – mucus – pain. I reckon the last flare-up was due to overwhelming stress. I had end of year exams, fearful of flying, and was very excited about travelling to Jamaica to meet unknown family.

* * *

Sat 13th Jun '98

Haven't opened my bowels for the last three days. I'm surprised, because I've been eating so much fruit, and thought this would make me go, and cleanse my digestive system. Maybe my bowels are taking a break, because they've been so active and sore over the last few weeks?

* * *

Wed 17th Jun '98

I'm not experiencing a flare-up, but I'm feeling very uncomfortable inside, due to constipation. It's now been seven days since I opened my bowels. I think it's useful to open bowels every day, since we eat daily? I need to get them working.

* * *

Fri 19th Jun '98

Used the Douche Can because it's now been over two weeks, and I'm still constipated and feeling really bunged up. I expelled small amount of sloppy stool, but it didn't reflect how much I've eaten in the last two weeks. Still, some is better than none.

* * *

Mon 22nd Jun '98

I've been administering enemas for the last three days. Bowels opened naturally – and the stool was normal, today! The stool was normal! It's been nearly six months since I've seen 'normal stool!'

* * *

Mon 6th Jul '98

I haven't written for over three weeks now. I've been busy relaxing on the beach, shopping, and socialising. And, I usually write at night, but here I feel so relaxed that all I want to do is sleep – and I do!

* * *

Thu 9th Jul '98

Been in Jamaica for over four weeks. I've been eating loads of fresh fruit and vegetables, doing lots of exercise, and resting. I feel great (and so do my bowels)! I've been opening them once a day and the stool is normal! 'The stool is normal!'

* * *

Mon 20th July '98

Haven't written in this journal for over a week! I think the 'need' to write is usually due to stress, and it offers a medium to off load. So, the lack of writing is a 'good' sign.

* * *

Wed 20th Aug '98

Over the last six weeks I've felt very well. I've visited several places, Kingston, Montego Bay, The Bob Marley's Museum, University of the

West Indies, Rose Hall, and Appleton's Rum factory. I've got so much energy! And, I'm wondering where this so called 'incurable bowel disease' has gone.

* * *

Fri 22nd Aug '98

For the last week, I've eaten at least three grapefruits per day. They're in season, and they taste beautiful! I feel great.

* * *

Tue 25th Aug '98

'Spoke too soon' (questioning where this so called 'incurable bowel disease' has gone'). My bowels have started playing up. I feel constipated, but I'm opening my bowels! A sticky black tar-like stool has been expelling along with small amounts of normal stool. I'm getting severe contracting in my sides, when I open my bowels (it feels like my insides are heaving, like when you vomit violently), and I've been experiencing fever. It's not the familiar abdominal pain, associated with UC and there's no blood – wind – mucus – pain.

* * *

Thu 27th Aug '98

Bowels aren't getting any better. I thought about taking those awful tablets, but because I'm not getting the familiar symptoms of UC (blood – wind – mucus – pain), I don't think it's worth it. I'll see what happens over the next couple of days. I'm sure things will settle down? Wonder what this is all about, if it's not UC.

* * *

Sat 29th Aug '98

Still constipated and only expelling small amounts of that sticky black tar-like stool. I'm still experiencing severe contracting in my sides, sweating and shivering. I've been using the Douche Can with water for the last two days (day and night), but it hasn't helped – the water is as clear coming out, as it is going in. Still no blood – wind – mucus – pain. I really don't know what to do. These symptoms don't reflect the so called 'incurable bowel disease', so I'm reluctant to take the medication. But if things don't improve soon, I'll start taking the tablets, because 'I don't know what else to do'.

* * *

Mon 31st Aug '98

I've been eating so much fruit hoping that this will relieve the constipation, but it hasn't helped, it's actually making symptoms worse. Still, I'm managing to get about. It must be the sun, sea, and fresh food that's boosting the energy. And, I can't afford to let constipation disable me, and allow experiences with Jamaica to slip by.

* * *

Tue 1st Sept '98

Started taking medication today even though symptoms don't favour UC, because 'I don't know what else to do' and I'm feeling desperate.

* * *

Sun 6th Sept '98

I've now been taking medication for five days, and bowels have really settled (just slight discomfort/soreness). I think this will ease by itself so I'm going to stop taking medication – don't want to over-do-it.

* * *

Tue 8th Sept '98

It's been two days since I stopped taking medication and my bowels have started playing up again! Wonder if my body has got used to me taking the medication? Or perhaps it's because I've been thinking about going home. I'm anxious about resuming study and I hate flying. Started taking medication again. I feel like a slave to this so-called 'incurable bowel disease'.

* * *

Sat 12th Sept '98

It's now been five days since I started taking the medication again, and it isn't working! I'm on full dosage, and administering the Colifoam enemas morning and night, but it's not helping. Actually, my bowels seem to be irritated by the enemas, because they open about five minutes after I've inserted them. This is so scary. The symptoms – and the fact that the medication isn't helping. My bowels are opening about seven times per day. I need to stop stressing – I need to relax.

* * *

Sun 13th Sept '98

I'm now opening my bowels about nine times a day, with lots of blood – wind – mucus – pain. I'm also sweating and shivering, and experiencing dizziness. The flight isn't until 5.50pm tomorrow, which seems like a long time. My fear of flying seems to have disappeared. I need to fly – I need to get home. I need to sort my bowels out. I feel very, very ill.

* * *

Mon 14th Sept '98

Departing Jamaica in a very sickly state. For almost the last three months – I've been well. I thought I'd be returning to London healthy and ready to resume study. But I'm leaving Jamaica feeling very un-well. Actually, worse than when I left London.

* * *

The Loss and Gain of Living

Tue 15th Sept '98

London – Heathrow.

1.15pm: arrived home. Mum and Dad had solemn expressions. Aunty Celia is dead?! My favourite Aunty and friend is dead?! They told me she 'passed away' last Thursday. Mum said everyone agreed that she should wait till I came home to tell me. I cried hysterically.

I went to Aunty Celia's home – for confirmation. I needed to 'see her absence'. Aunty Celia is dead? When I got to Aunty Celia's – she wasn't there, and her son's and our friend's faces disclosed the 'truth' – Aunty Celia was dead. I felt panic and then numb.

I left in a daze and I don't remember how I got home.

When I did arrive, I dashed to the toilet and expelled several times with the most force and pain I've ever experienced. I don't know what came out – and I didn't care. Aunty Celia is dead?

* * *

Wed 16th Sept '98

11.20am: didn't sleep much last night. Symptoms have got drastically worse. The severity of pain and I'm unable to control my bowels – I'm literally running to the toilet. I peered in the pan on few occasions to see what was coming out (I wish I hadn't) – fresh blood – lots of it. Still taking medication that isn't helping. I've opened my bowels about twelve times during the night and this morning. I feel physically weak – and mentally numb. And Aunty Celia is dead?

* * *

Thu 17th Sept '98

9am: my bowels are now opening about fifteen times a day and I'm

28

experiencing fever. Last night I sweat so much that I needed to change my nightie. It's been nine days since symptoms of UC have returned and they're getting worse. I'm not fond of orthodox medication, but felt in desperate need of help – so I called Toni. She said I should go and see her 'in clinic' – today! I thought she might advise over the phone (perhaps to increase medication). I visited her 'in clinic' and she prescribed an added drug (Prednisolone) to take for seven days, along with Mesalazine and Colifoam enemas! She said if I don't see any improvement after seven days – I should contact her 'immediately'. I don't want to take these synthetic drugs.

I must relax and seek some alternative remedies. I know this flare-up is due to distress – the thought of resuming study after such a long break. And, Aunty Celia is dead?

* * *

Fri 18th Sept '98

I want the death of Aunty Celia to be a nightmare. They told me four days ago that she was dead, but she can't be.

* * *

Sun 20th Sept '98

The Prednisolone seems to be working. I'm opening my bowels about ten times now, (it was fifteen times, three days ago). I'm sure I'll be better by next week. I can't wait for next week to come, so I can resume study and stop thinking about Aunty Celia.

I want to get back to normality – I want to be out of bed – I want to be studying – and I want Aunty Celia to be alive. And – Shit! I feel sooo ill.

* * *

Mon 21st Sept '98

What the fuck's going on?! Mum asked if I wanted to see Aunty Celia in the morgue?! 'No I don't,' I told her angrily. I don't want to hear anything about this 'death?'

I want to get back to normality – I want to be out of bed – I want to be studying – and I want Aunty Celia to be alive.

Still opening bowels ten times.

* * *

Tue 22nd Sept '98

Aunty Celia's funeral. The coffin was closed – I didn't see her dead? But they tell me she is, and I haven't see or spoken to her since returning. Still opening bowels ten times.

* * *

Wed 23rd Sept '98

Thinking about yesterday. The ceremony – the sad faces – the burial. And still it doesn't make sense to me. Where has Aunty Celia gone?

8.30pm: in bed trying to rest (again) – must get myself fit for University…

My bowels are now opening eight times per day.

* * *

Thu 24th Sept '98

It's been eight days since taking Prednisolone (extra medication) and I'm now opening my bowels just eight times a day. When I started taking this medication I was opening fifteen times.

Toni said I should contact her immediately if I didn't see 'some improvement' after seven days, but I have seen 'some improvement?' Well, I'm not eating much, since it increases my bowel activity. So, there hasn't 'really' been any 'improvement', because if I ate regularly – my bowel activity would increase. 'I hate this'.

* * *

Mon 28th Sept '98

Back at University. It was a struggle to go – I feel so weak, even after five days of lazing in bed! How much rest can a body need?!

I'm still opening my bowels about eight times a day, but the bloatedness and pain is less severe.

Still not eating much.

* * *

Tue 29th Sept '98

Went to University and couldn't concentrate on the lecture. I was worried about my stomach growling and having to rush to the toilet. Actually, going to University was a waste of time. Still at least I went.

* * *

Sat 3rd Oct '98

It's now been seventeen days since taking Prednisolone, and I'm still opening my bowels eight times per day. I extended the 'improvement' period of seven days, by ten hoping symptoms would reduce, but I'm getting weaker – I'm not able to eating properly – and I feel like a zombie. If this continues – I'll call Toni on Monday.

* * *

Sun 4th Oct '98

11.45pm: writing from a hospital bed! I was feeling so ill – and so desperate I 'had' to air-call Toni – today – on a Sunday! 'Hi, Toni. 'I've been taking the medication you prescribed for over two weeks now, and I'm opening my bowels eight times a day with loads of blood – wind – mucus – pain,' I informed nervously. 'Oh Sam, it sounds like you might need a more powerful medication to help this flare-up. I think you better go to A&E. You may need to stay in hospital for a couple of nights, so pack an over-night bag. I'll inform them that you're coming,' she instructed. I was in shock. 'Are you sure?' I queried. 'Sam, get yourself to A&E,' she sternly replied.

'I'm in hospital?!' It's scary that symptoms have been acknowledged as serious, enough to be admitted into hospital, but at least now I'll receive some relief, even if it does come in form of orthodox medicine. I use these remedies until I have the strength to medicate myself, with natural alternatives. And, I shouldn't be here too long. After tonight I'll have just one more night in here. Toni did say I 'may need to stay in hospital for a couple of nights'.

The nurse who escorted me from A&E to the ward had a terrible attitude. I asked her a few questions and she replied abruptly to all of them. I think she thought I wasn't ill (I certainly didn't 'look' sick). I felt like saying to her 'I don't want to be here you know, I'm sick'. But I didn't have the energy.

* * *

Mon 5th Oct '98

4.15am: woken up by a nurse pulling my hand. 'Can I take your Blood Pressure?' she asked with the attachment already around my arm! I was in such a nice sleep – and now I feel wide-awake.

8.45am: woken by two teams of 'specialists' (surgical and medical) from a deep sleep (having dosed off at 6am). The surgical team was 'headed' by Mr. Bows and the medical team by Ms. Suppressant. There were at least ten people around the bed. I felt swamped and frightened. One minute I was in a deep sleep – the next I was being gawped at – bombarded with a barrage of questions – my abdomen being prodded in the name of an 'examination' – and an anal inspection! Mr. Bows explained that I would be 'observed over the next few days'. 'The next few days?!' I told him I thought I'd be leaving tomorrow.

That Toni said I may need to stay in hospital for a 'couple of nights'. And I didn't feel sick enough to be 'observed over the next few days'. My expressions were ignored – or at least without a response worthy of remembrance.

* * *

Tue 6th Oct '98

7.30am: Ms. Suppressant visited. 'Hi Samantha, how are you? She asked cheerfully, opening a file at the end of the bed. 'No better,' I replied sadly. 'Ummm. Okay. Tell me, what's been happening?' she asked looking at me with interest. 'I've been opening my bowels about ten times, and every time I eat, it causes stomach cramps and bowel movement,' I explained. 'We'll need to do a Colonoscopy to see what's going on. We'll do it tomorrow,' she informed. My heart began pounding and I asked, 'What's a Colonoscopy?' 'It's a procedure were we insert a camera into your bottom,' she explained calmly and left. 'A camera into your bottom' – sounds flipping awful. I can't wait to get out of here.

* * *

Wed 7th Oct '98

They did the Colonoscopy – no sedation. It was so fucking painful – I screamed. They said I might need an operation?! Apparently my Colon is 'badly diseased'. I don't know what they mean by 'badly diseased'. But I'm not having an operation. I asked what percentage of my Colon was affected to try and understand the extent of the 'disease' – they couldn't say?! I'm sure they don't know what they're talking about. So, I'm going to have to keep a record of what's going on.

I opened my bowels ten times today (was only eight times when I arrived). I'm sure this increase is due to the stress of being in here. Constantly being disturbed, prodded, pricked, monitored, and questioned. 'I need to get out of here'.

* * *

Thu 8th Oct '98

4.50am: I want to know what's going on (well, part of me does). So many measurements, blood tests – blood pressure – monitoring of temperature – and bowel openings. So many medications, painkillers – antibiotics – and anti-inflammatory drugs. No-one's telling me the 'results' – and I'm not feeling any 'improvements'.

Toni said I'd only be in here for a couple of nights, but I've been in this dreaded place for five now. 'I need to get out of here'.

* * *

Fri 9th Oct '98

I was put on intravenous medication – Hydrocortisone steroids. Right into the vein – through my whole system – and my brain. I doubt this will help – nothings helped so far. I hate orthodox medication. I need to seek natural remedies.

Today I opened my bowels nine times (an 'improvement?'), but I'm losing weight (can't keep nothing in). This situation is crazy. 'I need to get out of here'.

* * *

Sat 10th Oct '98

Today I opened my bowels eight times – things seem to be improving. I passed formed stool today – and I ate – and I haven't vomited.

* * *

Sun 11th Oct '98

Opened my bowels ten times and vomited yellow bile! One minute I'm getting better – the next it's all going fucking wrong. I thought these steroids were supposed to help?

I must ask friends to seek out 'natural remedies and start taking them'. I don't care that orthodox views of medication are not fond of natural remedies, and are concerned with how they interact with 'their remedies'. Because, orthodox medication isn't working.

* * *

Mon 12th Oct '98

10.30am: dietitian visited. She prescribed Enlive drinks, which are apparently 'nutritional' and easy to digest. She advised that I eat extra 'fatty snacks', like biscuit's and cakes to gain weight?! Sounded crazy to me. What about clogging up my arteries?! Still, I guess it wouldn't do too much damage to eat a few 'fatty snacks', since I rarely eat what she suggested. So I had a buttered scone with jam and a cup of Chamomile tea. Apparently, Chamomile is good for relaxation and I'm experiencing a lot of stress in here. It's also recommended to reduce inflammation, so I'm drinking loads of it, since UC is just inflammation of the colon.

3.30pm: told Ms. Suppressant that I'm experiencing dizziness and swollen joints. She explained that these were side-effects of Hydrocortisone!

I've only opened my bowels five times today. Wonder if this reduction is due to orthodox medication or Chamomile tea? I'm confused about this improvement. I'm happy that my bowel activity has reduced, but I don't appreciate the side-effects of orthodox medication – 'recovering' in one area and promoting 'sicknesses' in another. 'This situation is crazy'.

* * *

Tue 13th Oct '98

Appetite is definitely improving. Today I managed to drink two Enlive drinks, ate a cheese sandwich, a packet of crisps, and a piece of cake!

I told Lucy (Senior House Officer to Ms. Suppressant) that I was still feeling dizzy – that my joints were now so sore, it was difficult to bend or stand – and that I was now experiencing tightness in my chest. She said it was 'unfortunate' that I was experiencing these side-effects, but at least my bowel activity was improving! I thought 'Great! – I'll soon be passing out, become disabled and have a heart attack! But at least I'd be rid of UC!' 'This situation is crazy'. And I've now been in this place for nine nights – Toni said I might need to stay for 'a couple'.

* * *

Wed 14th Oct '98

Told Toni I've been experiencing severe burning when opening my bowels, for the past few days. She examined my anus, and said I had a 'Prolapsed Pile' and prescribed GNT ointment to reduce the pain. I read the leaflet that came with it. Possible side-affects included headaches, and light-headedness. More medication – more possible side-effects. 'I need to get out of here'.

I asked Mum what I could do about my pile (a specialist in the field, having suffered with piles for over twenty-six years). She suggested placing ice between my buttocks and gently pushing the pile back in – I'll try this natural remedy.

Bowels opened seven times today. The first opening was induced by water! This is getting frightening. My body is rejecting water! I think I'm 'very sick' – but I will get better? I haven't been able to eat anything today.

* * *

Thu 15th Oct '98

An x-ray showed stool lodged in part of my Colon, and I was prescribed a laxative – seems ironic when I'm opening my bowels so much! However, I expelled a black-tar-like stool (similar to that passed in Jamaica) and feel better (not so bunged up). Hope this will spur recovery. 'I need to get out of here'.

3.30pm- a ward nurse told me that I need to 'mobilise'. 'Get out of bed, and walk around,' she said in a commanding voice, implying I was lazy. If only she knew how tired and weak I am: I can't 'walk around!' Even if I tried, my Pile is so big and sore – I'd have to walk like I'd been sitting on a horse for a week!

Today I opened my bowels six times – and haven't eaten anything, 'again'.

* * *

Fri 16th Oct '98

3.30pm: Ms. Suppressant explained that I'm not getting any better, and that I need to consider surgery as an option! I told her I 'was' getting better, since I was now only opening my bowels about six times. She said, 'But you're still unable to eat, and you're losing weight.' I told her, 'I'll be fine, once my bowels clear-up. It's because my bowels are sick that I'm not eating,' I reassured. She asked to see the observations I'd been recording. I handed them to her. They noted times I'd eaten (and what), number of bowel openings (describing what was expelled, i.e. sloppy stool/blood/mucus), number of times vomited (and what, i.e. bile/food/tablets) and medication taken. She handed the observations back to me with a heavy sigh and said, 'Sam, you're not getting better.' I didn't reply. My notes and body 'said', 'I wasn't getting better'. But I can 'get better?' And to 'get better' doesn't include having surgery – 'I'm not that sick'.

* * *

Sat 17th Oct '98

2am: woken up with severe cramps in abdomen. My nightie and the bed sheets were soaking wet with sweat – I had to change them.

My bowels opened ten times today, with a fifty/fifty balance of sloppy stool and blood. Still unable to eat – food is making me feel sick – I've lost a stone – and I'm feeling very miserable. I've been in this place for thirteen nights now. 'I really want to go home'. Toni said I might need to stay for 'a couple'.

* * *

Sun 18th Oct '98

Wasn't able to speak much to visitors today, and when I did I was defensive. Dad asked if I was 'feelin beta today', and I snapped, 'No.' His eyes looked sad and his facial expression displayed hopelessness. I felt guilty. Why was I snapping at him? It wasn't his fault that I wasn't 'feeling better'. Dad called one of the nurses and told her that he wanted to meet with the doctors. 'Look pun she! She can't keep nothin in! If she nut vomiting – she passin trew de back passage. Me naw understand wat dese doctors a do. She nut gettin any beta, and me want fee see de doctor in charge,' he ordered angrily. The nurse replied, 'It will have to be tomorrow, since it's the weekend.' 'Right, mek sure you write dat me want to meet wid hymn,' Dad replied in a stern tone. The nurse wrote in my file.

I haven't been able to tell friends and family what the Consultants had advised (that I'm not getting any better and that I needed to consider surgery). I felt sad when Dad said that, I'm 'nut gettin any beta', because I know I'm not. But I can get better?!....

Today my bowels opened ten times. No sloppy stool – No mucus – 'just blood'.

* * *

Mon 19th Oct '98

7.45am: surgical and medical team visited. I was unable to respond in my usual helpful manner, because I was feeling so miserable. Ms. Suppressant picked up on my mood and tried to humour me. 'Are we feeling a little depressed?' she said with a chuckle, but I didn't think her comment was funny. I felt like telling her to piss off', but 'my health was in her hands'.

Today I opened my bowels thirteen times.

* * *

Tue 20th Oct '98

Dad met with Mr. Bows who explained everything to him. He said the teams had informed me that the medication wasn't working – that they had discussed surgery with me – and that I'd been reluctant to acknowledge the serious condition of my health. Dad looked me straight in the eyes and I felt guilty, because I hadn't kept him informed. I didn't want to tell people what was going on, because I knew they'd encourage me to have surgery, once the doctors convinced them it was 'the only way I'd 'get better'.

After hearing what Mr. Bows had said, I knew what Dad wanted to say. He wanted to say that I should have the operation. So before he could say it, I said in a sombre tone, 'Dad, I'm not having surgery.'

I opened bowels just seven times today – I think I'm getting better (again).

* * *

Wed 21st Oct '98

Today I vomited breakfast, undigested tablets, and green bile. But although I've vomited – I am getting better. The reduction in my bowel activity says so – I've only opened my bowels five times today.

* * *

Thu 22nd Oct '98

7.30am: feeling totally exhausted. There's far too much disturbance, and routine in this hospital. When they're not checking my blood pressure, temperature, or pulse (throughout the day and night) – I'm woken up for breakfast, lunch, or dinner! When the monitoring or meals are not causing disturbance, then doctor's visits are.

11am: Mum came to visit and I told her that 'I can't stay in this place any longer – that I needed a break – and that I needed to go home'. She didn't think it was a good idea, but I insisted, and kept repeating, 'I can't stay in this place any longer'. I went to the Nurses Station and told them that I wanted to go home 'today'. They said I should wait to speak to one of the Consultants.

1pm: Ms. Suppressant visited. I told her that I was going home. She tried to discourage me, by saying, 'Samantha, you're not going to get better by going home.' I explained that the hospital environment was disturbing and that I thought part of my illness was due to me not getting ample rest. And, I told her I thought I was only going to be in hospital for a 'couple of nights' – and that I'd now spent eighteen! I insisted that going home was 'for the better' – and discharged myself.

* * *

Fri 23rd Oct '98

9.30pm: glad to be back at home with familiar surroundings and com-forts. My own room – don't have to tolerate the disturbance of ward activities, or company of other patients, and their visitors. Cosy carpets – that I can walk on without having to wear slippers due to cold lino, and the risk of contamination from dirty floors. The kitchen – I can eat when I like – and what I like! Don't have to store food in case I get hungry, when breakfast, lunch or dinner isn't 'served' and there's no staff available! I'm snuggled under my quilt with the soothing smell of fabric conditioner. In these conditions – I'm guaranteed a good nights sleep. And, best of all there are no measurements – no timetable – no routine – and 'I'm in control'.

* * *

Sat 24th Oct '98

7.30am: had one of the best nights sleep, in what feels like a very long time.

Started the day by drinking 'Periwinkle tea' (which is another herbal drink recommended to reduce inflammation). It tastes awful (just like all the other herbal remedies), but, I'll drink it, because it's supposed to help.

Today I've opened my bowels ten times (double the amount since leaving hospital). Wonder why the symptoms are getting worse – still I'm feeling better 'mentally'.

Dad saw me on the landing, crouching over in pain, and hobbling to the toilet and looked scared. He said he didn't think me coming home was a good idea, I ignored his comment.

* * *

Sun 25th Oct '98

Today I opened my bowels fifteen times, and vomited once! My body feels so weak and I'm expelling a lot of blood. Periwinkle doesn't seem to be helping – in fact it seems to be making things worse!

Dad suggested that I return to hospital, today. I do need help. But back 'to hospital?!' I wasn't getting better in there, and I'm scared to go back, because their 'help' means 'surgery'. 'I'm not having surgery'. Still, I told Dad if there was no 'improvement' by tomorrow – I'd return.

* * *

Mon 26th Oct '98

Back in fucking hospital! I've opened my bowels twenty times – vomited five times – and have a high fever! Been drinking plenty of water and herbal teas, to purify my body of the toxins from the medication, but my detox doesn't seem to be working. Nothings working! The natural remedies – the bed rest – the orthodox medication. For fuck sake! What's going to make me better (tears are rolling down my face)?

2.30pm: Mr. Bows visited with a team of five students. 'Oh, Sam, you're back. Tell me what's been happening,' he said, sitting on the bed. 'I've opened my bowels twenty times, vomited five, and have a high fever, since Saturday,' I replied wearily. He tapped my shin and said, 'Right let's examine your abdomen.' I lifted my nightie to allow the examination to take place. I wasn't wearing any knickers and so my vagina was exposed. Mr. Bows hastily covered me with the bed sheet and looked embarrassed – and so did the students. But, I didn't care that my vagina was exposed – I'd lost my dignity. 'So, they could all see my vagina?! It was 'just a fucking vagina!' Right now – all I need is to 'get better'.

* * *

Tue 27th Oct '98

Took Buscopan (an anti-spasmodic drug) to reduce bowel activity, but

I'm wondering if that was a good idea. Will it not mask what's happening inside? Suppose something serious is happening? How will I know?

Today I opened my bowels nine times – yesterday it was twenty. Wonder if this drastic reduction is due to Buscopan? And I'm wondering how 'good' this is as a life-long remedy.

* * *

Wed 28th Oct '98

Had an ultrasound scan today (not sure what for). So many tests – so little results – such tiny benefits.

7.30pm: asked 'permission' to leave the ward and walked to the front of the hospital. I stood at the entrance feeling like a prisoner. I want to leave this place, but I'm 'forced' to be here – UC dictating. I didn't want to return to the ward and sat at the entrance to the hospital reception in a daze feeling miserable, and sad. I was pleasantly 'interrupted' by Mr. Bows (I like him) who came and sat with me. 'We were talking about you today. We really think you need surgery,' he advised with a sad expression and reiterated sternly, 'You need to consider surgery.' 'What are you still doing here at this hour? You came to see me at 8am: it's now nearly 8pm! Haven't you got a life outside of this place?' I asked in a jovial manner, ignoring his comments. 'You people are my life. See you tomorrow,' he replied tapping my shoulder as he left.

As I sat alone again, and repeatedly heard Mr. Bows's comments, 'We really think you need surgery.' – 'You need to consider surgery.' But, I'm not having an operation. I've only opened my bowels ten times today – and vomited just twice. 'I'm getting better?'

* * *

Thu 29th Oct '98

Dietitian came to check–up on my intake of Enlive drinks. She said I wasn't drinking enough. I wanted to tell her that it's a waste of time drinking them, because I vomit them moments later. But I couldn't be bothered, she'd only tell me to keep trying. So what I'll do is provide the drain with these drinks.

Today I opened my bowels eleven times with no pain and can't feel the movement. I guess this is due to Buscopan and don't like the suppressing. When you're opening your bowels eleven times with blood – wind – mucus, you're naturally supposed to feel pain. I've vomited four times.

* * *

39

Fri 30th Oct '98

Still reluctantly taking Buscopan – still got a prolapsed pile. Opened my bowels nine times today – and vomited twice.

* * *

Sat 31st Oct '98

I've decided to stop taking Buscopan, because it's now causing nausea, which has kept me awake. I think it's 'safer' to take Paracetamol to take the edge off the pain, and feel the movement of my bowel. Today I opened my bowels eight times and vomited 'only once'.

* * *

Wed 4th Nov '98

12am: nil by mouth, because of CT scan (examination providing pictures of internal organs) planned later.

10.30am: had to drink a liquid, which was to assist in gaining clear results of the examination (more junk into my system). The scan was terrible. They tried to administer some dye intravenously, but it caused so much pain – I screamed. They stopped the investigation and looked disappointed. 'Was it that painful?' one of the operators asked in a sarcastic tone as she came out of the 'protective cabin'. I wanted to say 'No, I just felt like screaming,' but I didn't answer.

As I sat waiting for the porter to take me back to the ward – I felt guilty – I'd wasted their time. And, questioned, 'maybe it wasn't that 'painful' – perhaps I was imagining it?

When I returned to the ward I expelled three times in twenty minutes. 'I need to get out of here.' I've opened my bowels sixteen times today. But I haven't vomited (which is good).

* * *

Thu 5th Nov '98

9.15am: Mr. Bows visited. I told him about the new symptom of my fingers locking stiff, and that I sometimes can't bend them. He advised this was another side-effect! He asked how many times I'd opened my bowels yesterday. I didn't want to tell him the truth (sixteen times), but I did. I didn't want to be honest, because I knew what he was going to say. I guessed he was going to say, 'you need to consider surgery' – and he did. Yet again, I ignored his suggestion, and informed excitedly, 'I didn't vomit yesterday.' 'But did you eat?' he questioned. I didn't answer, because I hadn't – and he knew. 'Routine tests are indicating that you are getting very sick,' he added in a serious tone, and left.

Today I 'only' opened my bowels eight times – 'I am getting better'. Must tell Mr. Bows tomorrow. 'I'm not having surgery'.

* * *

Fri 6th Nov '98

11am: Ms. Suppressant visited. She recommended a second Colonoscopy, but told her 'I'm getting better' and refused to have it. 'I only opened my bowels eight times yesterday,' I explained. She didn't say anything, but took my Medical File from the end of the bed, and sat beside me. She opened the file and began reading the results of tests (x-rays, blood, electrolytes). The results meant nothing to me, and I sensed she was trying to convince me that I wasn't getting better. However, I insisted that I felt 'I was getting better' – and that's what was important. She asked me to sign medical notes where she had written that I was 'at risk of perforation' and that I had 'refused a Colonoscopy'. She warned that should anything fatal happen to me over the weekend – they wouldn't be responsible. I signed the statement with confidence, because 'I am getting better'.

4.15pm: Mr. Bows visited. 'Sam, you really should have let the medical team carry out a second examination,' he expressed pitifully. 'But I'm getting better. I only opened my bowels eight times yesterday,' I said enthusiastically, and added sternly, 'I'm not going through that pain again.' 'Ummm. You didn't have sedation with the last Colonoscopy and your colon was very sore. Will you let me carry out the investigation on Monday? I promise it won't hurt. I'll give you double dose to sedate you,' he said in an almost pleading voice, and continued, 'We're very worried about you. We need an up-date on the current activity and severity of the disease.' I reluctantly agreed to have it done. 'They needed an update – I didn't'.

* * *

Sat 7th Nov '98

9.20am: I'm in total shock. Just been weighed – I weigh just six stones and three pounds! I couldn't believe it, so went to the bathroom to look at myself in the mirror – to confirm this. 'The image' displayed the evidence. Black sunken eyes – protruding cheek bones – knee caps sticking out! How and when did I get to this?! As I stared at the reflection of me – of Sam? – Huge tears rolled out of my eyes and ran down my puny face. And, I cried almost all day.

4.30pm: 8pm: I told visitors that 'I wasn't getting better' – and that the 'Consultants were right' – I now had 'no option', but to have 'surgery'. It was time to stop fighting – the battle was over. 'UC had won'.

* * *

Sun 8th Nov '98

9.30am: I told the doctor on call that I'd decided to have surgery. He said I'd 'made the right decision' and wrote a note in my file stating that I'd decided to have the operation. It was now official – 'I was going to have surgery'. I don't really know what this operation entails, but I do know that I'll be shitting in a plastic bag from my abdomen.

Yet again, I cried almost all day – and repeatedly told visitors that 'I now had no option', but to have surgery. Most of them didn't know what to say, but tried to pacify with comments like, 'At least you'll be better', and 'it'll be alright, they do these operations all the time'.

11.15pm: I'm sitting in bed and looking at the many cards, flowers, and gifts around me, and recalling the comments offered by visitors. And I've just realised that 'Family' – 'Friends' – 'Wealth' – or 'Possessions' can't help me. My physical body has lost the battle with UC and none these can help. And I've just realised that 'I have no control of what will happen to me'. I think there's 'something' or 'someone' else in control of all of this? And it feels strange to admit, because I can't see this 'something' or 'someone' else, but sense it – 'Spiritually?'

* * *

Mon 9th Nov '98

7.30am: Mr. Bows came to visit. I immediately started crying and blurted, 'I weight just six stones and three pounds! I never realised I was 'that sick'. If I knew on Friday, I would have had the second Colonoscopy, then. I've got no option, but to have surgery'. He wiped the streaming tears from my cheeks, and calmly said, 'Lets see what the Colonoscopy shows.' His manner was sincere and tinged with a hint of sadness. I'd never experienced such compassion from a white person – and something inside my heart shifted. And, my perception of the importance of 'race' disappeared.

1.30pm: taken to the Day Care Centre for the examination on the bed (too weak to walk). 'Here's your double shot of rum – now's the coke,' were the words of Mr. Bows, as he injected the drugs that induced unconsciousness. When I woke up he was looking pitifully at me, and said, 'I'd like to operate tomorrow, even though the Theatre List is full. Your colon is very inflamed and at risk of perforation.' His words had no effect. I was too weak to reply and wasn't 'in charge'. And, I'm going to let that 'something' or 'someone' else in control take care of this situation.

4pm: Toni came and stuck a transparent plastic square on the right hand side of my abdomen, and with a felt-tipped marker placed an 'X' on it. She explained that this was where the 'stoma' would be formed.

And although I'd seen pictures and been told what a stoma was 'I still didn't really know what she meant'.

7pm: Mr. Bows visited to explain 'the procedure', but I didn't want to know, or care. I was going to let that 'something' or 'someone' else in control take care of this. I sat looking at him blankly, and so he directed his speech to Dad sitting in the visitor's chair, and who was keen to know 'the procedure'. I heard snippets. '...Won't bleed too much'... – 'a risk...' – '... infection...' He then said, 'Sam, I think you're putting on a brave face.' I didn't answer, but forced a smile. This wasn't about 'bravery'. It was about me not being able to continue like this – it was about me 'doing' or 'dying'.

* * *

Surgery:
The Ruthless Remedy

9.30am: Today is the day of the operation. They're going to remove my colon?

10am: Aunty Bernice arrived to be with me until 1pm: until I to go to 'Theatre'.

10.45am: had severe pain in my abdomen and felt the need to expel. As I approach the toilet I went dizzy and just about managed to sit on the seat, where my bowels violently exploded – 'nothing'. I then had a hot flush and lost my vision, but could 'see' bright white specks in darkness. I shouted in a panic, 'I can't see – I can't see', and began hyperventilating. Aunty Bernice rushed in the toilet and calmly said, 'Alright Sam, put your head between your knees.' I sat on the toilet for about ten minutes – in a panic.

12.15pm: the Anaesthetist visited and I told him about the severe pain and incident in the toilet. I asked him if he was sure that I was well enough for the operation. Can't remember exactly what he said, but the implication was that I was too sick, not to have it. Wonder if I'll wake up from this operation? Still, surgery may not kill me, but UC looks like it could.

12.35pm – Sherilyn (my cousin) came and prayed for me. She asked that 'God protect me' and that 'the surgeons be guided by his wisdom'. She knew that 'something' or 'someone' else was in control of all of this.

1pm: a nurse entered the room and a porter swiftly followed behind her. 'They're ready for you,' she announced. My heart started racing. The porter began wheeling the bed (and me) out of the side room – the nurse and Aunty Bernice followed. They were 'ready for me', but I wasn't 'ready for them'. I wanted to change my mind – but, I wanted

44

to get better. I felt like screaming 'I've changed my mind – I don't want to have surgery', but I wanted 'to get better'.

The nurse, porter and Aunty Bernice seemed to be marching, as I was wheeled along the cold corridors. Suddenly, there was an abrupt halt at heavy double doors marked, 'Theatre – Only Patients and Staff Beyond This Point'. Aunty Bernice lent forward and pitifully whispered, 'See you later,' and gave me a hug and kiss. I felt like crying, as I wondered if I would 'see her later'. The nurse and porter pushed the bed into the heavy doors and we entered an empty cold area. The porter disappeared round a corner leaving myself and the nurse alone. She smiled at me, awkwardly. I heard the porter say 'Samantha Shakes' and moments later he returned with the Anaesthetist who smiled and said, 'Samantha Shakes?' I tried to answer 'yes', but no sound came out, so I nodded. He then asked, 'is your date of birth, the twenty-fifth, of the first, nineteen seventy two?' I nodded again. It was as though my 'spirit' didn't want to be part of this – so my voice wouldn't work. It didn't want 'Samantha Shakes' born on 'the twenty-fifth, of the first, nineteen seventy two' to have surgery. The Anaesthetist wheeled me through to another area, where Mr. Bows was and I felt a slight sense of relief at seeing him. He gave me the 'thumbs-up' sign – I nodded and forced a smile. The Anaesthetist inserted a syringe into the cannula on my hand, and said, 'Don't fight it Samantha.' I whispered 'I won't.'

8pm: woke up in the familiar side room on the ward. The lighting appeared to be very bright. Mum and Dad were in the room with me, but Mark (my brother), Sidiki and Doreen (my sisters) were hovering at the entrance, and peering in with fearful faces. I wondered why they looked so scared and was perturbed by their expressions. What's so scary – I thought? I wanted to say 'come in', but I couldn't get my mouth to work. I wanted to wave to them and indicate that they should come in, but my arms wouldn't work either. There was a tube in my nose with a bag collecting bile from my stomach – there was a tube in my throat attached to a feed bag – another one was in my hand for antibiotics – another attached to a pain control machine – one attached to a bag of blood – a catheter was attached – and I was wearing an oxygen mask. I felt stifled and restricted. I tried to take the mask off to breathe better, but Dad came over and stopped me. 'No, na tek it awf, Sa-man-ta. It fee help you', he said in a tone that sounded almost like a whisper. But, the oxygen mask didn't feel like it was helping – I felt like I was suffocating. And, I wanted to say 'I can't breathe with this over my face', but couldn't – and my heart began to race with panic...

* * *

Wed 11th Nov '98

3am: woke up to see Dad sitting in the chair in the corner of the room,

45

smiling at me. He walked over to me and whispered, 'You al-right?' I nodded and in croaky voice replied, 'Yes.' I felt guilty that Dad was here at this hour, but I was glad he was. I'm finding it difficult to breathe, and need someone to watch over me (in case I stop). I noticed I don't have that familiar nagging in my abdomen.

1.50pm: a physiotherapist visited. She made me get out of bed and sit on the chair. She said it would make me 'feel better'. She taught me how to clear my chest and lungs, by taking deep breaths and exhaling violently. It felt so uncomfortable. My chest felt loaded with phlegm (due to surgery?). She explained that I needed to 'sit up and be mobile', if I wanted to 'get better'. 'Phlegm will collect on your lungs if you don't sit up,' she sternly warned. Sounded serious and a wave of panic struck. 'I felt so weak – I couldn't 'sit up and be mobile', but I want to 'get better' and I don't want 'phlegm to collect on my lungs'. When she was leaving I asked her to help me back into bed. 'Don't you want to sit out for a bit longer?' she asked. I replied, 'No.' 'It would be good if you could,' she said in a harsh tone. I shook my head and she reluctantly helped me return to bed. I felt disappointed that I couldn't 'sit out for a bit longer' – I want to 'get better', but I 'needed' to lie down.

4.15pm: Sharon (new Stoma Care Nurse) visited and asked how I was. I told her, 'I was tired', hoping she would leave, but she stayed and asked if she could examine the stoma. She seemed to stare and fiddle with the stoma forever, through a large clear plastic bag attached to my abdomen, and she looked intrigued. I was irritated at her curiosity and angry at my lack of interest in this 'new thing pouring shit out of my abdomen'. So, I forced myself to look at 'the stoma', but saw 'nothing'.

5pm: Mr. Bows and Ms. Suppressant visited with their team of students. 'How are you feeling?' Mr. Bows asked towering over me. 'Tired,' I replied, pausing as I tried to breathe. 'And, I don't have that nagging feeling in my abdomen.' 'So you're feeling better already,' he suggested with a smile and looking round at his colleagues. 'The operation went well, Sam. Have you got any questions?' I shook my head. 'See you tomorrow, then,' he said tapping my shin and left.

* * *

Thu 12th Nov '98

11.15am: woken by a nurse tugging on the large clear plastic bag attached to my abdomen. She was emptying a greeny/brown liquid (my new shit) into a measuring jug! It felt very intrusive and I thought 'I must do this myself' – I can't have people managing my stool – I'm not a baby!

I'm feeling very irritated by feelings of hunger (I haven't felt hungry

46

for a long-time) so this is a good sign of recovery. I asked if I could have something to eat, and was told I couldn't?! That I could have just 10ml sips of water! I feel like a fucking child! They're managing my stool – I have to ask for permission – to eat – and to leave the ward! I'm a flipping 'adult' – and a 'patient' – not a child! I feel 'totally out of control' and I 'really fucking hate this'.

9.30pm: had the urge to open my bowels and panicked. I thought my bowels wouldn't be active anymore? That everything would now come out of the stoma? I grabbed a cardboard sick bowl and struggled hastily out of the bed. I stood with the bowl placed under my bum, and expelled a mixture of fresh blood, and pinky discharge – that filled the bowl. Shit! Where had all that come from – and what was going on?! I thought about buzzing for a nurse, but I needed someone to see this 'now' – I couldn't wait for them to answer my call. So I hobbled to the Nurses Station and showed a nurse my discharge who didn't look impressed at my offering. She advised that this was 'residue from surgery' and that she didn't 'think it was anything to worry about'. 'Residue from surgery?' What the fuck did that mean?! And I didn't care what she 'thought'. I told her that something might be going wrong inside, since it's only been two days, since surgery. She said she would show it to one of the doctors when they visited 'later'. 'Later!' I hobbled back to my room and sat worrying. 'Later?' I 'needed' to know what was happening now.

* * *

Fri 13th Nov '98

3am: woke up feeling upset and angry. Their aftercare treatment is shit! Still only allowed sips of water and I'm so hungry that I'm now feeling sick and light-headed. And my joints are very swollen (due to steroids), restricting me from bending and standing (again).

I buzzed for a nurse. When she arrived I told her that I had swollen joints, and was feeling very sick. She examined my knees and ankles, and said, 'They're not swollen, Samantha.' I was shocked by her conclusion. 'Not swollen?!' I could see they were – and I knew swelling was a side-effect of the steroids. Unbelievable – nursing staff can't identify swollen joints! Now I'm convinced these people, who are 'caring' for me don't know much, or what they're doing, so, I've got to start looking after myself. I told her to stop the intravenous steroids and antibiotics. 'How am I supposed to get better, when I'm being pumped with this rubbish and no food?!' I angrily asked. She didn't answer, but looked at me with troubled eyes as she stopped the flow of medication.

3.45am: the nurse returned. She tried to comfort me by saying, 'You've been through the worse, Samantha. Everything will be okay.' I know she was trying to 'help', but she sounded patronising. How did she know that I'd 'been through the worse' and that 'everything will be okay?' Did she have UC? – Was she shitting from her abdomen?

8am: Mr. Bows visited with his team. 'How are you?' he asked with a smile, as he read my Medical Notes. But before I could answer, he said with shock and disappointment, 'Samantha, you've stopped the treatment!' I looked him straight in the eye and retorted angrily, 'Yep! I've stopped the treatment. I'm not getting any stronger, or better, because I'm not eating... Being fuelled with just medication is making me feel sick. I need to eat!' He looked alarmed at my outburst and calmly explained, 'When major surgery takes place, the stomach stops working, and it could be fatal if you eat before it is ready to receive food. You can carry on having 10–30ml sips of water. If you continue to tolerate these, then you can have clear fluids. You must continue taking the steroids. It's very dangerous to stop this treatment abruptly. It needs to be gradually reduced,' he informed. 'Sam, you won't be on this medication forever, just see it as a part of your road to recovery,' he reassured in a comforting voice.

When the team left – I cried hysterically. It could be 'fatal if I ate before [my stomach] was ready to receive food?!' And I 'must continue taking the steroids', because 'it's very dangerous to stop this treatment abruptly?' How can it be fatal to eat?! And how can steroids with nasty side-effects be a medicine?! This is crazy. And now I have no choice, but to let them dictate. Now only they know how to deal with this unnatural and mutilated body. I fell asleep – crying.

* * *

Sat 14th Nov '98

Yesterday, I sipped loads of water, hoping I'd be 'allowed' to have clear fluids for breakfast...

7.30am: breakfast was served. 'Look, I've drank another 30mls. Mr. Bows said it was okay for me to have clear fluids, if I was able to tolerate 10–30ml sips of water,' I eagerly told the nurse, holding up my empty plastic measuring cup. She reached for my Medical Notes and I thought 'Oh here we fucking go. She's not going to listen to me, but adhere to the out-of-date notes'. She said, 'the notes say you're only to have '10–30mls of water'. I repeated as calmly as I could, 'Mr. Bows said it was okay for me to have clear fluids, if I was able to tolerate 10–30ml sips of water – and I have. Those notes were written before he said this.' She replied, 'I have to go by what the notes say,' and left.

Spurred by frustration – I started crying. What was the point of me drinking all that water, if I was still unable to start on clear fluids – 'now'. I need to get better – 'now' – and I need more than water and medication. I need food to help my recovery (my body tells me so). This 'Aftercare' is hindering my recovery. I thought hospitals were a place for people with ill health to get better?! I need Mr. Bows to visit 'now'. I need him to approve that I can have clear fluids. 'This is crazy.' I need permission to drink 'clear fluids?!'

9.30am: peered out my room to see if Mr. Bows was coming...

9.50am: out of bed again – looking for Mr. Bows, but there's still no sign of him.

10.15am: walked around the whole ward in search of Mr. Bows, but nursing staff tell me he still hasn't arrived yet.

11.20am: shit (woke up in a panic) – I'd dosed off! Hope Mr. Bows hadn't visited me whilst I was sleeping! I hobbled hastily to the Nurses Station and blurted, 'Has Mr. Bows visited?' 'No, we've not seen him yet,' one of the nurses replied. I returned to bed feeling relieved.

11.50am: Mr. Bows still hasn't arrived (he usually visits in the morning). Hope he comes before lunchtime (12.30–1pm) else I'll miss another opportunity for clear fluids.

12.15pm: I'm trying to read, but can't. All I can think about is having clear fluids and what time Mr. Bows will arrive.

12.45pm: I walked to the entrance of the ward and peered out of the windows. Still no sign of him.

1pm: lunch is being served and it smells lovely. Lovely? Hospital food smells lovely?! I must be really hungry! My stomach is going crazy with hunger pangs and making me feel even sicker.

I wanted to ask one of the nurses when they expected the doctors to arrive, but was afraid to go out and see the food, because I thought of stealing a lunch off the trolley. But remembered Mr. Bows saying it could be 'fatal if I ate'. So, I waited until they'd finished serving before I went out onto the ward. I tried not to look at people's lunch, but couldn't resist. Poached fish (that looked like rubber) – boiled potatoes (full of black bits) – carrots and cabbage (soggy and water logged) – Mmmm, looks delicious?!

2pm: surgical team arrived (without Mr. Bows and too late for clear fluids served at lunchtime). I was feeling really pissed off. I eagerly told Harry (Senior House Officer to Mr. Bows) that I'd been able to tolerate up to100mls of water and he said I could have clear fluids at dinnertime! I was so happy (even though I had no idea what 'clear fluids' meant – they had to be better than just water!). Harry advised that 'clear fluids' was soup without foods. He said I should pick out 'all the food' in soup. I asked if I could have fruit juices, tea, coffee, milk, yogurts, since these didn't contain food. He said I couldn't, and that I should continue sipping water, before and after my soup. He said he would review my diet tomorrow, once observations had been made of how my stomach had reacted to 'clear fluids'. 'How my stomach had reacted to clear fluids?!' Sounds ludicrous – how would a hungry stomach react?!

2.30pm: its three and a half hours till dinner is due. It feels like 6pm will take 'forever' to come. I considered sleeping to pass the time away, but haven't been able to, due to hunger pangs, and fear of missing dinner. I tried reading, but couldn't concentrate. I read the same page three times, but still couldn't grasp what I read! So I sat in bed – staring at nothing – and thought about eating food again.

6pm: dinner has arrived! It smells really nice. Wonder what the soup of the day is...

6.30pm: still waiting for my 'clear fluid' – soup! Dinner never takes this long to distribute. I went to the Nurses Station and asked where my soup was. 'There's nothing for bed six. Did you order dinner yester-day?' she asked in a blasé tone. 'No. I wasn't allowed to eat yesterday, so didn't order.' 'Well meals must be ordered a day in advance. So there's nothing for you,' she informed. My heart skipped a beat and my head started pounding. I snapped, 'I've got to have a soup! I haven't eaten for six days and it's making me sick.' 'Alright, Sam, calm down. We'll get you something to eat, as soon as we can,' the nurse calmly replied. She sent an agency nurse to find me a soup from another ward. The agency nurse returned and gave me a complete dinner! I imme-diately started gulping the soup. I was so tempted to drink the orange juice, and have a piece of bread (more than 'clear fluids'), but I resisted. The soup had onions in it, but didn't pick them out, because they were well cooked and I didn't view them as 'food'. The soup was beautiful. It was a great appetizer – and I felt very hungry after having it. I wanted – no needed more. Knowing the agency nurse was unaware of my restricted diet, I asked her if there was a spare soup, since I didn't want anything else from the meal. She ignorantly went in search of a soup, and returned with one! I knew I shouldn't be having another one, but I felt sooo hungry, and thought, a bit more liquid won't hurt. I started on the second soup, and finished it. I really wanted – no 'needed' to eat something heavier. My appetite had been opened and I felt ravenous. I thought 'a piece of bread won't hurt and was about to take a bite of the bread roll, when the nurse 'looking after me' entered the room. I quickly placed the bread back on the tray, hoping he hadn't seen it in my hand, but he had. 'Samantha! You know you're only allowed 'clear fluids. You could make yourself very ill,' he shouted rushing over to me and snatched the tray away. 'I was only going to eat half of the tiny roll!

I'm so hungry,' I retorted. 'You'll be okay. You won't die from hunger. Your IV fluids will keep you going,' he replied angrily and left. My stomach felt cheated. After being deprived of food for nearly a flipping week – it was teased with a couple of light soups – and wanted – no needed more. I felt like crying, but what for? – Food?

* * *

Sun 15th Nov '98

7.30am: Doctors visited. 'How are you feeling Samantha?' Harry asked with a smile. I replied in a miserable tone, 'I tolerated the soup yesterday, but it wasn't enough. I was still hungry afterwards.' Harry chuckled (I don't know what amused him – what I'd said wasn't funny?). 'Okay, you can start having light meals – a low residue diet. That means you can have any fluid you like, and light meals in small portions. Cereals like Rice Crispies or Corn Flakes, as opposed to Oats or Bran Flakes. For lunch – mashed potatoes, and small amounts of meat/fish – no vegetables,' he said. This was good news and I was eager for breakfast to arrive. I sat thinking what I'd have when it did. 'Fresh orange juice' – followed by 'cereal' – and then a cup of 'tea' – what a treat!

8.15am: breakfast arrived and I consumed all of the above, but it wasn't a treat – it was like punishment. The orange juice and tea caused a burning sensation in my stomach. And the Rice Crispies caused bloatedness and nausea. I vomited! I'm not supposed to feel sick after eating – I'm supposed to feel better! Shit! I can't fucking eat?! I felt so ready for food, but my stomach is telling me something else. Can't let the doctors know about this – they'll say I'll have to stop eating again. So, I poured the orange juice, cereal and vomit down the toilet, and disposed the vomit bowl in the bin.

When the nurse came to collect the tray, I said, 'That was the best breakfast ever! I feel so much better after eating!' (I had to do this so it would be noted that I was eating and tolerating foods – that I was getting better – that I could go home). 'Good,' she replied. 'What did you have?' 'Orange juice and cornflakes and I'm going to finish off with my tea,' I lied with a smile, looking at the cup. She made notes in my file. And when she left – I poured the tea down the sink.

* * *

Mon 16th Nov '98

9.30am: Physiotherapist came and hassled me. She made me, sit up in a chair – walk up and down the ward – and climb stairs! She said I would get stronger by exercising. I wanted to stay in bed. I haven't eaten enough to gain the strength to do exercise.

2.30pm: Sharon came to teach me how to change the bag. To change

51

the bag? There was another one?! This was forever?! Even though I 'know' it's 'permanent', I was still 'hoping' that this stoma would eventually go. Like the other attachments that had disappeared over the last few days, the bag collecting bile from my stomach – the feed bag – the antibiotics, – the pain control machine – the catheter – and the oxygen mask. But, this 'demonstration' of 'how to change the bag' made me realise that, this 'sticky plastic attachment and stoma with shit pouring from it' will be a permanent fixture. 'I hate this'.

* * *

Thu 19th Nov '98

10.15am: Surgical team came to check how the incision along my torso was 'Healing'. They removed the metal staples from the cut and it split open! 'It's because of the steroids, they can sometimes slow down the healing process', they explained after the event! If they knew this, why the heck did they remove them so soon?! Now I have a weepy wound covered with gauze. I suppose if I bend, or move too much, it will open up completely, and I'll see my stomach? Now I'm definitely not going to do anything, but lay in bed, regardless of what they say about 'being mobile'. I know they'll think I'm being 'difficult', but it's so obvious that 'they don't know what they're doing'.

3pm: Sharon visited. She wanted me to change the bag by myself. I didn't want to, but I didn't want her to either (I don't want anyone cleaning up my shit). I asked her where the soap was to clean my skin properly. She said I shouldn't use soap to clean around the stoma, just water to avoid skin irritation! So, I rubbed the skin harshly, trying to remove all the adhesive, and clean off all the shit – without soap?! She said, 'You don't need to get it 'all' off, if you rub your skin that hard, you'll make it sore.' No soap – and no rubbing! – I felt so dirty – I had to keep this 'thing' as clean as possible. Didn't she understand? – I had shit coming out of my abdomen – for fuck sake!

* * *

Fri 20th Nov '98

Mr. Bows said I can go home tomorrow! I've been in here for seven weeks (minus three days break at home) and I can't wait to be 'released' and back at home! Sharon visited and gave me some information. An IA journal – A booklet titled 'Going Home with an Ileostomy – and a leaflet with the heading 'Ulcerative Colitis and Crohn's Disease: The British Digestive Foundation' (already had the last leaflet – given in April – when I was first diagnosed). As I put the latter leaflet in my bag, I thought, 'It's too late for 'information' now – the damage has already been done.'

* * *

Sat 21st Nov '98

4pm: I'm home! In my newly decorated bedroom (complete with nice smelling fabric conditioned bed sheets) – I can smell the aroma of Mum's flavoursome cooking – and have enjoyed the welcoming of sisters, and brother.

7.30pm: lying in bed thinking. 'When Mr. Bows said I could go home yesterday, I thought, 'I can't wait to be released and back at home!' But now I'm feeling scared – really, really scared. Suppose I can't cope with this 'thing' on my abdomen? – Suppose there's 'an emergency?' Ironically, part of me felt 'safe' in hospital – and part of me wants to be back there – hospital feels more like home. And, I can't believe I'm feeling like this.

* * *

Sun 22nd Nov '98

Changed the bag today. I wanted to change it yesterday, but couldn't face it, and our bathroom is no 'home' for a stoma. There's nowhere to put the appliances (unlike at the hospital, where there were shelves and clinical cupboards to store stoma bags, plastic bowls and gauze). And, there's no lino flooring that can be easily cleaned if shit ends up outside of the toilet bowl (how thorough can you clean runny shit out of carpet?!). Our bathroom is far too cosy and comfortable for a stoma – it needs somewhere 'clinical' and 'practical' to be 'dealt' with.

When I took the bag off, the stoma started shitting and squirted onto my leg, and nearly on the carpet (I jolted back so the shit would end up in the toilet bowl). Every time I cleaned around the stoma, it started shitting. I tried to stop it by pulling in my stomach, but it continued. For a few moments, I sat and watched the shit pour out – out from a red fleshy thing on the side of my abdomen. And as the moments passed – my amazement increased. 'I'm shitting from a red fleshy thing on my abdomen?' It was disgusting. I began feeling frustrated, 'When would the shit stop pouring out?!' 'When would this nightmare be over?' Every time I attempted to put the bag over the stoma – it started spurting out shit! On one attempt shit went on my finger! I felt 'hysterical' inside. I wanted to scream: and shout – and cry. But for the sake of the family and for the sake of needing to 'exercise some control' – I didn't.

* * *

Mon 23rd Nov '98

1am: still experiencing colicky pains. They started yesterday about 4pm (one hour after eating) and have gradually got worse – hope it's just indigestion.

1.45am: getting severe cramping and there's no stool in the bag – just liquid. I didn't think I'd experience abdominal pain after surgery, since I no longer have a colon – no longer have UC. Wonder if something technical is happening inside – something to do with surgery.

2.15am: the pains are unbearable and I haven't experienced pain like this even with UC. I definitely think this has something to do with surgery.

2.35am: vomited green bile. Woke Mum up and told her that I needed to go to hospital. She packed a hospital bag (nightie, knickers, toiletries and slippers) and called for an ambulance.

3.05am: in A&E. The Consultant prodded my abdomen and inserted his finger into the stoma. He told me the stoma had stopped working. 'The stoma can stop working?!' He said I was to have 'nil-by-mouth' until they were, 'Sure what was going on' and to 'give my bowels a rest'. He said the symptoms 'could be' a result of adhesions – a blockage – or a kink in the bowel. Intravenous fluids were prescribed and I was offered Pethidine (pain relief), but refused (I want to feel what is going on). The Consultant asked what I'd last eaten. 'Rice with kidney beans, broccoli, roast potatoes, and lamb,' I informed. 'Don't you think that was a bit much?' he asked in a tone that stupefied me. I didn't answer. But thought, 'Did he think I wanted to get 'ill' again? If I'd thought it 'was a bit much' I wouldn't have eaten what I had – would I?! What the fuck is going on?! I thought this operation was supposed to make me better?! But now, I've got more to consider than UC – 'Adhesions' – 'blockages' – 'kinks in my bowel'.

4.35am: taken to Cut-up Ward (I'd only left two days ago). Thinking about what the Consultant in A&E had said with regards to what I had eaten. 'Don't you think that was a bit too much?' I thought of the advice regarding a 'low residue diet' and realised that perhaps it 'was a bit much' (bowels sore and in need of rest) – and maybe 'I'd caused all this'. 'I hate this'.

5.25am: woke up to find stool in the bag and iron capsule! Stoma is working and I feel a lot better. I think it started working due to the Consultant inserting his finger into the stoma. Great 'natural' remedy. I'll know what to do next time – 'stick my finger in the stoma!'

10.30am: Sharon visited and suggested that the blockage could have been caused by the iron capsule that I took yesterday, since it was un-digested and quite large. 'It might have had trouble getting through the stoma,' she advised. 'The blockage could have been caused by the iron capsule?' I want my health back – so, 'I need to take supplements. I need to combat anaemia and restore my energy (I feel so tired – I'm sure I'm lacking iron)'. Now I don't know what to do for the 'best' – I might cause a 'blockage', if I take supplements that may help regain my health. 'I hate this'.

* * *

Wed 25th Nov '98

9.30am: Mr. Bows visited. He examined my abdomen. 'Well Sam, looks as though things have settled down. It appeared to be nothing more than a blockage'. 'Nothing more than a blockage'. 'Nothing more than a blockage' had me in severe pain. 'Nothing more than a blockage' was enough to have me back in hospital for two days. And, 'nothing more than a blockage' had me back on intravenous relief! He continued, 'From the notes I can see that it might have been caused by an iron capsule. Why are you taking iron?' 'I think I might be anaemic, because I feel so tired,' I explained. He flicked through my Medical Notes. 'All your blood tests were fine.' Your tiredness is probably a result of the anaesthetic and having had major surgery. Don't expect too much from yourself. It's only been fifteen days since surgery and you were very ill. It could take up to three months before you really start feeling well again. You don't need to take supplements,' he advised. It's amazing (I thought). They (the medics) think they can dictate what I 'should' and 'shouldn't' be doing even when I'm out of hospital…

1.30pm: discharged.

* * *

55

An Unrecognisable Me

Sat 28th Nov '98

4.30pm: in my room feeling very miserable. Returned home four days ago and 'should be happy', but I'm not – I feel so isolated. I can't believe people are 'out there' walking around with stomas. And I can't believe people are living a 'normal' life. I think people with stomas must be 'indoors people', because I've never seen them. But Sharon told me that people live 'normal lives' and suggested I contact IA (Ileostomy and Internal Support Group) to speak to someone who has a stoma.

7.30pm: decided to contact IA (although it's Saturday) – couldn't wait until 'business hours' – I needed to speak to someone – 'now'. I nervously dialed the number, hoping I wouldn't receive an ansaphone message. 'Hello,' a man with a jolly voice answered. 'Hello, can I speak to Rod please?' I nervously asked. 'Speaking,' the man replied in the same jolly tone. 'Oh, hi – my name is Sam. My Stoma Nurse gave me your number – she said it would be okay to call you – I had a stoma formed eighteen days ago,' I rapped. 'Okay. How are you finding it?' he asked adopting a calm tone. 'Well. I don't like it – I'm scared that the bag may burst – or the clip undoes – and I can't believe that people live 'normal' lives with a stoma,' I blurted without taking a breath. 'Oh,' he replied and continued, 'Well the bag can burst and there are the occasional batches of faulty clips, but this rarely happens. I live what people call a pretty 'normal' life… I have a job, children, and go on holidays.' But he sounded too 'normal' – and so did his life. How could you go outdoors and live 'normally' with shit hanging from you, and with a 'weakened body'? I wasn't convinced that he had a stoma so asked, 'When did you have your stoma formed?' 'In nineteen-eighty-two. So I've had mine for sixteen years,' he shared. 'Why don't you come along to our Annual General Meeting to meet me and a few others?' he invited. I said I'd 'think about it'. I disconnected the call in shock. He'd had a stoma for sixteen years – and he was still okay? This man was working – looking

56

after his children – going on holidays – and assisting to run a support group. He was 'living a normal life' and I thought if he can – so can I.

* * *

Mon 30th Nov '98

My friend Sonia filled out an application form for 'Incapacity Benefit. I didn't want to apply for this 'support', but Sonia said I should because, I was 'entitled to it'. I've never 'claimed benefits' in my life. 'Incapacity Benefit'. So now it's official – I'm 'disabled' – 'Physically' – and 'Financially'. More 'dependency'.

5.30pm: Experiencing severe pain (like the pains on Tues 24th). I suspected another 'blockage'. So I've stuck my finger in the stoma (like the Consultant did in A&E). I've pushed my finger directly in, and around, and up and down.

9.10pm: pain is increasing and still no stool – and I've now vomited...

* * *

Tue 1st Dec '98

12.50am: back in hospital (I've only been home for five days). The x-ray didn't show 'adhesions' – a 'blockage' – or a 'kink in the bowel', but something wasn't right. When they said 'nothing showed up on the x-ray', I wondered if I was 'imagining the pain', but my vomiting and swollen abdomen confirmed I wasn't. I asked why this is happening. 'Why does the stoma stop working?' I was again told that it could be 'adhesions, a 'blockage', or a 'kink in the bowel'. But, basically, they were 'suspecting' (which is very frightening, since they've mutilated me, and now nature doesn't know what to do). For fuck sake! I don't want to become a 'revolving-door patient', who's in and out of hospital all the time – who knows the staff on first name basis – and is familiar with the routine of the wards and hospital policies. I've been back in hospital twice (in seven days) and hospital is more familiar than home. And, I thought this operation was supposed to make me better?

* * *

Wed 2nd Dec '98

Sharon advised that I avoid certain foods (at the moment), since my diet might be causing the problems. She gave me a leaflet of the 'forbidden foods':

Wholemeal bread, pastry or biscuits	*Wholemeal cereals*
Wholemeal cereals	*Wholemeal and brown rice*
Wholemeal or spinach pasta	*Pulses including peas and lentils*
Green beans	*Baked beans*

Green vegetables, i.e. lettuce,	*Sweetcorn*
cabbage and spinach	*Celery*
Cucumber	*Onions*
Heavily fried foods	*Skins on all fruit*
Fruit with pips in, i.e. strawberries,	*Pineapple*
raspberries, kiwi fruit	*Popcorn*
Nuts...	

Mostly healthy foods and the foods that I like, and I'm wondering what I can eat.

4.30pm: Doctors visited. 'How are you feeling?' A young Student doctor quizzed sounding insincere. 'Better,' I replied. 'Can I feel your tummy? He asked, leaning forward pulling up the bed sheets, and raising my nightie without waiting for a reply. 'Ummm, you don't feel tender,' he agreed and advised, 'I think you can go home.' I asked if they were sure, this could have been due to 'adhesions', a 'blockage', or a 'kink in the bowel?' Can't remember the answer and basically wasn't convinced. I don't think they know what's going on. If they did then, 'Why aren't they able to rectify me/this?' 'Why are there so many 'reasons' why this operation is displaying not to be a 'remedy'?' They've mutilated me and now they're unable to help. And, I'm wondering if surgery went well like they say it did – it doesn't feel like it. 'I hate this'.

* * *

Thu 3rd Dec '98

7.30pm: at home and scared to eat anything. I don't want to cause another 'blockage'. Mum keeps trying to encourage me to eat. 'Just a little something', she keeps suggesting and she's getting on my nerves. She doesn't understand the fear of spurring a blockage, and having to endure excruciating pain, or the trauma of being in hospital. Eating has too many consequences – right now, 'eating is not healthy'.

* * *

Fri 4th Dec '98

12pm: feeling very hungry, so ate a yoghurt and packet of crisp (low residue). Not much nutritional value in these, but I guess something is better than nothing?

I read one of the information leaflets that Sharon had given me, because I still don't know 'exactly' what they've done to me....

> *Usually all the colon is removed due to disease.... The ileum is brought to the surface of the abdomen to form the stoma... This is where faeces will now pass from the body... there is no sphincter muscle around the stoma, therefore you will have to wear a bag to collect the faeces...*

Ohhh! So, that's what they've done to me?! They've 'removed my co-lon'.... And, 'the ileum [has been] brought to the surface of the abdomen to form the stoma'.

* * *

Sat 5th Dec '98

I'm concerned that I've not been eating healthy foods, and can get vitamins in me, via liquid supplements, or by bursting the capsules. So I asked Mum to buy liquid iron, calcium, and Evening Primrose Oil. As soon as she arrived home, I gulped them down – one after the other. Hopefully, these will boost my battered body and surge the recovery process.

* * *

Sun 6th Dec '98

6am: just weighed myself to assess my progress. I wish I hadn't. I weigh just five stones and six pounds! 'Five stones and six pounds'. I looked at myself in the mirror to see if this weight was right. It was – I looked terrible. I don't want anyone to see me – and I don't want to see me. Back to bed with quilt over my head.

* * *

Wed 9th Dec '98

3.30pm: Sharon visited me at home. 'You're in bed!' She remarked with shock. 'I still feel weak, Sharon,' I replied defensively. But, the real reasons for me being in bed were that I looked terrible – I didn't want to speak to anyone – and, I didn't feel confident going outside shitting from this 'stoma'. 'You need to go outdoors and walk to get stronger. You should be going out every day, and walking for about fifteen minutes,' she exclaimed. When she left, I sat feeling angry. 'Go outdoors' (she couldn't be serious?). With shit pouring from my side, inside a plastic bag?

7pm: thinking about Rod and his 'normal' life, and about Sharon telling me that '[I] need to go outdoors and walk to get stronger.' I think 'I'm pathetic.' I need to 'stop feeling sorry for myself'. And, I need to adopt a 'low residue diet'. And, I need to 'go outdoors and walk to get stronger'. And, I need to have a 'normal' life. And, 'I need to stop shitting from my abdomen'. I'm crying. 'I hate this'.

* * *

Fri 11th Dec '98

Since, weighing myself (five days ago), I've felt 'depressed?' I need to 'snap out of it', but I can't. I wonder if these mood swings are to do with the medication (I remember in hospital hearing the doctors tell Mum and Dad that a side-effect of steroids are mood-swings). But I'm not experiencing much 'swinging' – I'm stuck in 'miserable' mode.

* * *

Sat 12th Dec '98

I've been spending all of my time in my bedroom. I don't want anyone to see me – and I don't want to see me.

I've created a hospital setting in my room:

- I've got four pillows behind me (similar support to the metal head-rest on hospital bed).

- I have a spare blanket folded up at the bottom of my bed (I usually just have a quilt on my bed, but I've made the bed resemble the hospital bed covering (there was always a cotton sheet, and a blanket at the bottom of the bed).

- I've got a basin placed at the side of my bed (cardboard sick bowel).

- I've got a bucket to pee inside my room (there was an en-suite toilet in the room at the hospital).

- The blinds are set to allow just enough light in, promoting a dusk shade (in the hospital the room was never brightly lit, nor ever in darkness. There was a constant 'shade').

- I cleaned out one of the my drawers, and filled it with clinical items (sterile water; disposable wipes; syringes; incontinent pads; circulation socks; adhesive tape; etc).

- There's a lamp that keeps away the darkness at night (like the light above my head in the hospital).

- There are chairs placed at the foot of the bed (visitors chairs).

- My slippers are at placed at the side of the bed, so I can slip them straight on (in hospital I never wanted to place my feet on the cold dirty floor).

I have a pole that I bang on the floor to alert family in an 'emergency' (hospital buzzer)!

I'm also practicing the hospital mealtime routine. I'm watching the time and thinking, 8.30am: should be eating breakfast... 12.30pm: should be eating lunch... 6pm: should be eating dinner. And when I don't eat at these times I feel agitated.

* * *

Sun 13th Dec '98

3pm: went outdoors for the first time, since being discharged from hospital (ten days ago), with a bag for shitting in, hanging from my side. I 'had' to go to the doctor's to deliver a prescription for appliances. Mum and Sidiki offered to take it, but I'm fed up of people doing things for me – for the sake of this stoma. Still, I was glad the doctor's was only a five minute drive away and that Trevor (x-boyfriend) drove, because I was worried that people could see the bag or that it might leak. As soon as Trevor stopped the car outside the surgery, I moved as quickly as possible. I darted out of the car – posted the prescription – and was sat back in the car (out of breath), in what seemed like a lifetime to me. 'Blimey, that was quick,' Trevor said when I got back in the car. 'Was it?' I quizzed.

I had a good talk with Trevor. Got loads off my mind, and feel a lot better. I told him that I couldn't see me coping, when it came to sex. 'I can't imagine having sex with this bag on the side of me,' I said. He laughed and said, 'Can't see you coping without having sex!' And I laughed. I laughed?! This was the first time I'd laughed regarding an issue with the stoma. And I continued, 'No, seriously. What will I do with the bag?' I didn't expect him to have an answer, but he replied, 'Don't you just fling it to the side?' 'Oh,' I thought, 'of course you do.'

* * *

Mon 14th Dec '98

Went to University with Brendon (friend), who drove. I'm keen to catch-up on what I've missed and want to resume study in February when the second semester starts. I need to gain 'some normality'. Still I'm worried about incidents that might happen like, suppose the bag leaks – bursts – or the clip undoes – or there's no toilet when it's time to empty – or the stoma makes a noise and people hear it. I keep telling myself that I can't live by 'what might happen', but no matter how much I tell myself this – I do. I can't get rid of these 'fears'.

* * *

Tue 15th Dec '98

4.30pm: contacted Henry (lecturer) at University to tell him the reason for my absence. When I explained the consequence of surgery (shitting out of my abdomen in a plastic bag), he replied, 'That doesn't sound very nice.' I told him I wanted to resume study in February. He said that he wouldn't 'advise it' and suggested that I 'take the whole year out'. 'Take the whole year out!' I need 'some normality' – now! 'Take the whole year out' – stupid advice – and I didn't ask for his fucking opinion!

7.30pm: thinking about what Henry said. He's right. How can I think about returning to study, when I'm worried about incidences that might happen like, suppose the bag leaks – bursts – or the clip undoes – or there's no toilet when it's time to empty – or the stoma makes a noise and people hear it. How can I be thinking about returning to study when I only feel able and 'safe' to go out in a car? How will I cope being in lectures, seminars, the canteen, or using public toilets? Fuck! I don't want to think – and I don't want to see anyone. Retreated to my safe haven (room) and back to bed with the quilt over my head.

* * *

Wed 16th Dec '98

Sharon visited. I told her I had been out twice – 'in a car'. I thought she would have said, 'Well done!' but instead she reiterated her last advice, 'You need to go outdoors and walk to get stronger. You 'should' be going out every day, and walking for about fifteen minutes', but this time it sounded like a command. I didn't say anything I was 'afraid of the anger' that was rising within in me. I was 'afraid of being out of control' and what I might say. This time I was a 'victim'. How dear she tell me what I should be doing by now – fucking cheek! I 'shouldn't' have had UC – I 'shouldn't' have had surgery – and I 'shouldn't' be shitting out of my abdomen!

I cried hysterically when she left. This wasn't my fault. I used to go out every day. I used to walk for more than fifteen minutes – before I was 'shitting out of my abdomen'. This wasn't my fault!!! But 'whose fault' was it?…

I remember reading that 'withholding emotions (especially anger) can affect our digestive system. I suppress a lot of my 'anger' and 'frustration'. I learnt to do this in my childhood. 'Childhood!' This wasn't my fault – it was my parents!!! They taught this damaging suppressive behaviour, that has caused me to be sick – to the point of disease and surgery. It's my 'taught behaviour' of 'withholding and suppressing' my emotions that has made me sick – not 'me!' And, parents need to know the influences they have on their children and the fucking consequences. I started an autobiography today, under the guise of a novel. The first sentence I wrote was:

Mum often said that I was 'full a cheek' or called me 'rude' when I asked questions she didn't like, or couldn't answer'.

* * *

Thu 17th Dec '98

11am: to Dalston to buy 'Thank-you' gifts for Mr. Bows, Harry, Toni,

Ms. Suppressant and her team. Dalston is not the best place to shop, but it's just a fifteen minute bus ride away (a safe distance). I'd wanted to buy these gifts before today, but couldn't leave the house. However, I had to go out today – 'Out-Patients' appointment.

2.30pm: Out-Patients visit with Mr. Bows, Toni and Nadeem. Mr. Bows greeted me in his usual cheerful manner. 'Hi Sam. How have you been? You look better,' Mr. Bows greeted. 'Yeah, I feel stronger,' I replied. 'Okay, will it be alright to examine your back passage?' he asked. I started shaking (inside and out) and my mouth went dry. 'Examine my back passage?' I repeated. 'I know it's not nice, but I would like to see how your rectum is getting on,' he explained. I reluctantly got on the bed and adopted the familiar position of laying on my side and buttocks out. My heart was racing. I thought I'd be rid of these examinations now that I'd had surgery and should be better. I had my back to Mr. Bows and when I heard the clinking of metal, I swung my head around in a panic. 'You can't use the regular instrument because I now have a rectal stump,' I blurted in case he tried to 'ram' the usual long instrument up me, and cause damage. He calmly said 'I know Sam,' and tapped my shoulder. He said there was inflammation, but 'it wasn't too bad', and that I should carry on administering Colifoam enemas (I didn't inform him that I'd stopped taking them about a week ago, because I was experiencing nausea and it appeared to be making the inflammation worse).

I gave him his present. 'Sam, what's this?' he whined. 'A gift,' I replied. I handed Toni and Nadeem their gifts. 'Oh, Thank You Sam, but really you shouldn't have,' advised Toni. 'I don't celebrate Christmas,' Nadeem explained. These are not Christmas gifts, they're 'Thank you' ones,' I told him.

I left the hospital feeling good – I like giving gifts. 'I hate having a stoma'. But I don't blame these 'medical professionals'. They treated me well considering their 'knowledge and experience' – which is why I 'Thank' them.

* * *

Tue 22nd Dec '98

Haven't been able to write anything for the last four days. I've wanted to – there has been a lot to write, but 'I'm scared to think'. I feel sad – disappointed – and lonely. I'm so angry about still being 'under the care of medics (out of control)' – about still experiencing UC – about having shit pouring out of my abdomen. A few days ago I thought, if I write (if I start to think) – I'll explode with anger – I'll be out of control – and I'm scared of what I might do, or what might happen to me. But, I forced myself to write today.

I've only been out of the house three times in seventeen days and I've stayed in my room most of the time. I only leave the room to empty a bucket that I'm peeing in, take dirty dishes to the kitchen, or to empty or change the bag. Haven't washed for five days (since Out-Patients appointment) – I don't see the point – I'm not going out.

* * *

Wed 23rd Dec '98

3.40pm: attended Ms. Suppressant's clinic. I asked her to take me off her list, since I was being seen in Mr. Bows's clinic. She said it might still be useful for me to remain under her supervision, because I was still taking medication. I insisted that it wasn't necessary, and that another patient could use my appointments. I want as little contact as possible with 'medical professionals' and 'hospital'.

* * *

Fri 25th Dec '98

8.30am: Christmas Day. Woke up with severe headache and pain behind left eye and down the side of my face. I 'had' to take Paracetamol. Stayed in bed and slept.

1.30pm: woke up without headache, but my knees are very sore, swollen and stiff (effects of steroids)!

2pm: the family insisted that I come down to the living room. 'At least to open your presents,' Mum said in a pleading voice. So I did. I opened my presents and waited until everyone had opened theirs. Then I immediately left. I couldn't wait to be out of all the fuss, and back to the safety of my room. I'm usually excited on Christmas Day and really enjoy how it brings family and friends together, but today I don't care. Today could be any day. Today I'm shitting out the side of my abdomen.

* * *

Sun 27th Dec '98

Woke up with pain behind left eye and down the side of my face again, and reluctantly took Paracetamol.

* * *

Mon 28th Dec '98

2am: woke up with severe headache, pain behind left eye and down the side of my face again. The severity of pain is frightening and I'm worrying about these headaches.

Slept and spent most of yesterday in my 'safe haven' (my room) and

I've been doing this for nearly a month. The blinds are always drawn for darkness – to block outdoors, and I'm unaware of time, until someone knocks to say 'Goodnight' or when daylight peeps through the blinds. I'm getting fed up of being in here, but now it feels 'strange to go out'.

* * *

Tue 29th Dec '98

Woke up feeling very desperate. I'm getting stuck – I 'need' to go out! I've got to push myself. Staying in this room most of the day and night is not healthy. I called Joan and arranged to go shopping with her tomorrow. We're going to Mare Street (which is local) – she drives (safer travel) – and there are toilets (to emptying).

* * *

Wed 30th Dec '98

Woke up with familiar headache and pain.

I wish I hadn't suggested to go shopping with Joan today. I thought about cancelling the arrangement, but I forced myself to go – and was glad I went. I didn't have time to dwell on 'illness', or the 'stoma', or 'surgery'. I didn't even think about the possibility of the bag leaking – bursting – or the clip undoing – or if there's no toilet when it's time to empty – or suppose the stoma makes a noise and people hear it. It felt equally exciting and scary being outdoors, but mostly it was a great break from 'thinking' and – I 'need' to go out.

* * *

Thu 31st Dec '98

8.30am: New Years Eve. Woke up feeling 'out of sorts'. I'm trying to be in a 'good mood', so I can see the New Year in – 'positively'. But 'good mood' is a struggle.

Filled out the 1999 diary that my sisters and brother bought me for a Christmas gift. Under usual personal details, I wrote the following:

I am an Ileostomist (had an operation – removal of whole colon).

DATE OF OPERATION:	10th Nov '98
I AM KNOWN AT:	Lank's Hospital
	Lanks Row
	London
	E26 1SS
PATIENT NO:	250172
MY SURGEON IS:	Mr. Bows
MY CONTACT IS:	Toni Helpful

I thought this would be useful in 'the event of an emergency'. Mr. Bows or Toni could explain 'exactly' what they've done to me.

11.50pm: Mum came to my room and gave me a glass of champagne. 'Come downstairs and see the New Year in with us,' she said in an encouraging voice. 'Oh Mum. I really don't want to,' I said sadly. 'Okay,' she said with empathy and gave me a hug. 'Happy New Year, Sam.'

Mum had invited friends over and I heard cheering from downstairs – it was obviously 12am. One by one family members and friends came up to my room and wished me a 'Happy New Year'. They raised their glasses of champagne and I raised my full one. And, I repeatedly replied, 'Yes, Happy New Year,' with a forced smile. What I really wanted to say was, 'Fuck off and leave me alone.' When Sidiki entered my room, I didn't 'act-out' – I could be honest with her. 'Oh Sam, come downstairs, just for a little while,' she said pitifully. I burst out crying, 'uncontrollably'. I don't know what spurred it. I think it might have been the sympathetic tone of her voice, or perhaps it was because, deep down inside, sadness was raging to be let out. She hugged me and said with tears in her eyes, 'Oh, Sam. We're downstairs having fun and you're up here in tears.' 'I'll be alright,' I sobbed. 'Go and enjoy yourself.'

When she left I sipped the champagne. Initially, it created a burning sensation in my stomach, but within moments a calmness prevailed throughout my whole body – relaxing every cell. I sipped more, especially liking the tranquil affect on my mind. I felt tipsy and peaceful when I finished the glass of champagne. I banged on the floor and Sidiki came up. 'Can you get me some more champagne, please,' I asked. 'Course I can. Having your own party?!' she teased with a chuckle. 'Yeah,' I dryly replied with a forced smile. I gulped the second glass of champagne, keen to encourage more 'relaxation' and more 'peacefulness', and felt quite drunk once I'd finished it. The champagne had relaxed 'every cell' – no tension anywhere, but best of all – 'no thoughts'. I fell asleep feeling 'peaceful' and 'almost merry'.

* * *

1999

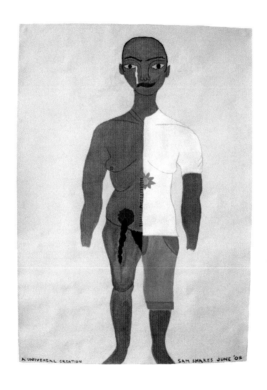

A UNIVERSAL CREATION   SAM SHARES JUNE '08

A Strange and Chaotic Existence

Fri 1st Jan '99

5.30am: woke up feeling tired and nauseous (I guess due to the champagne).

3.30pm: even though I've just woken up I still feel tired. I'm not sleeping well, because I can't lie comfortably on my stomach. I'm afraid the stoma might go in, or that the pressure on the bag might cause it to burst. So now I sleep on my back, which feels awkward. Sometimes I forget I can't lie on my stomach, but the bulging bag reminds me that, 'I must sleep on my back'. I'm also not sleeping well, because I need empty the bag at least three times during the night. I haven't had a decent sleep, since surgery. Now, I guess with this stoma – I never will.

Still experiencing blood – mucus – pulling/discomfort. And I'm thinking about administering enemas for quick relief (must source a natural remedy) – great start to the New Year.

* * *

Sat 2nd Jan '99

Since the beginning of December, I haven't been washing daily. I used to love soaking in the bath – so relaxing, but I can't do that anymore. The plastic bag floats on top of the water, reminding me that I've got shit pouring out of my abdomen, and it looks disgusting. I've tried covering the bag with my flannel, but it floats away. And, it feels so 'alien' to be bathing with a plastic bag stuck on my side – like washing with clothes on! In the bath you're supposed to be 'naked'. And when you wash, you're supposed to clean 'everywhere'.

* * *

Sun 3rd Jan '99

7.30am: woke up with severe headache, and pain behind my left eye.

Today, the pain is causing nausea, so I haven't eaten anything.

6.30pm: Joan rang. The conversation was so strained. She babbled about what 'bargains', she got in the 'sales'. 'Everything was fifty percent off,... but then I found a top with twenty-five percent off,... so I only paid twenty-five percent of the original price,....' As she rambled, her voice went faint. I was 'shitting in a plastic bag stuck to my stomach' – I couldn't give a fuck about her 'bargains'.

9.30pm: yet again, for most of today I've been consumed with 'negative' thoughts. I'm not getting good sleep, because of the stoma – I'm not gaining the benefits of a relaxing bath, because of the stoma – I can't go out, because of the stoma. Perhaps I'm 'imagining' these problems? There must be some 'positive' aspects to this surgery?

* * *

Mon 4th Jan '99

6.30am: woke up with a headache again! Bet it's got something to do with this surgery. I've never suffered with headaches before. I must tell Mr. Bows about these when I see him at clinic on Thursday.

1.10pm: Nathan (x-boyfriend) visited. He explained that he was on his lunch break, and boasted that he had a new job and was working around the corner. He continued in a blasé tone to inform that he'd 'heard I was in hospital' and that he'd 'heard I had cancer'. My mind raced with reflection upon what he said. 'He'd heard I was in hospital' – he'd 'heard I had cancer' – yet he didn't visit me whilst I was in hospital. He asked me to 'whip up one of those nice toasted sandwiches that [I] used to'. I thought he'd come to see me, but he'd come for lunch! And, my mind continued to reflect – he'd 'heard I was in hospital' – he'd 'heard I had cancer' – yet, he didn't visit me whilst I was in hospital. I gritted my teeth as I fought to contain my shock and anger, and told him to 'help himself'. I got up from sitting and the bag rustled. 'What was that?' he asked with a chuckle. 'Nothing,' I replied defensively. He laughed and retorted, 'Stop telling lies. Sounds like a plastic bag!' He came over and jostled with me, lifting the bottom of my nightie – trying to see the 'plastic bag'. As I fought to stop him – he was laughing – I wasn't. When he left 'bile' filled my stomach – 'Angry bile' that physically burnt...

* * *

Tue 5th Jan '99

1am: woke up thinking about Nathan. I kept seeing the scene of us. Him jostling with me, lifting the bottom of my nightie – trying to see the plastic bag. He thought having a plastic bag stuck on your abdomen to shit in was a joke?! The Fucking Bastard.

A STRANGE AND CHAOTIC EXISTENCE

* * *

Wed 6th Jan '99

3.30am: woken up by a very frightening dream and in a panic. I dreamt I stabbed Nathan. He was standing in front of me, and his facial expression didn't display that he'd been stabbed, but blood was oozing from his chest. He didn't say anything – but very calmly I said, 'See, what you made me do.'

This dream was distressing because in it, I thought the stabbing was justified and that Nathan had 'made me do it'. And, I found it very disturbing that I had no remorse. But, what perturbed me greatly, was that awake, I saw a reality. That I could stab Nathan – that it would be justified – and I would have no remorse. I feel dangerous.

3.45am: I needed to relax – and I needed to rid of these thoughts. Remembering how relaxed and peaceful I felt when I drank champagne on New Year's Eve – I drank 'four shots' of brandy with hot blackcurrant, I fell asleep feeling 'relaxed'.

9.30am: the clip undone! This is the third time this has happened. I was walking up stairs and all of sudden shit was everywhere! On my nightie – on my leg – on the stairs – in my toes – on the stairs – and I stepped in the shit! Incidences like this make me start wondering again, 'What if the bag leaks? – What if shit goes all over my clothes? – What if there's no toilet to empty? – What if the bag fills up and people see it? – What if the clip undoes? 'What if!' 'What if!' 'What if!' But, sometimes it's my fault. I'm leaving it too long to empty the bag, because I hate seeing it – and the stoma. So, the clip is overwhelmed with the weight of the stool. I must decide what I prefer – cleaning up shit, or seeing the bag and the stoma more.

This incident nearly changed my positive view of having a 'normal' life, and going out to seek information on courses tomorrow. But I composed myself by affirming that I've, 'Just got to start emptying the bag more often', because, I need to get out – and I need to keep busy. If I stay in, I'll think more – get angry – be sad – feel lonely – and I'll 'lose it'.

7.30pm: Sharaz rang and the conversation was strained (just like it was with Joan). She spoke about having the flu and not being able to go to work! Her 'problem' was flu! I felt like saying, 'I'm unable to go to University due to illness and surgery – and shitting out of my abdomen, and you're complaining about having the fucking flu?!' I ended the call feeling frustrated and needed to relax. I poured myself a brandy with hot blackcurrant.

* * *

Thu 7th Jan '99

3.30pm: Out-Patients appointment. 'Why do I keep getting severe headaches?' I asked Mr. Bows. 'It's due to 'dehydration'. Most of our water is absorbed in the colon, and you no longer have one. So you'll need to increase your fluid intake, to compensate for this,' he explained. I 'knew' these headaches were due to surgery – more fucking accommodation for this 'cure?!' 'Will the stoma go in if I lie on my stomach?' I asked. 'No,' he replied. 'Why do you think I'm feeling so tired. I think this 'constant tiredness' might be due to 'anaemia',' I answered my own question. 'Your last blood tests were 'fine',' he reminded and continued, 'Sam you were very ill, and you've had a major operation. It will take some time for you to recover.' I thought 'three months since surgery is ample time to recover. I think something still isn't right. And it isn't, else why am I 'still getting flare-ups?' 'How's your rectum, Sam?' he asked with concern. Containing my anger – I replied coldly, 'active'. But what I really wanted to say was, 'Why am I still getting flare-ups – I shouldn't still be administering awful steroid enemas – I now had to deal with a shit pouring out of my abdomen (as well as UC) – and I thought this operation was supposed to make me better?!' But I felt too angry. I would've exploded if I said all that. And it's not his fault. But fuck – it's not mine either! I weigh 6.13lbs.

4.50pm: rang College and requested information on short courses be posted to me. The woman asked if I lived 'local', I replied, 'Yes.' She continued, 'You could pop in and collect a prospectus. It helps reduce the cost of postage, and saves time.' I hesitated. This would mean 'going out!' I said, 'Do you think you could post it. I'm unable to come out at the moment.' I put the phone down and quizzed, 'I'm unable to come out at the moment?' Why did I say that? I'm 'pathetic'.

5.10pm: a woman at the leisure centre advised I should obtain a 'Leisure Card' to receive concessionary rates, since I was claiming 'Incapacity Benefit'. She said I needed to pick up a form from the centre – take it to the Town Hall to be approved – and I would need a passport sized photo for the card. I thought, 'What a palaver' – so much outdoor activity. To the leisure centre – to the Town Hall – have to take photos – and back to the centre! I wanted to collect the form today, but I needed to psyche myself up to go out. I'll go tomorrow.

* * *

Fri 8th Jan '99

7.30am: woke up feeling very 'dark' (low mood). It was hard for me to leave the house (I forced myself to go to the leisure centre) and the journey was awful – 'I felt scared being outside?' I walked briskly, but mainly trotted – wanting to get home as soon as possible. My heart was pounding – I kept thinking that 'someone was going to attack me'. I kept looking behind me, and at one point – I wanted to walk backwards. I'd been scared to go out, because of the 'What if's', regarding the stoma. But today I was scared to go out because I thought 'someone was going to attack me'.

5.30pm: Petrinella called. She asked if I wanted to 'go out' – to a 'restaurant!' I abruptly replied that, 'I didn't.' 'How could I risk eating at a restaurant?!' Most of the menu would probably consist of foods I can't eat anymore, and she knew I'd been in hospital with complications caused by foods. For fuck sake, 'What's the matter with these people?!' I needed to relax – and rid of my angry feelings. Drank three quarters of a bottle of wine.

* * *

Sat 9th Jan '99

10am: College prospectus arrived and there are few courses that think will be useful. The 'Introduction to Counselling' course looks good – client-centred, encourages listening and being listened to, and reflection for personal development. I don't want to be a Counsellor, but I think this course will be an opportunity to off load some of my 'frustration' and 'anger' – 'I'll contact them on Monday.' I never realised the benefits of 'singing' until I read an advert today. Apparently, singing is 'a great way to express your emotions'. At first I thought, 'I can't sing!' But I'm 'desperate to release my emotions, I'll 'try anything' – 'I'll contact them on Monday.' North East London University has a Black Studies course. I feel like I've 'lost myself', and will benefit from knowledge of the achievements of black people (of my history) – 'I'll contact them on Monday.' I've read about the benefits of Yoga, and this practice seems physically undemanding and effective to 'combat stress' – 'I'll contact them on Monday.' I'm keen to keep writing my 'novel', but I need support. I think a Writing course will be 'motivating' – 'I'll contact them on Monday.'

I've expelled five times today – blood – wind – mucus – pain. Alcohol seems to exacerbate 'UC' – but it's great for the mind.

* * *

Mon 11th Jan '99

Yet again, I had to force myself out of the house. I trotted (and sometimes ran) most of the thirty minute journey to the Town Hall. A tiny part of me wanted to laugh – why was I trotting – why was I running?! I felt stupid – 'Trotting and Running for no reason?!' But, there 'was a reason' – I thought 'someone was going to attack me'. Still, I kept telling myself that I was 'being stupid', and tried to stop trotting and running. But every time I attempted to stop, my heart began pounding, and I didn't feel in control of my legs. It was as though my legs were being controlled by another part of my mind – not 'me'. They were trotting and running even when 'I' was telling them not too. 'Part of my mind' didn't want to be 'attacked' – and wanted to be safe – back in my haven. Whilst, 'I' wanted to stop trotting and running – and 'being stupid'. 'I hate this'.

3.30pm: I've got to go out tomorrow because if I don't – I could lose 'the will' to go out – 'Forever'. Needed to relax – I drank some brandy and hot blackcurrant.

10.50pm: I've expelled blood – wind – mucus six times today. Must 'reduce my alcohol intake' for the sake of 'UC' – so 'I won't have a drink tomorrow'.

Never managed to make any calls.

* * *

Tue 12th Jan '99

10.30am: went swimming! Before I got changed, I sought out where the nearest toilets were. They were just five meters away from the pool (but still they were too far). I entered the pool with my towel wrapped around me, because I didn't want the chance of anyone 'seeing the bag' (even though I'd checked few times in the mirror and could see 'nothing'). I didn't remove the towel until my waistline (the bag) was safely out of sight – in the water. I swam the width of the pool rather than the length, because that's where the toilets were. I kept getting in the way of the other swimmers, but there was no way I was going to swim 'right the way' up the other end, 'just in case'.

3.30pm: at home and made the calls I was supposed to do yesterday. The course times are great! I can do all of them! Singing workshop: Mon 4.30–5.30pm: Black Studies course: Tue 7.30–9.30pm: Yoga: Wed 12.30–1.30pm: Creative Writing Course: Thu 7–9pm: Counselling course: Fri 9.30am–12.30pm. ... And go to Women's Morning every Monday between 9.30am–1pm, and aerobics, Fridays 6–7pm. 'I've got to keep busy'.

9.45pm: I'm in bed (early tonight), because if I stay awake – I know I'm going to have to have a drink – to relax my mind, but a drink won't help UC.

10.15pm: thinking about having 'just one glass of wine'...

10.55pm: still thinking about having a glass of wine...

11.55pm: eventually fell asleep without having the glass of wine that I so desperately wanted.

A STRANGE AND CHAOTIC EXISTENCE

* * *

Wed 13th Jan '99

It's been four weeks since I started writing the 'novel' and it's helping me to off load my negative feelings. I wrote about my earliest memory – when I was four years old. I was cutting up an apple to feed the birds with a sharp knife, and cut my finger. I've got loads of sad memories regarding childhood and adolescence. I feel 'let down again' by my parents and I'm experiencing similar emotions that I had during adolescence. I feel a lot of anger towards Mum – her inability to show 'love', 'understanding', and 'protect' me.

Today I 'should' have gone to practise Yoga. It's supposed to be beneficial for both 'mind' and 'body', which is the precise combination (remedy) – I need right now. I really wanted to go, but I 'couldn't force myself' out of the house. 'I'm pathetic'.

I needed to relax. I knew 'it' wouldn't help UC, but 'it's great for the mind'. Drank a glass of wine (remainder of what I'd opened on Monday), but it wasn't enough to offer relaxation, so I drank a few shots of brandy and hot blackcurrant.

* * *

Thu 14th Jan '99

I 'should' have enrolled onto the Black Studies course today, but didn't. I couldn't bear the forty minute journey to the University. Didn't go to Yoga yesterday – didn't enrol on course today. 'I'm useless'. Still, I went swimming on Tuesday, which was 'good' – I suppose? But, I 'should' be doing something every day. 'I've got to keep busy'.

* * *

Fri 15th Jan '99

5am: woke up feeling numb and I'm crying without a murmur. As I sit here writing – it's completely silent. It seems like I'm the only one in the universe awake. I feel 'invisible' and 'not alive' – 'everyone and everything unaware of my existence' and my 'sadness'. I feel 'unknown' and 'empty'. I think 'I want to die'. Huge tears are rolling out of my eyes at a constant pace – 'still no murmur'...

7.45am: still awake. I've been lying on my back staring at the ceiling, trying to figure out 'who I am and where I belong'. And, I'm wondering how I'm going to stay awake during the Counselling course that starts at 9.30am this morning. I'm shattered, but I'm definitely going. I've got that feeling of desperation again, of needing to 'do something' – needing to 'go out' – or risk 'losing the will to go out forever'.

9am: arrived at the college early to find out the distance from the toilets to the classroom. The nearest toilet was a short walk along the corridor, but it was a 'disabled' one. It was handy that a toilet was so near, but why did it have to be 'disabled?' If I have to use these toilets in 'an emergency', people will wonder why I'm using the 'disabled' toilets, instead of the normal ones (on the next floor) – I would have to explain.

Wonder if I'm considered disabled, because of the stoma? I am incontinent and incontinence is a disability (I think). I'm not like 'normal' people, who can hold their stool and wait for a convenient time and place to go. If I need to empty the bag – I 'need to empty it' – I have 'no control'. So, 'I think I am disabled'. Therefore, I have 'a right' to use the disabled toilets. I'm 'not normal' anymore – 'I'm disabled'. As we sat in a group, I scanned the sixteen students and wondered if they 'knew' I had a stoma.

Tutor explained that, 'The course requires a lot of listening', which I'm going to find hard, because my mind is so active. All I seem to be able to hear are my thoughts. Still, if I try to listen to someone else's thoughts, perhaps I'll escape my 'crazy' ones.

College information stated that 'if you have a medical condition that might affect you on the course, please inform your tutor'. I didn't know whether this stoma would 'affect [me] on the course' – I'd never taken it on one before.

* * *

Sat 16th Jan '99

7.30pm: Trevor called. He asked how I'd been, and what I'd been doing over the last couple of weeks. It seemed trivial to tell him I'd been swimming for the first time with shit pouring out of my abdomen, and how proud I was about this. So instead I said, 'Nothing really.' He told me he'd been working, playing football and been to a concert. I felt envious of his 'normal' life and didn't want to hear about what he'd been doing. His Life is steadily ticking – mine is just about ticking over.

8.35pm: opened a bottle of wine and didn't drink the usual three quarters of the bottle – I finished it.

* * *

Sun 17th Jan '99

Woke up feeling angry. I can't deal with the lack of understanding amongst people. Their 'trivial talk' about 'bargains', 'flu', and their insensitivity (going on about their 'normal' lives). I'm going to have to stop speaking to them. 'They're' causing too much 'frustration' and 'anger' – they're causing too much distress.

I heard the phone ring from my room, and Mark say, 'I'll just get her.' I listened to him stepping up the stairs – confirming the call was for me. I dived under the covers, and pretended to be asleep. Mark peered into my room, and said to the person via the phone, 'Oh, she's sleeping', and left. I felt 'guilty' afterwards, but it was worth it. I have to stop speaking to people – 'They're causing too much distress'.

Flare-ups are increasing. I expelled blood – wind – mucus – (with lots of) pain, eight times today.

* * *

Mon 18th Jan '99

10.30am: went to the leisure centre – swam and had a 'sauna'. I wasn't sure if it was 'safe' to have a sauna (even though I'd read that people with stomas have no problem), I thought the heat might steam the bag off and leak shit everywhere, so wasn't able to relax. And it was frustrating trying 'to cleanse' – to 'detox'. I wanted to exfoliate my bum and hips, but I couldn't, because I now have to wear pants (to hid the bag) – I don't want anyone to see it – I don't want to see it. Before surgery, I'd be butt naked. So, I 'had to make do' with dipping my flannel inside my pants to exfoliate my buttocks, which was so annoying – I didn't enjoy the sauna.

4.30pm: Singing workshop started today, but I couldn't go (too exhausted after swim and sauna).

7.45pm: Doreen entered my room and said, 'Tricia's on the phone for you.' My heart began to pound. I never heard it ring – else I'd have done my familiar act of pretending to be asleep! I 'wanted' to take the call, but I 'couldn't' – 'I have to stop speaking to people – they're causing too much distress'. So, I replied with a heavy sigh, 'I'll phone her back' with 'no intention of doing so'. Again, I felt guilty (I was lying to myself and I was lying to others) – and I felt miserable – and sad. I wanted to be honest – and I wanted to be happy. I needed to relax – I had a drink of brandy and hot blackcurrant.

* * *

Tue 19th Jan '99

6.30pm: I asked family members to tell anyone that called that I'd phone them back. Joan, Sharaz, and Petrinella rang today, and part of me really wanted to return the call, but 'I have to stop speaking to people – they're causing too much distress'.

* * *

Wed 20th Jan '99

Trevor called and left a message asking what I was doing for my Birthday. 'My Birthday!' 'Shit!' 'I forgot my Birthday?!' How near was it?! What date is it today (even though I'm writing dates almost every day – they aren't registering)?! Gosh, my Birthday is just five days away! No wonder so many friends have been calling. 'I always celebrate my Birthday'. I've got to arrange something for this Saturday – three days away! 'I always celebrate my Birthday' – and if I don't – I will be 'losing me'.

10.30pm: feeling 'guilty'. Friends were considering me – and I feel angry with them.

* * *

Thu 21st Jan '99

7pm: at Writing course. The tutor said the purpose of the course is 'to strengthen imagination'. Good! I hope I can get so creative, that I imagine good things about having a stoma – and start 'living!'

9.30pm: arrived home. Drank some brandy and hot blackcurrant to 'relax' and 'psyche' myself up before calling friends. Called friends and told them I'd be celebrating my Birthday this Saturday in a Wine Bar, and apologised for the late notification. The general response was that it didn't matter that they 'wouldn't miss my Birthday for the world!' I felt guilty when I heard their enthusiasm and words of kindness. It's not their fault they don't 'understand' what it's like to have 'shit pouring from your abdomen'. Not even I 'understand' and I'm the one doing it! All I know is that 'I'm shitting from my abdomen' and it's not 'natural' – it's not 'normal' – and I 'hate' it.

* * *

Fri 22nd Jan '99

9.30am: Counselling course. We were asked to, 'Reveal your anxieties and fears about the course'. I wrote: 'Relationship between parents might be discussed'. For another exercise we had to talk for two minutes about ourselves, with a partner. Two minutes seemed to take forever to pass (when I was talking), and there were uncomfortable silent moments. I didn't reveal that I had a stoma to my partner, even though we were asked to talk about 'ourselves' – and the stoma (shit pouring from my abdomen) is very much part of me? I felt quite deceitful. Part of me didn't want to start talking, because I thought if I did, I'd probably breakdown and cry, and wouldn't be able to stop. It felt 'safer' to listen. Still, when my partner did talk, I didn't hear what she was saying – my mind kept wondering off.

5pm: first aerobics class. During the class the instructor kept shouting, 'Abs in – abs in,' instructing 'someone' to pull in their abdominal muscles. I didn't think she was talking to me, because I had pulled mine in to the point where they were touching my spine! But she continued shouting, 'abs in – abs in.' I looked up, and she was talking to me?! When I looked at my abdomen – there was a bulge – the bag was full, and this is what she could see! She thought the bag was flabby abs! I nervously smiled at her and the other participants, feeling humiliated. 'I'm pulling them in as hard as I can,' I responded with a fake chuckle. At the end of the class I explained to the instructor that I had an 'ileostomy (stoma), wore a bag, and that was the 'bulge' she could see'. She looked embarrassed and apologised. I told her there was 'no need to apologise – that it wasn't 'her fault'. I wanted to apologise too – but it wasn't 'my fault' either.

* * *

Sat 23rd Jan '99

9.30pm: at Corks Wine Bar celebrating my Birthday. Joan and Sharaz made me 'laugh' (haven't done that in a while) and it was in relation to the stoma! They said, 'Oh Sam you can get drunk today. You've been through a lot.' 'Okay, who will help me to empty my bag when I'm too drunk to?' I teased. They looked at each other and Joan said, 'Sharaz will – she's your best friend!' 'No I'm not! You are, Joan!' Sharaz jokingly contended and we all laughed. I couldn't get 'drunk', and risk not being able to empty the bag. Suppose it burst and shit went everywhere – in a Wine Bar, where you're supposed to be impressing! How impressive would that be?! I had a close dance with Trevor. 'Trevor can you feel the bag?' I repeatedly asked throughout the dance. 'No, Sam. I'm enjoying dancing with you, and I can't feel the bag,' he kept reassuring. But I'm sure he could. I think he said he couldn't, because he didn't want me to feel bad. I 'sort of enjoyed the night'. I had just two glasses of wine – couldn't drink too much – I needed to be 'alert' to take care of the stoma.

* * *

Mon 25th Jan '99

Today is my Birthday, but because I've already celebrated it – it's really been just another day.

2pm: had a sauna with Lizzy. A woman asked how I got the scar on my abdomen, but before I could answer, Lizzy replied defensively, 'That's personal!' But I seized the chance to explain to the woman what a stoma was, and why I had it. The woman looked 'sympathetic' and was 'speechless'. I felt relived at disclosing this part of me and I realised that not telling people – not speaking about the stoma is a large part of my 'frustration' – 'anger' – and distress.

7.30pm: I needed to relax – and celebrate my Birthday. Drank some brandy and hot blackcurrant.

* * *

Tue 26th Jan '99

Done a lot of 'de-cluttering'. I bagged up excessive possessions that I'd had for years – filling three dustbin bags with clothes, unused gifts, and gold jewellery (little was spared – little was of use). My cupboards and wardrobe were almost bare once I'd finished. The visit to the wine bar, on Saturday spurred this 'clearing out'. The pretence of the glitzy environment – the fake drunken laughter – the women's make up – the dishonest chat up lines – the whole 'ignorance of the importance of life'. I needed to 'make some space for Life' and part of this was to rid of my excessive and unnecessary possessions.

Mum and Sidiki were surprised, when I told them I no longer needed the bagged up items (especially the gold jewellery). 'You're getting rid of your jewellery?!' Mum asked in shock. I explained that 'Wisdom was better than silver and gold' and 'health paramount', but neither of them appeared to appreciate what I was trying to share – 'that these materials were stifling 'Life', and not reflective of the importance of it.

As I shared this, I remembered the night when I was in hospital – when I realised the 'uselessness of wealth and possessions' – in terms of 'health' – in terms of 'Life'. My values and beliefs have been shattered. I'm blank – I have no idea of 'my ideals' – all I've known to be 'true' – have been 'lies'. And, I'm totally confused.

* * *

Thu 28th Jan '99

Still getting flare-ups and using steroid enemas to 'help', but this 'remedy' isn't working. As soon as I put them in – I've got to expel. The enemas are spurring bowel movement – instead of reducing them! I'm going to 'stop administering them again'.

Period came! I haven't had one since the sixth of October 1998! Never thought I'd be so happy about having back pain, sore breasts – a period! My body's getting 'back to normal!'

7pm: at Writing class. We were asked to choose a quote and elaborate on it, by writing what comes into our mind. I chose:

The prison is 'self' made really…

And wrote:

> 'I have locked myself away into this feeling of isolation, but there
> is hope. I have a burning desire to be free. Free from the hurt of
> being judged or ridiculed. There is a small part inside of me, which
> is ever so strong to win, although the mass is dark and negative.'

11.20pm: at home retiring feeling 'drained' and 'depressed' upon reflection of the expression I wrote in class. I'm going to find this course
mentally challenging, but I 'sense it will be good for me' – kind of
'therapeutic'.

I needed to rid of my depressing feelings – and I needed to relax. Drank
three quarters of a bottle of wine.

* * *

Fri 29th Jan '99

4.30pm: one minute I feel 'up' and the next I feel 'down'. I'm wondering how useful the Writing and Counselling courses are going to be.
What I wrote yesterday left me feeling depressed. This weeks Counselling course caused great frustration, as I listened to other people's
'trivial problems'. One student shared his 'challenging experience' of
coming to terms with the death of his goldfish! 'Challenging experience?!' They haven't got a clue. If only they knew, about living with a
shitty stoma! I don't think I should continue these courses, but, 'I need
to keep busy'. I'm totally confused. Drank a 'whole bottle' of wine.

* * *

Sun 31st Jan '99

Feeling perturbed. Thinking about my mood swings (one minute I feel
up – the next I feel down). And it seems ironic that 'I don't feel stressed'
(just having mood swings), but my back passage says so – by flare-ups.
And, the enemas aren't helping. I needed to relax and I know the alcohol isn't helping the flare-ups – but it helps relax my mind. Drank two
glasses of wine.

* * *

Tue 2nd Feb '99

Visited Grandma. I cleaned and tided her place, paid her telephone bill,
and made her a doctor's appointment. I didn't want to visit, but I need
to 'get out' – I need to 'keep busy' – I need to 'help others' – and I need
to stop 'playing victim'.

* * *

Wed 3rd Feb '99

Today is the first day I haven't taken a nap! I'm beginning to feel energetic, which is surprising, because my week is now quite hectic. On Mondays I attend Women's Morning (swim and sauna) – Thursdays I attend Writing course – Fridays I do Counselling course and Aerobics. The days I don't attend classes, I'm doing homework (writing), typing up notes from Counselling course, writing reflective journal, and visiting Grandma – doing her house chores.

I feel a lot happier. In fact – I feel very happy. Very, very, happy! Had a few shots of brandy and hot blackcurrant – I needed to relax.

* * *

Thu 4th Feb '99

7pm: at Writers course. One exercise was to write about a heading 'Sophisticated Sisters'. I wrote:

'Your world is fake; superficial and so are you.
You really are self-centred and can only relate to what 'looks good.
Completely unnatural –
Rosy apples with rotten cores.'

This was about me! Not any 'Sophisticated Sisters'. I feel 'fake' as I sit with a very 'unsophisticated' plastic bag stuck on my side, 'completely unnatural'. I might 'look good', but really I'm portraying a 'rosy apple' (my appearance) with a 'rotten core' (the stoma).

* * *

Fri 5th Feb '99

9.30am: Counselling course. At the end of the class a student recommended and handed me a book, *Inspirational Thoughts*, by Tycho Photiou. I had a quick scan of the book of quotations.

If we try too hard to force others to live in our world, because we think it is the real world, we are doomed to disappointment. (p29)

I realised that's what I've been doing with friends and experiencing. And,

One often learns more from ten days of agony than from ten years of contentment. (p76).

After reading these quotes I felt energised and hopeful. 'Where can I get a copy of this,' I asked with excitement, and travelled straight to the bookshop from College – I needed to get a copy 'now'.

Last week I was deliberating whether to continue this course, but although I'm finding it frustrating, I think there will be some benefit (even if it's 'just getting me out of the house'). And, I need to complete it – something's got to go 'right' – be 'good'.

* * *

Sat 6th Feb '99

Stayed at Tricia's. It was the first time I'd slept out since having the stoma and I didn't feel comfortable emptying the bag at her place. When I emptied it, I used what seemed like half a can of air-fresher to rid of the smell, but still the 'abnormal stench' overpowered, and I worried about what she might think.

We sat chatting and drinking brandy. Throughout the evening I nearly 'lost it' (my temper) several times, as she talked about her trivial concerns, arguments with boyfriend – bills – and work colleagues. I sat hearing her 'drone', wishing I was at home – alone in my room. I drank more and more of the brandy to be 'out of this reality'.

* * *

Sunday 7th Feb '99

I left Tricia's at 8.30am! I woke her up to say 'Goodbye'. She asked why I was leaving so early. I said that I had to go for a Gym Induction – and I did, but that wasn't until 1pm! I could have left at 12.20pm and been on time. The complete truth of the 'early departure' was that I couldn't wait to 'get away' from her – and to be in 'familiar surroundings'.

5.30pm: at home. Yet again, I'm feeling 'frustrated' and 'angered' by friends. I'm comparing whatever 'problem' they've got with having a stoma and 'nothing' can match, and although I appreciate the quote I read yesterday, about 'forcing others to live in our world' my 'frustration' and 'anger' prevails.

9.30pm: lying regretting forcing myself to speak to Petrinella and Sharaz earlier, when they rang. Because, yet again after the conversation the familiar emotions of 'frustration' and 'anger' visited, along with a new one – 'guilt'. I've been feeling guilty at the way I feel (especially after my Birthday), because my 'friends' are trying to accommodate. But, even though they may be trying to accommodate, they're not being supportive, or understanding, and so, I needn't feel guilty?…

I wrote a poem about 'friendship' and 'honesty'. I titled it, *I make no apology*.

> I make no apology…
> For being straight,
> For being honest,

And not a fake.
I make no apology…
For who I am,
Or what I say,
I don't give a damn.
I make no apology….
For myself and others,
Who energetically disclose –
What others may cover.
I make no apology…
I am who I am,
And ignorance maybe part –
Of my confident stand.
I make no apology…
For my feelings are true,
And I will not hide them,
For the worse of you.
I make no apology…
But feel quite sad,
That hostility is the reaction –
Can the truth be that bad?
I make no apology…
To, lost friends along the way,
When I expose the truth –
And they silently walk away.
I make no apology….
For it is your fears,
That evoke defensive behaviour –
At the truth that you hear.
I make no apology…
For authenticity is tough,
And understand, honesty with oneself –
Is extremely rough.
I make no apology…
But of the tone I use,
Which may offend –
The severely abused.
I make no apology…
For being a friend,
I wish I had someone –
Upon whom to depend.

I've got to cut myself off from 'friends' – for the sake of my sanity and 'good relationships'.

* * *

Wed 10th Feb '99

2.20pm: Out-Patients appointment via Toni's clinic. I told her the cut was 'still' open and weeping – three months after surgery! She administered silver nitrate. I asked how long it would take to heal. She said 'she couldn't say', and that 'steroids slow down the healing process'. I've been using steroids since October, and I'm still taking them via the enemas for my 'active rectum' – for 'UC'. Still being plagued with UC, nasty side-effects of drugs and a weeping wound. For fuck sake – when am I going to 'get better!'

11.45pm: had familiar night toddy (few shots of brandy and hot blackcurrant) to assist relaxation and sleep.

* * *

Fri 12th Feb '99

I bought another book written by Tycho Photiou titled, *You Are What You Think*. The blurb on the back of the book explained that it would 'enable you to improve any aspect of your life by reprogramming your subconscious for health and happiness' which is preciously what I need. I need to improve my 'health and happiness'. I need to 'improve my health' – to 'create some success' – I feel like a failure (I've failed my health).

I read sub-chapter seven first. It was titled 'Keep a positive attitude'. In it I read a quote,

Pain is inevitable. Suffering is optional.

Hmmm. I continued to read,

If we have a problem, what is more important is not the problem, but our attitude to it…

And,

We are only bothered by another man's words or actions if we allow his words or actions to bother us…

11.45pm: I've read half of the book – can't put it down! 'Now' I'm beginning to realise the power of the mind and our perception. Overwhelmed with realisation – I drank a bottle of wine.

* * *

Tue 16th Feb '99

7am: woke up and immediately started reading Tycho's book. A couple of quotes spurred great reflection. These were,

Our self image is the single, most important factor in determining our success and happiness in life.

And,

> *A negative self-image is one of the principle causes of failure. Our self-image creates the reality of who we are.*

If I hate the stoma – I hate my self-image. I've got to 'change my thinking'. This idea of 'self image' spurred thoughts about my 'body image'. I've been fooling myself – how I look 'is' important. And I recognise my destructive 'self-talk' and comments like 'I look flipping awful' – 'I'm useless' – 'I feel like a failure' – 'I'm pathetic' – and I've got to stop this negative 'self-talk'. Shit! I need to change so much of 'me' – I'm exhausted just thinking about it. Feeling stressed out – and needed to relax – had a drink of rum and blackcurrant.

* * *

Wed 17th Feb '99

4.30am: woke up thinking about body image. I used to love the freedom of wearing barely no clothes indoors. But now the bag protrudes out of my 'normal' knickers, reminding me that I'm shitting out my abdomen, and it looks awful. I need to 'hide this bag' so I can walk around indoors half naked again!

9.45am: went shopping for new knickers. Bought 'full briefs' (to cover the bag) and ones that have 'tummy control' (to hold the bag snug). A bit bigger, but great!

* * *

Thu 18th Feb '99

7pm: this weeks Writing class has been the most emotive session. We were asked to cast our minds back to 'childhood' and to elaborate on the sentence, 'I have always wanted to be.' I wrote:

> 'Loved; understood; understanding; helpful; knowledgeable; known.'

And when I read what I'd written – I started crying. These feelings weren't solely reflective of my 'childhood' – these were also feelings of today. I read the words over and over through blurred vision – created by the tears. 'I think I'm stuck in my 'dreaded childhood?' Or maybe surgery has spurred these similar needs?...

10.55pm: lying in bed thinking about the words I'd written 'Loved; understood; understanding; helpful; knowledgeable; known'. And I'm tossing and turning in bed...

* * *

Fri 19th Feb '99

12.45am: still tossing and turning in bed. Still the words 'Loved; understood; understanding; helpful; knowledgeable; known' are being repeated in my mind. I needed to relax – and I needed to sleep. I opened a bottle of wine – and finished it.

Feelings of guilt prevailed (I was hoping not to have a drink today – to stop drinking daily), but then I remembered that I needn't feel guilty. It was now the next day (12.45am). And, I didn't drink yesterday.

Tomorrow is Nada's (fellow University student) Hen Evening. Glad it's being held in her home, rather than a public place, because I still 'don't like going out.' I don't feel like celebrating – I feel miserable. I'm struggling to appreciate 'happiness' – 'joy' – or 'laughter' at the moment. Can't remember the last time I cracked a genuine smile, or 'recognised a joke'. I only know a joke when the person telling it laughs (or someone else does). Then with a delayed reaction, I force my stiff smiling muscles to work and react to the 'unrecognised' joke.

* * *

Sat 20th Feb '99

5.30pm: really enjoyed Nada's Hen evening (never thought I would). Nada's family and guests were very friendly and I felt at ease. It was nice meeting her Mum, whom I'd been speaking to via the telephone for over a year. She was keen to know how I was getting on with the stoma – she was 'interested in me' and 'the stoma?!' I felt great after speaking with her. She introduced me to older family members (in Farsi) and I think she explained that I'd had surgery, because most of them bowed their heads, with expressions of sympathy, at me. She didn't introduce me 'just as Nada's friend' from University – she acknowledged the whole me – 'Sam with a stoma'. I found this refreshing, because most people avoid talking about the surgery I've had – pretending nothing has happened – pretending that I haven't got a stoma – but I have.

10.30pm: arrived home and felt 'glad' and 'sad' to be appreciated as 'Sam with a stoma'. Had a drink and laid to rest – crying.

* * *

Wed 24th Feb '99

Second period since Oct '98 – came on time! It feels great! My body is recovering and gaining normal functioning (well at least in one area).

All week I've been trying to do the homework set from the Writing course based on our Childhood, but haven't been able to do it. I wish I could – more 'failure'. Had a drink.

* * *

Thu 25th Feb '99

7pm: at Writing course. I brought in a chapter from the 'novel' to share with the group, since I was unable to do this weeks homework (write a poem or prose related to 'Childhood'). When I finished reading people were looking at me in awe, smiling, or nodding their heads. They commented, 'Oh, you've 'got to' bring in the next chapter!', 'I want to know what happens to her', and 'wow, that was so emotive – I could really feel her anxiety'. I sat scanning the readers – wondering if their comments were genuine. And if these were true responses – I don't think I can share my writing – the feedback was overwhelming and caused 'stress'. The 'feel' of 'success' – frightening...

9.30pm: at home – drinking hot rum and blackcurrant. 'Who was Sam to gain such a positive response?'

* * *

Sat 27th Feb '99

Today Ashley (aged nine) and Shemika's (aged five) were having Birthday parties. I could have gone to both, but couldn't deal with the excitement (with children there is no excuse for snapping). Besides, I'm going to Nada's Wedding tomorrow, and one social a week is more than enough.

7.30pm: fed up of feeling unsociable and having to 'force enjoyment'. Drank rum and hot blackcurrant to feel happy.

* * *

Sun 28th Feb '99

Nada's wedding – couldn't miss this, especially after having such a loving exchange with Nada's family at the Hen Evening.

* * *

Tue 2nd Mar '99

Lynette at doctor's surgery was supposed to call regarding my 'Medical Exemption Certificate' – she didn't. I really haven't got the energy to be chasing people, especially regarding this surgery. I want to pursue activities leading a 'normal' life – not doing chores because of this wretched stoma.

Rang Blood Donor Helpline to find out where to give blood, but was told I can't give blood until I weigh 7.12lbs! I'm going to eat loads to put on weight. I must 'help others'.

9.30pm: feeling totally pissed off. Frustrated that Lynette's hasn't called – distressed at the need to put on weight – and the whole 'sickness'/'surgery'/'stoma' experience. Drank bottle of wine – needed to relax and stop thinking.

* * *

Wed 3rd Mar '99

Went for a drink and to the cinema with Sharaz, Petrinella and Joan. The 'good' thing about this evening was that we spent most of it in the cinema, so there wasn't much scope to talk. I'm so 'mixed-up'. I want to socialise, but I don't want to be in the company of people?!

* * *

Thu 4th Mar '99

7pm: last Writing class of the spring term. I wish it wasn't – I need to 'keep busy'. We shared our final piece of work. Mine was titled: *Someone's coming up the stairs.*

'I knew it was my sister, Sidiki creeping up the stairs. She was always playing tricks. Sometimes she'd throw herself on the landing, pretending to faint, or jump into my room to frighten me… today was 'roar like a lion day'… As she raced into my room. I pretended to be frightened and surprised at her display… Ha, ha! I frightened you… We laughed, but for different reasons. Hers was for the 'act', and mine of the 'effect (seeing her so excited by this exchange).

My sister is my Best Friend. We share more than the same parentage and siblings, we have a profound understating of each others needs and respect. Never failing under pressure or pain, or circumstance, that's why the only thing powerful enough to break our bond, is us.'

This I felt was more than a 'creative piece of work'. This was a revelation of 'love' – something I was realising for the first time. When I read this, I bawled and sobbed. I cried for every day of my life lived without realising love, and being loved – 9,855 days (plus).

* * *

Fri 5th Mar '99

7.30pm: I forgot to go to the Counselling course! I didn't 'remember' until Sonia called at 7pm and asked how it went. The class starts at 9.30am. It was 7pm and I still hadn't realised I hadn't gone. How could I 'forget' to go? 'I must have a lot on my mind?' Or am I 'losing my mind?' Feeling confused and scared – drank a bottle of wine.

* * *

Sat 6th Mar '99

7.30am: feeling quite relaxed (I think). Perhaps, it's because I'm going to a workshop, today. It's titled 'Connecting with the Goddess Within' and consists of meditation, writing and reflection. The aim is to encourage connecting with 'self' and 'spiritual growth'. During the workshop I wrote:

> 'I'm afraid of my natural growth.
> Others may not like it, but I will – I know I will.
> They don't know me and it's not their fault,
> I've hidden and been someone else for them.
> What they required of me – I was,
> But now it's making me miserable
> I need to breathe.'

I felt gratitude for realising 'what I've been' and the 'need to develop'. And, I know in time I will 'trust' and 'flourish' as I naturally should, and no longer retain aspects that hinder my self-development, and happiness.

8pm: at home reflecting on the workshop. The Guided Meditation was mind blowing. We were asked to 'Give advice and guidance to a child, so that they will grow-up to be a 'perfect' adult' (or something like that). My Goddess (the voice within) advised 'You have the knowledge and experience. Trust these and believe in yourself'. Upon 'hearing' this I realised, I've been 'suppressing all of what matters to me – all of my life'. Emotions surged to the top of my head like a volcanic eruption. And tears gushed from my eyes with the heaviness and abundance of a waterfall.

Today I was reminded that 'I'm not in control' – the 'Almighty Creator' is. And, I'm remembering the morning I had surgery. When Sherilyn prayed for me, asking 'God' to 'protect me' and asking for the surgeon to be 'guided by the wisdom of Him (God)'. She knew 'something' or 'someone else' was in control. We human – beings are not in control of this 'Life' – the Almighty Creator is.

9.20pm: my thoughts are racing – in my 'Childhood' – in my 'Adolescence' – in my 'Adulthood'. 'When I was four years old and cut my finger that dripped heavily with blood, as I used a sharp knife (unsupervised) – when I felt jealous and guilty because my new baby sister was getting more attention and 'love' than me – when I used to spend weekends at Aunty Bernice's and feel sad on the Sunday morning, because I didn't want to go home – when I was ridiculed for my 'skinniness' (my nervous tummy didn't want me eat) – when I was fourteen years old and condemned for smoking and drinking, because I couldn't cope with circumstances at home – when my grandma, aunts and uncles scolded me for not going straight home from school – when I was labelled 'useless' – when I 'failed' the expected 'C' grade with six of my

GCSE's – when I hated living with my parents from the age of twelve – seventeen years ('him' drinking – and 'she' not talking/mothering) – when I placed a chair leg on Rowels hand, because I envied him (his Mum showed him love – mine didn't) – when my survival and sanity was maintained via a best friend from secondary school – remembering the feeling of guilt and deep sorrow when I sincerely told my 'Dear Father' that 'we (siblings) would be better off, if he hung himself'.

'Why am I thinking about all this now?' It started with the writing exercise two weeks ago, that asked us to 'cast our minds back to Childhood', and the Guided Meditation has intensified the thoughts – they're unbearable. I thought meditation was supposed to be relaxing and encourage peacefulness? 'I feel so angry'. My mind feels like it's in a million pieces and these pieces are being flung about like shrapnel in a hurricane. So, many emotions 'sadness' – 'anger' – 'resentment' – 'despair' – and a feeling of 'total detachment from 'my – self' and everyone and the world. The only 'stable' ideas I have right now are that 'I'm not a wicked person' – and I don't think I 'deserve to feel this bad'.

10.05pm: needed to be with someone, but not family. I thought of Lizzy and called her. I told her I needed to talk – that I was desperate to get away from the family 'now'. 'I understand. Come over,' she empathised. I drove to Lizzy's and cried during the whole journey. I don't remember what route I took – all I know is that I arrived.

* * *

Sun 7th Mar '99

7.20am: woke up with the same tension headache that I went to bed with last night. I'm still thinking about past events – the stoma – 'Friends' and family – 'Me (wondering who I now am)'. However, the thoughts are not as intense I think it's because I got a lot off my mind speaking to Lizzy, last night.

3pm: in bath. It's becoming 'easier' to have a bath and change my bag. I'm not so bothered at seeing the bag or changing it – time can be a great healer.

* * *

Mon 8th Mar '99

8.15am woke up feeling relaxed and did for most of the day.

7pm: started thinking again – about past events – about the stoma – about my 'friends' and family – about 'me (wondering who I now was)'. I feel drained – and these thoughts are causing distress. I've tried listening to music and reading to stop the thoughts (to offer some distraction), but I couldn't 'hear' the music regardless of the volume, and when I tried reading, I could only 'see' the words – 'nothing was being registered'...

* * *

Tue 9th Mar '99

2.20am: unable to sleep due to hectic thoughts, babbling voices, and scenes of experiences. I needed to 'silence' everything. I drank a Guinness and six shots of white rum. I didn't want to drink this much, but it took this amount to stop the commotion.

7pm: contacted Tycho and felt extremely privileged to speak with him. I expressed the usefulness of his book and told him I considered it a 'Priceless Gem'. He asked if I'd read his other book, *You really are Responsible*. I told him the title sounded 'frightening'. He assured me that it contained no 'negativity'.

11.45pm: Feeling mentally drained. I'm thinking about 'everything' and 'nothing'.

* * *

Wed 10th Mar '99

Bought *You Really Are Responsible*, and began reading it on the bus. The first part I read was,

> *This book is all about self-empowerment... It is all about developing the attitude "I am responsible for everything that happens to me in my life" as opposed to "I am the victim of my circumstances over which I have no control"... We are not just helpless victims of circumstance, our life is a product of our consciousness...*

What does he mean 'I am responsible for everything that happens to me in my life?!' It's not my fault I got 'UC' and ended up with a stoma! And how can my 'consciousness' be a product of 'my life?!' Sounds like he's suggesting 'I asked for all this shit!' 'What a load of rubbish!' I aggressively closed the book and shoved it into my bag, and peered out the window. As the bus drove past Oxfam I suddenly thought, 'I want to go in there – I want to do some shopping?!' This felt strange – I've only ever been to Oxfam to donate. As I deliberated at this new idea – I missed the stop, but got off at the following one. As I approached the door I took a quick look round and darted in – hoping that no-one I knew saw me. As I browsed the clothing section, I could hardly believe that 'I' was thinking about purchasing 'second-hand clothes', and I realised after a few moments that I was attracted to the 'unconventional' garments. These clothes displayed 'difference' and 'I was different'. I purchased a blouse with a flowery design (not something your 'conventional' person would wear). The cashier was going to give me a bag marked 'Oxfam', but I told him I didn't need one, and squeezed the blouse into my rucksack – I didn't want everyone to know I'd purchased something from Oxfam! I darted out of the door as swiftly as I entered.

When I arrived home I showed everyone my blouse and was ridiculed. Not just because of the design, but because I'd purchased it from 'Oxfam'. 'Err, bet it's got fleas in it – get it away from me!' Mark teased. Mum said, 'Don't put that in my washing machine. You can wash it by hand.' Sidiki added, 'You better use bleach when you wash that – you don't know who's been wearing it.' I became defensive and shouted, 'Dirt only kills you if it falls on top of you' (repeating Dad's advice whilst I was in hospital, when I was distressed at not being able to wash daily). There was silence. I left the kitchen and took my outrageous, flea-bitten, second-hand blouse up to my room. Although part of me understood their reaction, I was angry that they 'didn't accept me' – they didn't see that 'I had changed and was changing' – they didn't appreciate that 'I was now different'.

9.25pm: took *You Really Are Responsible* out of my rucksack and I looked at the cover for some time. I was 'scared' to open the book – but I couldn't let 'fear' defeat me?' I'd experienced greater 'fear' than this – what of the morning of surgery? When I wondered if I'd survive the operation? Surely, I could appreciate that whatever was written was 'just an idea' and not a threat to my survival? I opened the book and began to read,

> *Progress in self-development comes when we look inside ourselves for the answers to our problems instead of trying to put the blame onto everyone and everything else.* (p8)

> *The qualities, both good and bad, that you notice most clearly in another person are usually qualities that you possess yourself...* (p16)

I can't see how I possess qualities like my family or friends 'anymore'. I consider them to be 'superficial' – focusing on materials and not appreciating life (health). I continued reading,

> *If we pay attention to someone's "unworthy" characteristic then this negative aspect of their character will grow...* (p24)

This is what I'm doing with family and friends?! I'm focusing on their 'unworthiness' and 'forgetting' how supportive they were whilst I was in hospital. Just because they don't understand and can't offer support now, doesn't mean they're 'bad'. I'm recognising so many negative aspects of my behaviour, and the more I read – the more distressed I'm becoming. I feel 'guilty' – 'angry' – 'frustrated' – and 'sad'. And 'I'm not sure of anything'.

11.55pm: poured few shots of rum and hot blackcurrant…

And few more. I fell asleep – feeling equally peaceful and numb.

* * *

Thu 11th Mar '99

Began the day reading *You Really Are Responsible*. What I've read so far has mainly caused 'distress', but I can't stop reading it. I'm reading information via titles such as *take responsibility*, *accept others as they are*, and *finding inner peace*. And, although what I'm reading is 'distressing' – it's also very liberating. And, I realise that I've got 'many changes to make'.

* * *

Fri 12th Mar '99

9.30am: Counselling course. We were asked to think about the helpful and unhelpful aspects of our culture. I couldn't think of anything 'helpful' or 'unhelpful' about being 'British'. I then wondered what might be 'helpful' or 'unhelpful' about being 'Asian' – 'African Caribbean' – or 'any other'! Couldn't see the relevance of this exercise. A more useful exercise might have been to think about what makes us 'helpful' or 'unhelpful' human-beings. Isn't it others views that make cultures 'helpful' or 'unhelpful?' As far as I'm concerned 'we're human-beings first – and culture second'.

6.30pm: Joan and Michael arranged a get together. It was to open a letter we'd written in June 1995. I didn't want to meet, but agreed to. I thought we were to meet in the Old Queen's Head Pub, but when I arrived they weren't there. I went to two other pubs, but they weren't there either – I was so glad! As I travelled home I thought, 'the universe is responding to my wants and needs. Now I understand what Tycho means when he writes, 'our life is a product of our consciousness.' My consciousness (mind) conveyed that I didn't want to meet with Joan and Michael – and the response was that our 'arrangement failed' – my true want and need met.

10pm: returned from visiting Sharaz. I must stop forcing myself in certain situations and start trusting my instinct. I felt 'uneasy' about visiting Sharaz, but thought 'I've got to start socialising'. I told Sharaz I was going to an Ileostomy and Internal Support Group (for people with stomas) meeting, hoping she might invite herself and offer some support, but instead she sarcastically replied 'Great!' I felt awful and went numb with shock and pain. Not just because she didn't offer to come, but because of her sarcastic reply. And, for a few moments her reaction literally 'disabled me' – mentally and physically. I understood her response. People who had a stoma were 'indoors people' – 'paraplegics' – 'old and smelly beings' – nothing like me. After her reply, I thought 'I shouldn't be going to this meeting'. And quizzed, 'What was 'I' doing with a stoma?!' I didn't want to have a relation with the 'Ileostomy and Internal Pouch Support Group'. I didn't 'want to have a stoma' and have 'something in common with these people' – 'indoors' – paraplegics' – 'old and smelly'. But I have – and I need to 're-identify myself'. I need to accept 'Sam with a fucking stoma'...

* * *

Sat 13th Mar '99

12.20am: laying in bed and feeling confused – sad – and totally pissed off...

3.30am: still awake. I desperately wanted to sleep, so I poured myself a white rum and hot blackcurrant... And another... And another. I drank till I was numb (again). And no-body knows... 'No-body knows'.

6.30am: woke up with a headache – not a 'hang-over' headache, but a 'tension' headache (pain on left-hand side of face and behind eye). My thoughts aroused me from sleep. My mind was racing – thinking about the visit to Sharaz's yesterday. I need to erase all 'negativity' in my life. This means not only changing 'my' way of thinking and behaviour, but also 'avoiding certain people'.

2pm: attended the IA social and Annual General Meeting. What a 'positive' experience! I felt welcomed and 'accepted!' The members understood what it was like to have a stoma and they were 'normal' – living ordinary lives! I agreed to be a committee member. 'I must keep busy'. And 'I must help others.'

* * *

Sun 14th Mar '99

Woke up feeling miserable. Today I'm going to be a Godmother, and I don't want to be. Nor do I want to go to Church – I'm not religious. I put on the blouse I bought from Oxfam. It wasn't what you'd wear to a Christening, but I didn't feel like 'dressing up'. Can't be bothered with 'all the fuss', or 'attracting attention'.

I wanted to go home after the church service, but I was expected to go back to the house to make a 'Godmother's' speech and join the 'party'. 'If you lose a friend – you gain an enemy, there's no in-between', explained Granny Pat, as we sat chatting in the party. She clarified, 'if there is no animosity you will be able to keep friendship, which is mutual respect and understanding of another point of view.' I thought, 'Ummm – she has a point?' I left with feelings of pleasure – I'd 'enjoyed' mingling.

10.20pm: at home and thinking about my feelings regarding friend-ship 'again'. 'Is my idea of cutting my 'friends' off being harsh?' 'Am I expecting too much?' 'Am I being too judgmental?' I don't know 'what's 'right' or 'wrong' anymore'. I had to have a 'break from my thoughts and the confusion'. I 'needed' to have a drink. I drank some white rum with hot blackcurrant – and I lost count of how many shots I poured...

* * *

Mon 15th Mar '99

4.30am: woke up to find the light and CD player on, and half a glass of cold rum and blackcurrant, on the floor. I turned the light and CD player off and tried to go back to sleep, but started thinking again – about my actions and thoughts regarding friends and family. I think 'I'm being harsh – I'm expecting too much – and I'm being cruelly judgmental. And, 'I'm beginning to hate my feelings – myself – and my life'.

1.45pm: I spoke at length this morning to the Almighty Creator, to try and 'strike a balance' – it can't be all 'bad'? Surely there 'must be something positive about me?' I talked about the operation and those involved in the experience. I thanked him for sending Mr. Bows to rid of my racist attitude, by showing me that 'white' people are first and foremost human-beings – just like me! I thanked the Almighty Creator for the experiences of dis-ease, and pain, and surgery, which have spurred invaluable reflection (even though it's agonizing – it's also 'very liberating'). I thanked the Almighty Creator for Aunty Celia and asked him to forgive me for missing her so much – for my own selfish reasons, and that he had the right to take her. I prayed that wherever she was – she was happy, and I told the Almighty Creator (and Aunty Celia, wasn't sure who I should tell) that I really loved her. I shared that I regretted not telling her this whilst she was alive – and from now on, I'll share my thoughts in the moment. 'Tomorrow is promised to no Man (or Woman)' – and regrets are useless. I thanked the Almighty Creator for the events, lessons and experiences that have developed my understanding of fellow human-beings – opened me up to trust Life – and assisted me to have faith in Him. After speaking with the Almighty Creator – I cried 'tears of joy and gratitude!' Knowing that if I'm Blessed with tomorrow, it would bring new experiences and more 'positive' emotions. It was refreshing to cry 'tears of joy and gratitude' instead of 'sadness and pain'. Praise the Almighty Creator.

* * *

Tue 16th Mar '99

7.30am: woke up feeling creative, and planned to write 'novel'. However, the Almighty Creator sent few distractions, so it wasn't possible to carry out 'my plan' – 'the Almighty's dictated'.

6.30pm: Brendon and Joan came to visit and throughout their stay my mind was on writing. At 8pm I felt irritated and considered asking them to leave, by saying I had writing to do. But then I thought, 'share yourself Sam' – don't 'try to control circumstances' – you 'said' 'friendship and support was what you needed'.

I think Brendon and Joan's visit was the Almighty Creator's response to my request (my conscious mind). And, I believe the Almighty Creator sent this interaction to remind me who is in control. I 'said' I wanted friendship and support – and so the Universe – the Almighty Creator provided.

* * *

Dilemmas, Changes, Realisations

Wed 17th Mar '99

5.20am: experiencing rollercoaster of emotions. One minute 'I'm happy, and content, and full of energy' (trusting The Almighty Creator) – the next 'I'm unhappy, confused and very tired'.

5pm: feeling very tired and didn't bathe again. Haven't washed since Sunday (for the Christening). Feeling lethargic and in need of a 'rest', but my mind wouldn't allow. Everything feels so demanding and tiring. Getting out of bed – being awake (thinking) – brushing teeth – washing – combing hair – eating – emptying bag – talking to people. 'I need to get rid of some of these chores'. I'm getting forgetful and vacant. I think it's because my mind is constantly preoccupied with 'reflection' and 'analysis'. I'm watching and analysing friends – parents – siblings – neighbours – and strangers 'behaviour'. When they talk, walk, or do an activity, I wonder, 'Why did they say that?' – 'Why did they do that.' – 'What are they going to do next?'

11.50pm: feeling shattered. Still 'reflecting' and 'analysing' behaviour – I'm fed up with this. I've been 'reflecting' and 'analysing' all day. 'I wish I could stop'. Drank some white rum and hot blackcurrant – I 'had' to – or be 'awake all night'.

* * *

Thu 18th Mar '99

7.45am: woke up and thought of one daily chore I could get rid of – combing my hair. I'm going to get my hair cut (shaved to 2mm) so I won't need to comb it?!

2.50pm: been deliberating most of the morning. 'Shall I cut my hair – or not?' It would be more than ridding of a chore – it would also be 'changing my image'.

3.30pm: decided that I'm going to do it (left in a rush and without washing)! Glad no-one was in, because if I told them what I was going to do – they would have tried to talk me out of it.

4pm: arrived at the hairdressers and sat in the barbers section. The barber double-looked when he saw me sitting in his area and informed, 'The women's section is over there,' and pointed towards the back of the shop. Looking at a man having his hair cut to about 2mm long, I replied, 'I know. I want my hair almost shaven, like his.' The barber looked surprised and said, 'You want to cut off all your hair?' I laughed and said, 'Well, not all of it. Leave on as much as he's got!' He replied slowly in a low tone, 'Okay. I'll be with you shortly.' When the barber ordered, 'Next. You Missy,' it sounded as if he bellowed. I was in deep thought, wondering, 'what I'd look like with virtually no hair', and 'whether I was sure'. I leapt from the 'waiting chair' and sat in one of the big black leather 'hair cutting chairs' – to get my hair shaved down to 2mm. The barber teased his fingers through my Afro with a frown. 'Are you sure you want to cut off this lovely hair? You know once I start, there's no going back,' he warned. For a moment we both stared at the reflection of me and my Afro in the mirror. My thoughts were rapid and confusing. It was 'lovely hair' – 'Did I want the old Sam to go?' – 'What would the 'new' Sam look like?' – 'What would people think and say?' There was a moment of panic, but then there was a sense of calm. I took a deep breath and said, 'If I don't like it – I'll wear a hat until it grows back!' The barber proceeded. He took a large pair of scissors and began to cut chunks of my 'lovely hair'. I sat and watched in the mirror, the clumps of hair falling from my head – onto my shoulders – onto my lap – and with each snip – a sense of liberation prevailed. This hair cut was freeing me of a chore. This hair cut was expressing change – embracing a new 'Sam'. This hair cut was stating freedom – from 'trivial' (hair). This hair cut was displaying an image that said, 'I'm not conventional – I'm different'.

When I arrived home Doreen shrieked, 'You've cut your hair off! It looks nice,' and she was smiling and swirling around me. Mark bolted from his room to find out what all the excitement was. 'Er, you look like a man,' he said with a fit of laughter and ran back to his room. I wasn't sure what reaction I preferred. I didn't want to 'look nice', or 'look like a man!' I went upstairs and looked in the mirror. 'Sam?' I questioned the reflection with a frown and smile. I liked this new image. I didn't care for the appearance – I loved the representation and expression that I thought it conveyed, 'I'm not conventional – I'm different'.

11.45pm: I've been constantly looking in the mirror and feeling my head! Can't believe I've cut almost all my hair off! Can't believe how good I feel about it – how comfortable the image and expression 'I'm not conventional – I'm different' – suits me. Feeling very happy. Drank a few shots of rum and Supermalt (nutritional drink with B vitamins – healthier than blackcurrant). Nice not to drink, because I 'need to be rid of thoughts' – nice to have a few drinks, because 'I'm happy and want to'.

* * *

Fri 19th Mar '99

7.20am: woke up feeling tired – too tired to attend Counselling course. Went back to bed.

11.15pm: stayed in bed most of today, dozing in and out of sleep, but I still feel exhausted.

* * *

Sat 20th Mar '99

Went to an Islamic event that was predominately attended by black people. I didn't appreciate the 'beliefs' – the notion that white people were responsible for all the unfortunate circumstances that black people found themselves in. They spoke about the underachievement of black boys – high rate of unemployment amongst the black population – and suggested foods marketed for black shoppers were being deliberately contaminated by white suppliers. The belief was that black people were being victimised by the white population. I wondered if they realised that black people had a part to play in these unfortunate circumstances. I wondered if they realised that foods in general were being contaminated with harmful additives and colours in supermarkets (on offer to all), not just black people? I wondered if they knew that white people suffer too? However, what I liked about this group was the 'intimacy'. These people had something in common, and were part of a group – and I envied their closeness. I want to share this type of 'intimacy' and 'be part of a group' – 'I'm fed up of being alone'.

* * *

Sun 21st Mar '99

2pm: went to Dad's for dinner and got a burning sensation in my stomach after one mouthful. I ate a second mouthful and aching in my abdomen followed. I groaned in pain. 'You al-right?' Dad asked in a voice of concern. 'No. I think the Peppered Fish is upsetting my stomach,' I replied. 'Oh, naw,' Dad said sucking his teeth with disappointment. 'Juss eat de rice and vege-tebles, den?' he suggested. I tried a small amount of rice, but my stomach didn't like that either. I resulted to just drinking water.

9.30pm: at home. The abdominal pains have increased. I drank hot rum with blackcurrant to numb the physical pain and mental distress. But when I sipped this 'hot alcoholic remedy' my stomach reacted as if I'd put a flame on petrol. I opened my mouth to allow some of the heat to escape, and dashed downstairs for water to 'put out the fire'. I gulped down the saviour and it took a few moments before the burning ceased. I stood in a bent position over the sink and drew a deep breath of relief, feeling calm for a moment. But then panic! Not because I was scared of the physical reaction, but as I thought, 'If I can't drink alcohol – I won't survive'.

* * *

Mon 22nd Mar '99

8am: woke up full of energy, but as the day progressed, started feeling tired.

7pm: haven't 'thought' much today – I've got that 'numb feeling' again.

* * *

Tue 23rd Mar '99

5pm: been in bed most of today 'again'. I'm getting fed up with this 'numb feeling'. 'I' want to get up and go, but my body and my mind are not permitting. Who am I? If not my body – if not my mind?

* * *

Wed 24th Mar '99

5.50am: woke up with abdominal pain. Hope it's not 'another blockage' or some other complication.

8.10am: pain is getting worse. Drank water and it induced cramping pains.

12.20pm: vomited. Reluctantly telephoned for an ambulance.

5.30pm: x-ray – drip attached – admitted to Cut Up ward. 'Back in fucking hospital!' 'This is the third time since surgery'. I'm beginning to feel like a burden. Mum and Dad were with me in A&E and I was thinking, 'Oh, here we go again' – and I 'know' they were too.

7pm: Nadeem (senior registrar) came to see me. As he approached the bed he smiled and said, 'Hello, Samantha. How are you?' I was agitated by his smile – what was there to smile about?! And what a stupid question – 'How are you?' I felt like saying, 'I'm fucking fine! That's why I'm in hospital!' But instead I forced a smile and said, 'I'm in a lot of pain.' He continued, 'I've looked at your x-rays. Looks like it could possibly be a blockage, or adhesions. I'm not sure.' I couldn't believe what he was telling me. 'Could possibly be a blockage' – I could have suggested that! And was it 'adhesions' or not?! I couldn't contain my anger. 'I thought this operation was going to make me better! This is the third time I've been back in hospital, and no-one seems to know what's going on,' I barked at him. His facial expression shifted from being relaxed to nervous. 'It's only four months post-surgery and it takes time for things to settle down. You may need to cut out certain foods, and change your eating habits. Sam, I'm sure things will settle down. See you tomorrow,' he replied in a dejected tone. I didn't say anything and thought, 'How could he be 'sure things will settle down?' 'Even with an x-ray – he didn't know what was going on'. My energy dipped and I asked pitifully, 'Will Mr. Bows come and see me too?' 'No, he's on holiday. He'll be back on Monday,' he informed. I thought, 'Back on Monday!' I can't wait till Monday to see him! But then he was the only one I trusted (well sort of) right now.

* * *

Thu 25th Mar '99

4.30am: really need to sleep – but it's too noisy and 'Ward Life' won't allow it. Staff are slamming bin lids, talking and laughing loudly, banging doors, and switching on lights. The entry buzzer to the ward is alarming – continuously. Fellow patients are calling out 'nurse', coughing, blowing noses, groaning in pain, or farting. And, after 7am it's impossible to get any rest in this place. There's breakfast – staff handover – bathing session – making of beds (whether you're ready to get up or not!) – curtains drawn – lights on – librarian visits – phlebotomists visits, Consultant visits – cleaners sweeping around you and the bed – blood pressure and temperature tests – drip change – the clutter of crockery. Then, there's the continue flow of patients visitors (strangers) in the intimacy of being in bed and feeling ill – and staff and visitors shouting at 'Mrs. Smith' (who's hard of hearing)!

7.10am: lying in pain – feeling tired and agitated. It's a fucking nightmare being in here! 'I hate this place'.

3pm: feeling totally pissed off. Still experiencing severe pain and I'm exhausted. 'I need to sleep'. And, I'm trying not to get angry – I'm trying to appreciate this experience. I'm trying to think of a 'solution' rather than dwell on the 'problem'. I'm trying to be 'positive'. But, 'I need to sleep' and 'I need to go home'.

5pm: lying in bed and began listening to the patient in the bed next to mine. She was 'talking to herself' with a childlike innocence and in an abstract style. She had a 'Smoker's Cough'. After a few moments I felt compelled to note what she was saying:

'Hurts your legs' – (cigarettes)'

'I had my leg off – I had my leg off.'

'Smoked too much.'

'60 a day.'

'I hate them now – the smell everything.'

'I used to smoke 60 a day, but 40 is still too much.'

'60 a day for 30 years.'

'They're now making mistakes, when they dress the stump with the 'wrong dressing'.'

'I'm 'always hot' – maybe too many cigarettes.'

'I can't go to the canteen without a wheelchair.'

'I can't get out of bed on my own.'

'I smoked 60 cigarettes for 30 years.'

Auxiliary nurse asks, 'What's for dinner tomorrow? 'Broccoli, pork, and fruits! But I'm not interested in anything,' she retorted.

I felt sad hearing this. I'd observed this patient who found it hard to breathe, yesterday. She sternly asked me to 'Leave the window open Miss – I need air to breathe'. My bed was alongside the window – I was cold during the day and night, but, I couldn't deprive her of the need for air. She was mostly awake during the night – and slept throughout the day. She lay with the covers revealing her scared tummy and her stump. She ate many fruits and drank lots of water – I guess 'trying to rectify the damage and dis-ease'. I felt very 'sad for her – and fortunate for me'.

* * *

Fri 26th Mar '99

Still in hospital – still in severe pain. Water brings on cramping pains and my abdomen is swelling. I don't know why, and nor do 'they' (the medics) – 'we make a great team?!'

9.30am: today was the last Counselling course lesson. I've missed the chance to say 'Bye' to the students. Can't 'plan' anything with this fucking stoma.

* * *

Sat 27th Mar '99

7am: feeling better. Still experiencing pain, but less severe and frequent.

Still only allowed sips of water – haven't eaten for four days now!

5.10pm: doctor visited and has 'allowed' me to eat.

6pm: dinner. Ate and it was so painful. I nearly (foolishly) asked for painkillers, but then thought 'if they know I'm experiencing pain, when I eat – they'll keep me in longer'. So I'm bearing the pain and 'I'm not telling'.

6.30pm: Mum, Simeon, and Brendon came to visit. People must be getting fed up of me being in hospital – I'm fed up of being in hospital. 'This is the third time since surgery'.

* * *

Sun 28th Mar '99

8am: I was scared to eat breakfast this morning, remembering the pain I experienced yesterday, but I had to. I needed to prove I was getting better. So I had a few mouthfuls of Cornflakes. Again, it was very painful, but at least I'd eaten.

12.30pm: Lunchtime. I forced myself to eat half a pilchard and two mouthfuls of mashed potato. There was 'some discomfort'. Well, it was 'a bit painful'. Actually, I was in 'excruciating pain'. 'I hate this'.

2pm: 'Doctor on call' visited and as he approached – I psyched myself up for 'action'. I sat up-right, and tried to show no sign of pain. 'How are you today?' he asked in an inviting voice. 'Fine. I've ingested and tolerated food, my stoma's completely functional, and I'm urinating regularly,' I ranted in 'medic' language (to further convince him). I then dragged my nightie up to my chest and began prodding my abdominal area. And continued to inform, 'Look – my abdomen is no longer distended – have a feel!' He looked embarrassed, and pulled my nightie down. He began examining my abdomen over the nightie. I couldn't conceal the excruciating pain induced by the prodding and cried out. 'It's no longer distended, but you're still very sore. I think you better stay till tomorrow to see Mr. Bows,' he said. My body slumped – feeling defeated. I felt like kicking myself. 'Have a feel!' Why did I invite him to examine me? Before that he had no reason, not to discharge me. Still, I need to see Mr. Bows. 'They' suggest that these blockages might be 'an ongoing occurrence!' 'An ongoing fucking occurrence!' I want to know what he has to say about this. And if this is going to be 'an ongoing occurrence' – I want these admissions to be as short as possible.

9.20pm: lying on this cold hospital bed feeling uncomfortable and very sore inside. I feel like crying, but there's a lack of physical energy and the mental pain would be too much too bear. Numbness prevails. I thought this 'operation was going to make me better'. 'I hate this'.

* * *

Mon 29th Mar '99

5.30am: feeling drained and abdomen is still sore.

9.30am: Mr. Bows (followed by four students) visited and my feelings of frustration and anger disappeared! He approached me full of energy and with a radiant smile. 'Sam! What are you doing in here?! I'll tell you – it's got something to do with that haircut!' he joked and we laughed. He asked if he could examine my abdomen. 'Mmmm, abdomen feels okay, but I can tell you're still experiencing pain,' he stated with inquisitive eyes. I maintained the eye contact and calmly said with a smile, 'I'm okay to go home.' He said nothing, but his eyes and raised eyebrows questioned, 'Are you sure?' I too voiced nothing, but smiled and nodded. There was a moment of silence. 'Right, then! Sam can go home,' he said lively, tapping my shin and continued, 'Take care Sam. See you in clinic.'

It was good seeing Mr. Bows. I no longer felt drained – I felt full of energy! Sometimes I wonder, 'Why do I appreciate him so much and is it healthy?' Sometimes I'm overwhelmed by his caring and seemingly sincere personality. Sometimes I'm reduced to tears.

* * *

Tue 30th Mar '99

8am: at home. Still experiencing soreness in my abdomen, and stomach, along with backache.

Hadn't drank since 21st March when I vomited (and wasn't able to drink due to being in hospital). I thought it might not be a good idea to drink of alcohol, because I was experiencing soreness in my stomach, but, thought it might be a good remedy to help my backache (I'm fed up of feeling pain). So I poured a glass of wine and took a sip. Moments later my stomach 'yelled out' in pain – but I ignored it (I'm fed up with feeling pain). And, I didn't care about the 'yell of pain' in pursuit of comfort and 'pleasure' – I knew that if I persisted – the pain would soon go – I'd be too tipsy to be aware of it. After the second glass of wine both the soreness in my stomach, and backache disappeared. And, I no longer felt miserable about 'being in pain' – or about the 'problems relating to surgery'.

* * *

Wed 31st Mar '99

8.20am: woke up feeling lethargic, but Sidiki raised my energy. She encouraged me to go out. I went shopping and when I arrived home – 'I felt useful and productive'.

11.55pm: to bed feeling exhausted and relaxed. Didn't have a drink.

* * *

Thu 1st Apr '99

6.30am: stomach is still a bit tender, but not as sore. Feeling very energetic and positive.

7.45pm: I've done lots of washing and sorting out clutter, and thought 'I deserve a drink!' Pondered on 'What alcoholic drink wouldn't cause pain?' Couldn't think of any, but thought since I hadn't drank yesterday (had a break), my stomach would probably be okay. So, I drank a glass of wine. There was an 'uncomfortable burning' sensation, but it wasn't severe pain, and I knew by the second glass – 'I'd be too tipsy to be aware of it'.

* * *

Sat 3rd Apr '99

11am: outfits delivered by clothing company. I've started Home Shopping (never done this before), it's not ideal, but at least I don't have to go out. I've been feeling unsociable for the last week and haven't felt like speaking to people. I think this is 'a phase'. I just need some 'time alone at the moment'.

6.35pm: feeling 'out of sorts'. 'Bored' – but don't want to be entertained. 'Tired' – but not sleepy.

11.10pm: thought I needed some air (haven't been out for five days), so I went for a walk. I felt scared (it was a bit 'late' and you never know who's out there), but I was desperate to rid of my 'out of sorts' feeling.

11.40pm: back, but still feeling the same. Lying in bed trying to relax, but 'I have a lot in my mind (again)'. Past events – The stoma – 'Friends' and family – 'Me (who I am)'. I needed to relax. Drank some white rum and Nurishment. It didn't cause pain – I guess it's because Nurishment is a milk based drink – alkaline versus acid. Wish I'd thought of this mix before.

* * *

Sun 4th Apr '99

10.40am: awake and feeling shattered. Didn't sleep well. Still got 'a lot in my mind'. Past events – The stoma – 'Friends' and family – 'Me (who I am)'. And now I've that feeling of numbness, 'again'.

4pm: Sherilyn invited me to a Christian concert. I decided to go since she seems so content and I thought, 'I might become satisfied by attending Church – by 'joining a group'.

At the end of the service the pastor invited people who weren't 'saved' to come up to the front to be 'prayed for'. I didn't immediately go up, but heard a voice somewhere inside me say, 'go up to be prayed for – you need help'. However, I remained in the seat – feeling paralysed, until my eyes met Sherilyn's. She looked at me with equally ordering and encouraging eyes that 'said', 'go up to be prayed for – you need help'. So, I made my way up to the front and knelt down – to be prayed for. Saved members awaited us. One held my left hand, whilst another placed their palms on my head. Moments later, the pastor began praying for us:

'Dear God – may these wounded sinners be Blessed with your presence – may they know you and walk in your shadow – may they turn themselves away from all evil – may they come to you in their suffering. Help them Lord for they are caught-up in the evils of the world and today they wish to be Saved. Lord set them free for they have suffered enough. Help them to heal their wounds by coming unto you – our Saviour. Lord they have seen the light today – and they have come to embrace you – have mercy upon them. Amen'.

I started crying (actually bawling) and so did all the other 'wounded sinners'. When I got up I felt 'hopeless' and 'weak'. This prayer confirmed that I would have to 'depend on something or someone else' to feel better. That 'I was not in control of all of this (Life)'. That 'God' – the Almighty Creator was in control. I think I was supposed to feel better knowing this (a sense of relief)? But I left the Church in despair – if I'm not in control – how can I really be sure I'll be taken care of? On the way home – all I could think about was the need to feel calm – the need to have a drink...

10.30pm: arrived home – at last (it seemed to take forever to get here)! I headed straight to the kitchen with my coat on, and poured some white rum with Nurishment. I took a gulp and immediately felt calmer. Yet again – no pain. Nurishment – great for the body. Rum – great for the mind.

* * *

Mon 5th Apr '99

7.30am: woke up this morning and definitely appreciate that 'something or someone else is in control'.

6.10pm: Aunty Bernice rang and we spoke until 5am! The talk cleared much of my confusion. I love this relationship. Thank you! A big 'Thank You' to the Almighty Creator for Aunty Bernice. I know you have sent her (and others) for the good of me...

* * *

Tue 6th Apr '99

5.35am: felt content and overwhelmed with happiness. I needed to relax. Drank few glasses of wine – and retired peacefully.

10.50am: awake and feeling refreshed! Just five hours sleep and I feel wonderful! I think it's because I went to bed with a peaceful mind.

Just realised I drink whether I'm experiencing eustress (happy stress) or distress (unhappy stress). And, I've just realised I've 'drank alcohol almost every day this year'. 'How did this happen?' Drank few shots of rum and blackcurrant.

* * *

Wed 7th Apr '99

6.30am: I 'need' to reduce my alcohol intake. 'I've drunk alcohol almost every day this year'. So I won't have one today.

11.50am: to Madame Tussauds Museum with Mark and Doreen.

8.30pm: arrived home feeling shattered, but relaxed. The visit gave a break from distressing and draining thoughts. Thank the Almighty Creator for this event.

11.15pm: drank Supermalt and rum. I said 'I wouldn't drink today,' but my mind has started racing again. Past events – The stoma – 'Friends' and family – 'Me' (who I am). And, I'm shattered – and I need to sleep. I won't drink any alcohol tomorrow.

* * *

Sat 10th Apr '99

Had an allergy test that suggested I avoid the following foods (as my body reacted 'adversely' to them):

Barley	*Monosodium*	*Mushroom*
Rye	*glutamate (E621)*	*Beer*
Cows milk	*Red wine*	*Yeast*
Yoghurt	*Wheat*	*Chocolate*
Pork	*Oats*	*Gin*
Orange	*Cow's cheese*	
Sugar	*Egg*	

I told the Consultant that I'd had an operation that involved the removal of my colon. He retorted 'that's impossible – you can't live without a colon!' I told him that's what they (medics) had told me – that they've 'removed my colon', and with the evidence of shit pouring out of my abdomen – I had no reason to disbelieve them. 'I think I am living and not a ghost!' I teased. He looked bewildered and forced a smile.

I pondered on what the Consultant had said, 'that's impossible – you can't live without a colon'. And, I wondered if 'they (medics)' had 'really' removed my colon?' And, I worried 'how long my body would last without this necessary organ'.

3.25pm: arrived home worrying. 'How long will my body last without my Colon?' And, I kept hearing the Consultants words, 'That's impossible – you can't live without a Colon'. However, I know you can live without a colon – I've seen people via IA. But now I'm wondering how 'well' I can.

9.30pm: feeling distressed. 'How well can I live without my colon?' Drank some rum and hot blackcurrant. Hadn't drank for two days (that's a 'break') – so, I needn't feel guilty.

* * *

Sun 11th Apr '99

7.10am: woke up feeling 'rough' and 'sad'. 'Rough', because I drank too much. 'Sad', because relief came in form of drinking 'again'.

1pm: went to 'Sistah's in Film' at Brixton. It was an event showing short films produced by people with 'alternative ideas'. I thought it would be good to attend, since there was a film that looked at 'childhood experiences'. I thought it would help with my distress at the moment (regarding 'Past Events') and that experiences shared might 'validate' mine.

When I arrived I was shocked by the audience that was ninety percent black women. I'd never been to an event with such a unusual crowd, and thought, 'Maybe I've found my group'. However, as I walked towards the front to sit, I was horrified at what I saw – two women kissing! 'Like a couple!' They were a couple?! I was at a lesbian event! I felt sick. I didn't belong here with 'these women' – I wasn't a lesbian.

Part of me wanted to leave, but I really wanted to see this childhood experience, so I headed towards the front – in a daze. I desperately looked for a row of empty seats (not wanting to sit next to any of 'the lesbians'). I found a seat with empty ones either side and sat with my head down (hoping that no-one would speak to me). But, after a few moments a woman approached with a radiant smile and said, 'Hi Sister. I'm Abigail. How ya doing today?' My heart began pounding and I replied without smiling, 'Fine,' hoping my unfriendly and defensive tone would have sent her packing. But she continued, 'What's your interest?' I felt like saying, 'Not you – I'm not a lesbian – so piss off!' But instead I replied in the same tone, 'I'm here to view the last film about childhood.' She continued, 'Oh, why's that?' I began to get agitated and folded my arms, thinking 'this woman isn't getting it! Can't she hear my tone? Or read my body language?' I continued with more harshness, 'I'm writing about childhood experiences.' She stopped smiling – she'd got it! She'd realised that I didn't want to speak to her and replied in a sad tone, 'Okay Sister. I hope you enjoy the film,' and she sat in a seat a couple of rows in front of me.

When the film started Abigail glanced back at me with 'sad eyes'. I felt guilty, 'Why did I speak to her like that? She didn't deserve it'. I dropped my head downwards. She looked at me a second time with the same 'sad eyes' and my guilt turned to sorrow for her. I smiled to offer some condolence, and she instantly displayed the same radiant smile, when she first approached me. Immediately, I knew I'd done 'wrong' – she'd taken my smile as an invitation to talk to me again, and I felt stupid for sending 'mixed signals'. I tried to leave as soon as the film was over, so Abigail couldn't get to me, but I was able to. A woman at the end of the row I was sitting in, was putting her coat on and I couldn't pass. Abigail was back! This time with a piece of paper and a pen! 'Hi, again Sister,' she said smiling. 'Did you enjoy the film?' I forced myself to smile and replied, 'Yeah. It was interesting. I must go'. As I hustled to get away, she held up the piece of paper and pen. 'Can I get your number, Sister?' she rapped in a desperate voice. I couldn't believe it – this woman fancied me! Couldn't she 'see' I wasn't a lesbian. I abruptly replied, 'No, sorry. Take care,' and rushed out of the building – to get away from 'the lesbians'…

* * *

Mon 12th Apr '99

1.15am: awake thinking about the way I spoke to Abigail yesterday. 'She didn't deserve to be spoken to like that just because she was a 'lesbian'. I was a horrible bitch. Yesterday, I failed to realise that 'lesbians' can experience 'all the emotions that I do'. Yesterday, I failed to realise that 'lesbians' are a 'creation of the Almighty Creator (just like me)'. Yesterday, I failed to realise that 'lesbians' were 'first and foremost human beings'.

3.30am: thinking about the comment made by the Consultant who done the allergy test, 'that's impossible – you can't live without a colon'. Even though I know 'everything happens for a reason' – 'I still have regrets'. Fuck! Why didn't I take the symptoms of 'UC' – the dis-ease seriously? Why didn't I have faith in what the Almighty Creator has provided for us to heal ourselves via herbs? Why did I place the 'cure' of my 'illness' in the hands of others, instead of him? And even though I know that 'One often learns more in ten days of suffering than ten years of contentment' – I hate the 'suffering' and I hate having a stoma. Still, I must give thanks to the Almighty Creator – I am alive'.

4.20am: Drank some hot rum and blackcurrant... And some more... And some more. 'Lesbians were first and foremost human beings' – 'Everything happens for a reason – I still have regrets'.

6.30am: retired peacefully and fell asleep – instantly.

2pm: woke up feeling tired (as usual) wonder why I wake up feeling tired no matter how much sleep I get.

* * *

Tue 13th Apr '99

10.30am: went shopping for 'new' foods based on the allergy test. I wondered around the supermarket trying to find appropriate foods, but 'everything' appears to contain gluten. Can't eat bread – can't eat crackers – can't eat cereals – can't eat biscuits... And what doesn't contain Monosodium Glutamate (MSG) – contains dairy... And what doesn't contain gluten – contains MSG! I left the supermarket feeling distressed – with no 'new' foods and wondering 'what can I eat'.

7pm: just realised if I don't write in this diary for one day – by the next day I've forgotten what has happened. 'What's happening to my memory?' Drank a bottle of wine and didn't feel guilty – haven't drank for two days.

* * *

Wed 14th Apr '99

1.30pm: at the barber's and experienced severe cramping pains, whilst getting my hair cut. The barber jested in a Jamaican accent, 'Gal! Ah wah yuh neyam laars nite dat ah bun yah belly suh?!' I was unable to reply, but forced a smile as I wriggled in the chair.

4.30pm: arrived home and took two Paracetamols (was desperate to rid of the pain), but the medication had no effect and the pain was getting worse.

5.30pm: lying in excruciating pain – hoping that whatever is going on will stop. 'I don't want to go to hospital.'

6.50pm: doubled-up in pain, but tried to resist it, hoping that this 'possible blockage' would clear itself. 'I don't want to go to hospital'.

8.45pm: vomited green bile and while I was bowed over the toilet bowl, Mum came in the bathroom. 'Oh, Sam, you're not well. I think you better go to hospital,' she said in an equally ordering and querying voice. I reluctantly gave a nod of approval. Fuck! 'I don't want to go to hospital!' I felt like crying, but thought, 'that won't help'. Mum dialled 999. The ambulance arrived and drove me to A&E...

10.20pm: taken for x-rays. Doctor on duty advised that the x-rays hadn't confirmed a blockage, but because the stoma had stopped working and I was experiencing severe pain, and vomiting – 'something must be going on'. He advised that Mr. Bows would make a second opinion – 'Tomorrow'. 'Tomorrow!' This meant I was going to be admitted – this meant staying in hospital! I was hoping that they would have done something in A&E, and I would be discharged after a few hours – not admitted! Doctor wrote necessary notes for my 'admission'. 'I hate this'.

* * *

Thu 15th Apr '99

7.30am: Mr. Bows looked surprised when he saw me. 'Sam! What are you doing here?!' he asked in a jovial tone. 'I don't know!' I replied smiling, whilst at the same time quizzed in my mind, 'Ummm, what am I doing here?!' He continued in a jovial manner, 'It's your new haircut, I tell you!' I chuckled, feeling slightly offended, and continued, 'I suspected a blockage, but the x-ray hasn't confirmed this. Anyway, I feel fine now,' I tried to reassure (hoping he'd 'authorise' discharge). But, he examined my abdomen, and said, 'Sam, you feel very tender and quite distended. You need to remain in hospital for intravenous fluids – to give your bowels a rest, and for observation. See you tomorrow,' he stated, leaving without any opportunity for me to contend. At hearing this, misery prevailed and the little energy I had – seeped out of me. I lay on the bed and curled up into foetus position, covering my head with the cold cotton sheet, and flimsy blanket. 'I hate this'.

* * *

Fri 16th Apr '99

7.30am: Mr. Bows arrived. 'Morning Sam. Oh, you don't appear happy,' he said with a pitiful look. I didn't change my miserable expression and I didn't reply. 'Can I exam your abdomen?' he asked. Again – I didn't reply. He continued to carry out the examination. 'Mmmm, feels better. Right, the fluids can be removed,' he said looking at one of the student doctors who then wrote in my Medical Notes. 'Sam, you can start drinking sips of water and if you're able tolerate liquids for the day, you can have a light dinner. If dinner stays down – you can go home this evening. How's that?' Mr Bows advised and asked. I smiled and sat up. 'Can I try lunch. I feel a lot better,' I asked enthusiastically (hoping that if I was able to tolerate lunch, I could go home sooner). Mr. Bows looked at me with a frown and said, 'Sam, don't rush things.'

6pm: Dinner is due, but hasn't arrived...

6.10pm: still not arrived...

6.20pm: still waiting for dinner…

6.30pm: dinner still hasn't arrived! 'I need to eat – I need to go home'.

6.40pm: dinner arrived (at last)! I gobbled two mouthfuls of the mashed potatoes and a small piece of chicken. Moments later I had excruciating pain in my stomach and couldn't eat anymore. But I had to pretend that I'd eaten this dinner, else discharge wouldn't be permitted. So, I wrapped most of the remainder of the dinner in a paper towel and threw it in the communal clinical waste (not in my bin – a loyal nurse might checked it).

7.05pm: buzzed for a nurse. 'I've eaten and tolerated dinner,' I lied. 'Can you please remove the cannula so I can go home?' 'How much have you eaten?' she asked looking at the dinner plate, and then answered her own question, 'Oh, you've eaten quite a lot. Well done! I'll go and get the necessary bits to take out the cannula'.

7.10pm: still waiting for her to return.

7.20pm: she still hasn't come back! I walked to the Nurse's Station to find her, but no-one was there.

7.30pm: still waiting.

7.40pm: buzzed again. Five minutes later – the same nurse arrived looking agitated and explained that there was an 'emergency with another patient' and that I'd have to wait for night staff to remove the cannula. I couldn't wait for 'night staff to remove the cannula'. By the time they'd 'handed over' it would be after 9pm. I needed to leave 'now'. I got dressed and removed the cannula myself (covering the gaping hole that was gashing out blood with a tissue, and pressure, just as I'd seen them do it).

8.05pm: made the bed and lied again to a different nurse at the Nursing Station that I'd tolerated dinner and was now 'entitled' to be discharged. She said she'd write up the discharge notes.

8.45pm: discharged. Travelled home by bus.

9.25pm: arrived home. Mum asked why I hadn't called to ask someone to collect me. 'I'm not an invalid Mum! It's alright for me to make my own way home,' I angrily retorted. Doesn't she realise that I feel 'like a burden' when I ask for assistance? Doesn't she realise that I'm 'totally pissed off with this 'backwards and forwards to hospital?' Doesn't she realise that, I don't want to 'bore anyone else with this shit?' And, doesn't she realise that, I need to 'regain my independence' – and 'control?'

* * *

Sat 17th Apr '99

10.30pm: desperate for an alcoholic drink (haven't had one for three days due to being in hospital). Feeling distress. I hate this 'backwards and forwards to hospital' – pain – vomiting – distended abdomen – drips – can't eat – can eat. I felt desperate for a break from these thoughts, but I resisted having a drink. I need to exercise some 'control.'

* * *

Mon 19th Apr '99

I've started noting all the foods that I'm eating to identify what might be causing 'possible blockages', and will definitely go shopping for 'new' foods – 'tomorrow'.

* * *

Tue 20th Apr '99

Went shopping for 'new' foods as planned and bought,

Goats cheese	*Spring onions*	*Smoked Salmon*
Soya yoghurts	*Apples*	*Honey*
Sesame Seed Snaps	*Kiwis*	*Cucumber*
Vegetable Rice pasta	*Soya milk*	*Broccoli*
Tuna in brine	*Egg-free mayonnaise*	*Bananas*
Ready salted crisps	*Rice Cakes*	

When I arrived home I unpacked the 'new' foods and felt excited. What could I try?! I topped rice cakes with salmon slices, goats cheese and thinly sliced cucumber. Ummm – I was pleasantly surprised. They didn't taste 'nice', but they didn't taste 'awful' either! I could acquire a taste for these 'new' foods. I only ate four rice cakes (didn't want to overwhelm the stoma with too much fibre and encourage a blockage). But, I was still hungry. So I topped up with a 'soft food' – soya yoghurt, and felt satisfied.

* * *

Thu 22nd Apr '99

7pm: started the Summer term of Writers course. Glad to be back and part of this group. We were asked to think of something we love or hate and describe it. I thought about 'love' and wrote,

My Dad. Large round gleaming face and head, small eyes, big forehead, that extends to his balding head. A glorious smile, that always seems to chuckle.

We were then asked to re-write what we'd written from the opposite perspective (hate). I wrote:

Head large and scary. His smile too glorious to be true, pretence. Eyes small and sly, the look, judgmental, scheming, scanning.

Amazing how 'perceptions can differ'.

10pm: arrived home feeling overwhelmed with enlightenment – the 'powerful realisation' of how 'perceptions can differ'. I needed to relax. Drank white rum and hot blackcurrant.

* * *

Sat 24th Apr '99

Drank a bottle of wine – because it's the weekend.

* * *

Tue 27th Apr '99

7.45pm: felt 'bored' and 'numb' for most of today. Had a drink of rum and blackcurrant.

* * *

Wed 28th Apr '99

Delivered Neil's (nurse at Lank's Hospital) leaving card. He 'cared' for me whilst in hospital and was extremely compassionate. He made me feel like 'I was a person' rather than 'a patient'. And I 'had' to let him know that his care was appreciated.

* * *

Fri 30th Apr '99

I haven't written much in the last week. Not much to note. I haven't been overwhelmed with activities or thoughts. The only thing to note is my alcohol drinking. I've been drinking alcohol almost every day. Sometimes I consider it a 'problem' – sometimes I don't.

* * *

Sun 2nd May '99

Drank – since it's the weekend.

* * *

Thu 6th May '99

7pm: we were to attended an event at Saison Poetry Library, Royal Festival Hall (RFH) instead of our usual Writing class. The RFH seemed like a million miles away and I didn't want to be in unfamiliar surroundings. And, I didn't want to meet new people, so I stayed at home.

9.30pm: I wish I'd gone to the event. How could the journey there 'seem like a million miles away?' It's up the road and 'I need to get out'. 'I'm useless'. Drank a bottle of wine.

* * *

Fri 7th May '99

I've been drinking from Fri – Sun for the last three weeks, because 'it's the weekend'.

* * *

Mon 10th May '99

12pm: reluctantly went to Grandma's to be there when Cable TV arrived. Must 'keep busy' – must 'help others'.

* * *

Thu 13th May '99

2.25pm: attended Out-Patients appointment. 'How are you, Sam?' Mr. Bows asked in his usual cheerful manner. 'A lot better than when you last saw me – in hospital,' I informed with a smile. 'Oh, that's good,' he replied. There was a silence. 'Sam, have you thought about having pouch surgery? You could get rid of the stoma and bag, you know. You're young and would probably recover well,' he suggested in a serious tone. I was horrified and snapped, 'I'm not having anymore surgery! I don't think I've fully recovered from this one.' He replied in a defensive tone, 'Not right now. But it's something you might like to consider.' I replied, 'Yeah, maybe,' and hastily put my coat on – ending the consultation. 'Right, see you in eight weeks,' he said. 'Okay,' I reluctantly replied. I left thinking 'this man is crazy'. 'I'm not having any more surgery!' I want to resume study in October – I want to get back to 'normal life'. More surgery would mean postponing study 'again'. And fuck! 'I don't want any more surgery' – but, 'I do want to get rid of this stoma'.

3.15pm: arrived home feeling distressed. Mr. Bows's words kept repeating in my head, 'Sam, have you thought about having pouch surgery? You could get rid of the stoma and bag.' I desperately want to get rid of this stoma, but 'I don't want any more surgery'. Surgery is not an option – but it's the only way to rid of the stoma. I needed to stop hearing Mr. Bows's words. Drank hot blackcurrant with loads of white rum.

* * *

Fri 14th May '99

9.30am: thought I might have to go to hospital again, because of pain, but they ceased. I'd eaten a banana, apple, and a packet of crisps (maybe too much fibre?).

11am: grudgingly made a doctor's appointment. My left eye has had a sore on it for over a week now, and a 'gel film' has formed over the top of it, and I don't know what to do. I reckon it's got something to do with this fucking surgery and stoma – I've never had a sore eye like this before.

* * *

Sat 15th May '99

6.30am: feeling totally useless. Questioning 'what I'm here on this earth for?' Can't help myself – and find it hard to help others.

4.25pm: sitting in front of the TV hoping to be distracted from my discontented mood, but I vaguely saw the images or heard what was being said. However, I did hear the words, 'Do something amazing today. Give blood', via an advert. I forgot that I used to donate blood – this would 'help others!' I leapt up from the settee – and I noted the 0800 number. I immediately rang it. An advisor informed me of my local point, and also advised that I needed to weigh at least seven stones and twelve pounds, before being fit to give blood. I disconnected the call feeling useful! I just need to put on four pounds to help others! To rejoice – I opened and drank a bottle of wine.

* * *

Mon 17th May '99

4.40am: feeling unsettled and unable to go back to sleep, so I wrote some of the 'novel'.

9.35am: Sharon called. She thought I'd be good at supporting people pre- or post-operatively for stoma surgery. She said, 'I'd make a good 'Ostomist visitor – and an ideal 'role model'. 'An ideal role model?' she was seeing someone completely different to 'me' – I can just about support myself. Still, I agreed to meet to discuss this. I must 'help others'.

11am: arrived at Middlesex University and spoke to a Health Advisor regarding returning to study. She advised that 'a link had been identified with UC and study'. And that I 'Re-think resuming study, if I didn't want to become ill again!' I then spoke to a Student Union Advisor who suggested that it is 'individual' and encouraged 'you could succeed at gaining a degree – if you're determined'. I left the University – confused. I don't want to 'become ill again' – but, I want to 'succeed at gaining a degree'.

5pm: at home. 'I don't want to 'become ill again' – but, I want to 'succeed at gaining a degree'. Drank some rum and hot blackcurrant to rid of my distressing dilemma of 'what to do'.

I'm drinking about every two days. I was drinking every other day. I thought my drinking was a problem, but it's actually reduced. Don't know why I thought it might be a problem – it hasn't stopped me carrying out daily activities or plans. Actually, I think it's helping me mentally, by offering breaks from my thoughts. And, if I didn't have these breaks – I think I'd have gone insane by now.

* * *

Tue 18th May '99

9.30am: attended a doctor's appointment. I entered the room feeling anxious. 'My left eye has been sore for over a week, with a gel film on the surface, and I've been experiencing vaginal thrush for at least three weeks,' I nervously told him. 'Okay,' let's have a look at your eye then,' he replied in an agreeable tone. He picked up an 'eye torch' from his desk and shifted closer to me by dragging his feet on the floor and moving his swivel chair. He pointed the 'eye torch' at me, whilst pulling down the skin beneath my eye. 'Look up!' he instructed and moved the apparatus closer to my eye. I got anxious (heart began pounding) thinking the tool was so close that it might poke me in the eye. He abruptly moved away and advised, 'Yes, you have an infection,' and continued, 'Right, you think you have vaginal thrush. Do you mind if I take an internal examination?' I replied, 'No,' but thought, 'I could do without this intrusion'. 'Ummm, looks like thrush, but I need to send away swabs to confirm that it's nothing else,' he informed. He returned to his desk – peered at the computer screen, and began writing a prescription to remedy both my 'eye infection' and 'vaginal thrush'. As he wrote, he explained, 'Eye infections and vaginal thrush are classic symptoms of taking steroids regularly, and on a long-term basis' (he'd obviously been 'enlightened' by reading my 'history' via the computer. But, little did he know that I hadn't actually been 'taking steroids regularly and on a long-term basis' – even though they'd been prescribed). I couldn't be bothered to enlighten him, but again questioned, 'how effective orthodox medical opinion and remedies were?' I was going to ask him if I should avoid alcohol whilst taking his prescribed therapy, but decided it couldn't be 'that dangerous to take medication and drink alcohol?' And, alcohol (unlike orthodox remedies) has been useful for me.

'I hate seeking orthodox medical advice'. Perhaps, it's because I have to admit that I'm 'ill' or 'in need of help'. Or perhaps it's because having taken orthodox medical advice before – I don't feel remedied. Must find the time to seek natural remedies.

7.30pm: reluctantly administered the prescribed eye-drops and Canesten cream. 'Medicating side-effects'. 'How ironic!' I'll use the prescribed medication for now, because I don't have the energy to source natural remedies.

9.30pm: drank a bottle of wine. My 'prescribed' remedy.

* * *

Thu 20th May '99

7.30am: I weigh seven stones and ten pounds – only need to gain three pounds to give blood! 'Must help others'.

10.15pm: arrived home from Writing course. An exercise during the class required us to write about journeys – physical or spiritual. I wrote about travelling by car to meet my cousin who cancelled our get-together, whilst I was on route (I'd travelled seven miles). She cancelled, because one of her false finger nails had fallen off, and she now needed to go for a manicure (she thought fixing false nails was more important than sharing time with me)! I expressed immense disappointment and anger via this exercise. Whatever exercise is required via this Writing course – I mostly express 'disappointment', 'anger' or 'sadness'. I seem to be withholding these emotions – and although it feels distressing as I discover this – it's therapeutic and relieving.

11.40pm: had a drink of hot rum and blackcurrant.

* * *

Fri 21st May '99

10.50am: went to University and felt like an alien. The building looked very strange (even though not much has changed). I saw Mehmac (a lecturer) walking towards me and a sense of belonging and excitement generated in me. This was someone I knew – a reminder me that I had a connection and reason for being at University. I eagerly began a conversation before we had come in talking distant. 'Hi Mehmac! I had to take a year out due to surgery, but....' He interrupted, 'Yes, yes I know. Harry told me. What are you doing hanging around this place? The academic year doesn't start till October,' he rapped and began waving his hands towards the doors. 'Go on – out of this place! Enjoy yourself 'til October,' he concluded in a commanding voice. I felt like telling him, that 'sadly' this was 'my enjoyment – that I needed to 'familiarise myself' with the University 'again' – that I needed to 'see' what had changed – that I needed to 'start preparing now' for my return (to reduce the possibility of getting stressed – of getting ill). But instead of telling him all this, I secretly hid my sadness, and replied in a calm controlled voice, 'Yes, you're right.' I made my way off the campus – 'prematurely' and with 'tears rolling out my eyes'.

12.55pm: arrived home and I headed straight for a bottle of wine. I hastily poured a glass and gulped a whole mouthful. I kept hearing Mehmac's 'encouraging', yet 'painfully received' words, 'Enjoy yourself 'til October'. 'October was too far away – I need to be part of a group 'now'. And, I need to be 'productive now'. And, the question, 'What am I here on this earth for,' began to dwell in my mind – 'again'.

* * *

Sat 22nd May '99

10am: helped Aunty Louise and Uncle John move to a new home. Got to 'keep busy' – Got to 'help others'.

* * *

Sun 23rd May '99

2pm: visited Grandma and she was so grateful for the visit. I only stayed for an hour and when I was leaving she said, Samantha, it was nice seeing you. When you coming again?' 'Soon' I replied. I didn't say a day or time, because I didn't want any 'pressure', 'commitment', or to 'disappoint' Grandma. I left feeling under pressure – I wish Grandma wasn't so grateful for the visit. It was nice seeing her smiling and happy, but 'I don't want to be outdoors'. However, I've got to 'keep busy' – and I've got to 'help others'.

4.30pm: arrived home and drank some rum and hot blackcurrant.

* * *

Mon 24th May '99

7.30am: I weigh 7.13lbs – now I can give blood!

* * *

Tue 25th May '99

10am: went to give blood, but was advised I couldn't, because I'd had surgery in less than a year! I thought this 'can't be right'. Surely if blood tests after surgery hadn't indicated anything contagious or dangerous, it wouldn't mean exclusion?

11.30am: I rang the Blood Donor Helpline to get a second opinion. 'Do you mind telling me the reason for surgery?' the advisor asked. 'No. I had it for Ulcerative Colitis. I've had my colon removed,' I informed. 'Mmmm. That's an 'auto-immune disease',' she commented. Yes, the information you was given is correct,' she assured me and continued, 'I'm afraid you won't be permitted to give blood anymore.' 'Why's that then?' I asked abruptly. 'Because you suffer from a condition that causes destruction of tissues by the body's own antibodies. So, your blood is not acceptable,' she replied in a sympathetic voice. There was a silence, as feelings of sadness prevailed within me. 'Oh, Thanks,' I replied in a low tone, and pressed the button to disconnect the call. This didn't make sense. So what if I had an 'auto-immune disease'. There's nothing 'wrong with my blood' – there's nothing wrong with me...

9.20pm: 'my blood is not acceptable' – because of the so-called fucking illness (UC). 'I'm useless' – 'What am I here on this earth for?' Drank loads of white rum with hot blackcurrant.

* * *

Wed 26th May '99

10.30am: met with Toni and Sharon to discuss being an Ostomist visitor. 'Sam, I think you'll make an 'excellent' visitor. A 'perfect role model'. You've 'coped really well' with having a stoma,' Sharon commented with a smile. 'Yep! I think you'll offer people a 'positive outlook' to having a stoma,' Toni agreed. 'Will it be okay for you to met with our other visitor who'll tell you how she fills this role?' Sharon asked. 'Yeah,' I replied, feeling overwhelmed.

9pm: been wondering how I'm going to be 'an excellent visitor' and 'perfect role model', because at the moment I hate having a stoma – I think it's disgusting – and I've been using alcohol to manage since having it. I 'should' have told them 'I wasn't ready to be a visitor', but this would have meant that 'I wasn't 'excellent' – or 'perfect' – and I wouldn't have 'coped really well'. It would have meant I'd 'failed'. And, I must 'keep busy' – 'I must help others'.

9.30pm: feeling mentally exhausted and completely misunderstood. Drank bottle of wine.

* * *

Thu 27th May '99

6.30am: woke up with a brilliant idea – to train to be a First Aider! I rang St. Johns Ambulance and was advised there was a course starting on Sat 12th June. Yeah!

11.30am: opened a bottle of wine and drank two glasses – I might have 'bad' blood, but I can still 'help others'.

3.25pm: finished wine and fell asleep feeling happy.

* * *

Wed 2nd Jun '99

Rang Josie (former Ostomist visitor) regarding visiting role and arranged to meet next Wednesday. Feeling very nervous about this responsibility but, I must 'keep busy' and I must 'help others'.

* * *

121

Thu 3rd Jun '99

'Novel' going well – chapters one, two, and three are complete.

* * *

Fri 4th Jun '99

3.30pm: I'm writing less in this journal. Too much to note and don't know where to start. So many thoughts about – 'Past events' – the stoma – 'Friends' and family – 'Me (who I am)'. But I don't feel as distressed when I have these thoughts – not like before. Perhaps it's because I'm writing the 'novel' and off loading some of these issues.

9.45pm: to bed. Relaxed and sober.

* * *

Wed 9th Jun '99

11.30am: met with Josie and discussed the role of an Ostomist visitor. She approached me with a wide smile and said, 'Hi, Samantha,' whilst she scanned my attire – from head to toe. She tried to do this discreetly (not moving her head, and fully exercising her eyes), but I saw, and her facial expression was one of 'disgust'. She was wearing a glittery brown and black shirt, with a black skirt – and shiny black shoes – 'to match'. I was wearing a baggy shirt that hung over a pair of jeans, with trainers. She explained the importance of offering 'positive advice' and 'listening' to the new or potential Ostomist. She ended our meeting saying, 'Oh, and on a visit you should wear something smart.' I silently chuckled and thought, 'What a cheek! She thought I looked a mess!' But I already 'knew' this from her scanning and look of disgust.

I left in amazement thinking, 'even a 'Visiting Ostomist' didn't understand that it was our mental state that really mattered. That looking 'smart' was secondary. That the new or potential Ostomist would need to deal with the outcome of a 'mutilated body', with shit pouring from their abdomen'. For fuck sake! 'Where's the empathy for the psychological affect'.

* * *

Thu 10th Jun '99

There's a Stoma Support Group meeting at Lank's Hospital, but, I'm unable to go due to a 'Lecture Taster' at University. Feels great to disregard 'stoma business' to fulfil 'normal' life commitments – 'priorities are changing'.

* * *

Sat 12th Jun '99

7.30am: first day of First Aid course that lasts all day (9am-5pm).

6.15pm: at home feeling exhausted. Really enjoyed today – learning First Aid means I can 'help others'.

7.30pm: Mark came into my room with the phone. 'Sam it's for you.' 'Who is it?' I asked with irritation. 'Joe,' he replied. As I took the phone from him I quizzed, 'Joe.' I didn't know a 'Joe'. 'Hello,' I said abruptly. 'Hello Samantha,' the person replied and I knew who it was immediately – and began smiling. It was Joe – (Joseph) my former boss. 'Joseph,' I said with excitement, 'How are you?!' 'Fine. I'm calling to see how your exams went and if you're enjoying the summer break?' I was in shock – he was interested and aware of what I was supposed to be doing! I told him about the operation and the years break from study. I told him about the 'positive' aspects regarding surgery that 'I'd been considered an 'excellent role model' and asked to be an Ostomist Visitor. That I was training to be a First Aider – and that I would be resuming studies this October. He listened with interest and sympathised with my experience of illness and surgery. He praised me regarding the 'positive' roles I was doing. I never told him that 'I hated the stoma – and that I was 'using alcohol almost every day' to comfort myself – and to cope.

We spoke for about forty-five minutes – me for forty! He must have thought I'd been gagged for the past year (when we last spoke)! I haven't spoken to anyone on the telephone for that duration in a longtime. I told him it was 'nice to hear from [him]' and that 'I'd keep in touch'. I've said this before to others – and not meant it, but this time – I did.

* * *

Sun 13th Jun '99

9-5pm: First Aid course. One of the practices was 'abdominal thrusts' (a technique to assist someone who's choking). You had to apply pressure on the abdominal area in upward strokes. I was scared that my partner would damage the stoma, but luckily he done the procedure wrong and didn't go near it. However, I wondered 'what would happen if I was choking and someone did these abdominal thrusts right? They'd damage the stoma'. Still, better to be alive with a damaged stoma – than choke to death? Travelled home feeling perturbed with this thought that I considered a paradox.

7pm: at home. Opened a bottle of wine to celebrate me completing the first part of training – and to relax. 'Better to be alive with a damaged stoma – than choke to death?'

* * *

Mon 14th Jun '99

Toni phoned and timidly asked, 'Sam, how are you?' 'I'm fine. How about you?' I replied surprised at her call. I was even more shocked when she said, 'Sam I want to ask you a favour. Would you mind speaking about your experience of stoma surgery at City University to student nurses?' I was dumbstruck and her words echoed. 'A favour?' – 'Would you mind' – 'speaking about your experience of stoma surgery' – 'City University' – 'to student nurses'. There was a long silence. 'Sam, are you still there?' Toni asked abruptly. 'Yeah,' I replied hesitantly. 'Well... do you think you could do this for me? You wouldn't have to talk for long, 'bout fifteen minutes would be good,' she explained. 'Yeah,' I replied trying to give a clear response in my astonishment. And then hastily added, 'But Toni, what would I say?' she replied, 'Just tell 'em what it's like to have UC and stoma surgery. I'll send the details in the post.' I slowly pressed the button to disconnect the call. She made it sound so easy, 'Just tell 'em what it's like to have UC and stoma surgery.' Never thought anyone would be interested in hearing 'what it's like to have UC and stoma surgery'. And talking about it to a 'group of people' – 'student nurses' – at a 'University'. I feel sort of 'privileged' and 'special' – but most of all – I feel 'scared'.

* * *

Wed 16th Jun '99

6.30pm: First Aid Exam.

9pm: at home worrying how I'd done in the exam. Drank some rum and hot blackcurrant.

* * *

Thu 17th Jun '99

9am-5pm: First Aid course (Babies and Children).

7.30-9pm: creative Writing course.

9.30pm: at home exhausted. I feel useful and happy! It's been a very productive day. Too tired to eat, and struggled to drink two glasses of wine. I 'had' to have a couple of glasses of wine – I'd earned them.

* * *

Fri 18th Jun '99

9.30am: post arrived with a letter from Toni confirming that 'Sam Shakes' would be the 'Guest Speaker' for the *Patients' Perspective*. 'Friday 25th June 1999'. At 'City University'. 'It was official!' And, I was struck with dread.

11am: poured a few shots of rum with hot blackcurrant.

* * *

Sun 20th Jun '99

6.30am: Fathers Day. Feeling nervous – I've invited Dad for dinner and will be cooking for the whole family (not sure it will turn out okay).

10.30am: opened a bottle of wine and began cooking. If I'm relaxed – I'll make better judgments.

1.30pm: Dad arrived and I was tipsy. 'Samantha. Ya drunk at diss time!' he exclaimed with concern, but tried to hide his worry with a false chuckle. 'Yep! It's called lunchtime drinking,' I replied confidently.

9.45pm: thinking about today. It's the second time I've drank in the morning. 'What's happening to me?'

11.40pm: had a few shots of rum and hot blackcurrant. I've 'drank twice this week 'in the morning'?'

* * *

Thu 24th Jun '99

9am–5pm: First Aid course (Babies and Children). Really enjoyed the training.

8.30pm: thinking about me drinking in the morning. It's not such a 'bad thing' – I'm still able to carry out commitments.

10.50pm: thinking about the talk I'm to give tomorrow at City University. 'Just tell 'em what it's like to have UC and stoma surgery'... Toni said. But, I'm not sure anyone will be interested in hearing 'what it's like to have UC and stoma surgery'. And, I'll be talking to a 'group of people – student nurses'. At a 'University'....

* * *

Fri 25th Jun '99

12.20am: still thinking about the talk I'm to give tomorrow.

1.35am: still thinking about the talk.

2.50am: feeling exhausted, but I can't sleep – 'I'll be talking to a 'group of people – student nurses. At a University tomorrow'. I needed to relax or be awake all night – thinking. Drank a bottle of wine.

5.45am: woke up in a panic – I'm giving the talk at a University today! My heart began pounding – my mouth went dry – my temples started thumping – and my stomach was in knots. What was I going to wear?

I needed to look smart – people would be gawping at me! I flicked through the clothes in my wardrobe – nothing looked suitable for this event – 'Nothing!' So I grabbed anything – a blue sixties styled skirt that I'd purchased from Oxfam and hastily starting flicking through the clothes again – I needed a top. I continued flicking through the clothes to the end of the wardrobe – and back again. 'Nothing!' Aargh! Grabbed a white blouse – it would 'have' to match. Time was ticking and I didn't want to be rushing – I didn't want to get stressed. But, I already was.

9.45am: as I approached the University I felt tension in my abdominal area. I entered the building and my heart began pounding. 'What was I doing here?' I silently questioned. I walked to the Welcome Desk and said to the receptionist, 'Hi, I'm here to give the *Patients' Perspective*. 'Oh, yes. You're in room B12. It's on the second floor,' she replied with a smile. As I climbed the stairs the tension increased. With every step – my heart pounded greater. With every step – my temples thumped deeper. And, with every step – an extra knot was added in my stomach. Then shit! There it was – room B12. I found it too soon – I wasn't ready. I tried to compose myself before entering, by taking a few deep breaths, but it didn't help. My heart was still pounding at great speed, my temples felt like they were going to explode, and the knots in my stomach were now causing nausea. I entered the room and Sharon was sitting at the front, near an Overhead Projector. 'Hiya, Sam. Good to see you,' she greeted with a smile. 'Hi, Sharon. I'm so nervous,' I replied. 'You'll be alright. Just see this talk as an informal chat,' she reassured. I dug in my bag and took out a crumpled sheet of paper – my notes. 'Here Sharon. These are what I was gonna talk about. What do you think?' I asked, handing her the notes. She read aloud, '*Before Surgery – Having Colitis – Living with a Stoma – Friends and Family's reaction*',' and continued, 'Sounds perfect. I think they're really going to enjoy your talk.'

10.20am: the talk was to start at 10.30am. Students began filing in. I counted eight and hoped that no more would arrive, but they kept coming.

10.35am: Sharon rose from her seat and said, 'Right. I think we'll make a start.' I began shaking inside as I counted fifteen bodies – fifteen pair of eyes staring at me! 'As you know this part of the course is titled the *Patients' Perspective* and I'm pleased to introduce Sam Shakes who is going to tell us about her experience of having Colitis, living with a stoma, and how she's managed to cope.' I thought 'Am I?!' I smiled nervously at the audience. I didn't know whether to sit or stand, and bobbed up and down, until I decided that I didn't want to be any more obvious – so remained seated. 'Hi,' I timidly greeted, in a croaky voice. I looked at my notes and the paper was flittering – my hand was shaking. I began, 'I was diagnosed with Ulcerative Colitis in April 1998, whilst studying

126

– (like you) and living what I would consider a 'normal life….' I spoke for twenty minutes. And, 'Sam Shakes' received a rapturous applaud from the group?! I travelled home smiling. 'I could have a stoma and be appreciated?' The response from this talk made me realise two great wonders: 'One – that I still have some use' – and 'two – having a stoma really isn't 'that bad'.

11.45am: arrived home. To celebrate these 'positive' realisations. I drank a bottle of wine.

* * *

Sun 27th Jun '99

9.15am: woke up to the sounds of Doreen and Mark arguing. I need a break from this place – I need some peace.

I thought a week at Dad's and Uncle Ted's would be ideal. They're both out working all day and I could enjoy the peacefulness of 'no-ones company' for that time.

11.10am: called Dad. 'Dad. Will it be okay to spend a week with you and Uncle Ted. I really needed to get away from this house,' I asked in a pleading voice. 'Yeah. You naw hav fe ask! Wen ya a come?' he questioned, sounding concerned (I guess at my need to 'get away'). 'This Monday, alright? Perhaps, you can collect me on your way home from work?' I suggested. 'Dat, alright. See ya den,' he replied. I felt relaxed and happy after speaking to Dad. I knew some solitude was soon to come. To maintain the feeling of relaxation and happiness – I drank a few shots of brandy with hot blackcurrant.

* * *

Wed 30th Jun '99

6.30am: thinking about returning to University. I didn't enjoy studying English Literary Studies, and think studying a subject I don't enjoy will add unnecessary stress. I want 'a degree' – I want to 'succeed', but 'I don't want to 'become ill again'.

9.30am: decided that I must change the course to prevent unnecessary stress. So, I went to local career's office. 'I'm interested in studying a course related to health,' I told the advisor. 'At what level?' she asked. 'Degree,' I replied. She recommended that I look at the 'Health Studies' degree course at Middlesex University. I looked it up and the course modules included *Stress and Health*; *Health Psychology* and *Patterns of Health and Illness*. These subjects were exactly what I wanted to learn more about! I contacted the University and was advised of an 'Open Day' in August – that I immediately placed in my diary.

* * *

127

Sun 4th Jul '99

10.20am: travelled to Southend with Uncle Solomon. I really enjoyed his company. He's one of the few people I can tolerant at the moment. 'Something's gone wrong in heaven,' Uncle Solomon said as he peered out the window. 'What do you mean?' I asked. 'I'm not being treated right,' he replied with a heavy sigh. 'Why?' I quizzed. 'I don't know, but I'm not getting what I need,' he sadly explained. 'What do you need?' I enquired. 'Money and good food. I'm not getting enough money or good food. Someone must be stealing it. I can't see who, but someone must be stealing it because I'm not getting enough. Something's gone wrong in heaven,' he rapped. 'How do you know?' I asked. 'I think it was 'Niber Sam' (Niber Sam: Uncle Solomon's Grandfather who died before he was born). He told me – I heard him say when he came to see me,' he explained.

I found this conversation insightful (and most of our conversations give me 'food for thought'). Uncle Solomon isn't religious, yet believes there's a 'God', and that God wants good things to happen to people. Therefore, because of his lack of money and fresh foods – 'something' wasn't right.

They (the medics) consider his conversation 'nonsensical'. This was nonsensical?! Made 'sense' to me. They (the medics) say he has a 'mental health problem'. He 'hears voices' – and 'sees ghosts' they exclaim! Uncle Solomon's behaviour isn't 'conventional' as he responds to hearing and seeing 'Niber Sam'. So what? He doesn't hurt anyone and has never expressed that hearing or seeing 'Niber Sam' is a problem. Yet, it is (according to the medics). He's been diagnosed as 'Schizophrenic'. Amazing – 'just' because we don't articulate or behave in a particular way – we are made 'ill' and considered having a 'problem'. 'Orthodox medicine mostly has Wellbeing and Life 'wrong'.

9.30pm: arrived home and rang Joe. I'd wanted to call four days ago, but never had 'a reason' – I just wanted a chat? Anyway, today I had a reason to call – to tell him that I was going to change my degree course. 'Hi Joe. Just thought I'd let you know that I'm going to change my degree course to Health Studies,' I nervously announced. 'Oh, Sam that sounds good, because you're interested in health, and it will make studying easier. I loved history and I think that's why I got a first class grade,' he informed me proudly. 'Either that or you're a boffin!' I jested and we both laughed. We talked for an hour and twenty minutes! I told him it was nice speaking to him and he said it was nice speaking to me. We ended the call laughing. I sat for a while after disconnecting the call. 'I'd just been speaking to someone for an hour and twenty minutes – and enjoyed it?'

* * *

Upheaval of Ideas – Distress of Changes

Mon 5th Jul '99

6.30pm: Dad collected me and we drove to Uncle Ted's and his home.

8.10pm: arrived at Uncle Ted's and Dad's. 'Hi Samantha – nice to see you. How have you been?' Uncle Ted greeted. 'Oh, up and down,' I replied in a blasé tone. 'Okay…,' he said with a nervousness, not knowing what to say. 'I'll be alright. Just need a break from home. A bit of peace,' I explained, breaking the uncomfortable atmosphere.

10.30pm: 'Right. Me go a bed,' informed Dad, as the news on TV finished. 'Me too,' Uncle Ted shared. They both said they generally retired at this time. 'What time do you leave in the morning,' I enquired. 'Bout seven,' Dad replied. 'I leave about seven-thirty,' Uncle Ted added. Both informed that they returned home between 6-6.30pm. This was going to be good. I'd only have contact with them four hours per day.

* * *

Tue 6th Jul '99

6.30am: woke up to the sounds of Dad and Uncle Ted. One was downstairs in the kitchen and the other was in the bathroom. I lay in my temporary bed – smiling. There was no pressure. It was 'early', so I needn't feel obliged to interact and say 'Good Morning.' They'd think I was still sleeping – and I'd soon have this space all for myself for nearly twelve hours!

7.15am: 'Check you later, Ted,' I heard Dad say, and front door slam. I thought, 'One out – one to go.'

7.25am: I heard the front door open and close – Uncle Ted leaving. It was now 'safe' to come out. It felt strange coming out of isolation into greater solitude. 'I wasn't obligated to do anything'. I didn't have to wash – I didn't have to speak – I didn't have to hide in a confide space.

129

I had the whole house to myself for the next twelve hours and a sense of 'freedom' prevailed!

* * *

Wed 7th Jul '99

6.30pm: I emptied the bag and the smell was particularly potent. Dad used the toilet soon after. I heard the lid of the air fresher pop off, violently followed by a long spray. He then shouted from the toilet, 'Pooh! You should empty dat bag in de outside toilet.' I was in 'my' room. I went numb. His words pierced my soul. I forced my mouth to work and replied, 'Oh, sorry. Next time – I will.' I tried to resist his comment 'Pooh! You should empty dat bag in de outside toilet' from piercing my soul, but it forced its way in – upsetting the whole of me. I didn't feel angry or sad – I felt 'pain'. I was glad we weren't face-to-face when he said this. Moments later, he popped his head in 'my' room and said, 'Me a go shop. Ya want anytin?' I replied in a croaky voice, 'No.' 'Ya al-right?' he asked looking me straight in the eyes. 'Yeah. Just tired,' I lied. 'Oh. Soon come,' he said and left. Almost simultaneously, as I heard the door close – I burst out crying 'uncontrollably'. Every cell in my body was vibrating from intense sobbing. My mind cried – my heart cried – and my stomach cried. I heard his comment over and over again 'Pooh! You should be emptying that bag in the outside toilet' – attacking my mind – my heart – and my stomach. And every time I heard his comment, 'a fresh set of heavy tears rolled out of my eyes'. I'd been desperately trying to convince myself that 'the stoma wasn't disgusting'. That it was 'just a new way of going to the toilet'. But Dad's comment destroyed all my mental work. My 'fantasy' that the 'stoma wasn't ghastly' – but actually, it was. I sat at the edge of the bed feeling hopeless and drained of energy. I needed to rid of this hopeless feeling. I thought about asking if I could open a bottle of wine, but didn't want to drink whilst here – in an ideal place to relax? I then remembered one of my saviours in desperate times – 'Tycho'. I took his book *Inspirational Thoughts* out of my bag (I always have it for moments like this) and read the following quote:

> *It's the way we look at the scenery that needs changing and not the scenery itself.*

I felt less distressed. Yes – I needed to change the 'way I looked' at the scenery – 'the stoma'. I needed to stop viewing it as something 'bad' and 'disgusting'. I needed to realise that the stoma was 'just a new way of going to the toilet'.

8.15pm: my distress wasn't getting any better and I uneasily asked Dad if I could open a bottle of wine. He said I could, but didn't sound sincere. I think he's concerned at my drinking habit, and a small part of me felt embarrassed asking to open the wine, yet a larger part of me didn't care. I selected a bottle from the wine rack. 'Do you want some?' I asked Dad and Uncle Ted, hoping they'd say no (less than a bottle wouldn't satisfy me and I couldn't ask to open another). 'Naw. Me alright,' Dad replied. 'Not for me,' Uncle Ted answered. I poured myself a glass and tried not to gulp it. I wanted to be drinking the second glass before I'd drank the first – I wanted to rid of the pain and sadness instantly. 'Shame' I drank today – it would have been four days without drinking.

* * *

Thu 8th Jul '99

6.30am: woke up feeling sad and in 'need of a drink'. I forgot how effective alcohol could be at drowning unwanted feelings. And I didn't want to feel sad – not in the place where I was seeking refuge and supposed to be feeling 'good' and 'happy'.

7.30am: I waited until Dad and Uncle Ted left and opened a bottle of wine. I began to feel better'. 'Pooh! You should be emptying that bag in the outside toilet' – I heard Dad's comment repeating in my mind. I responded to it, 'So what if it smells?! Doesn't his shit stink?! Doesn't everyone's?! It's only a fucking smell!

10.30am: finished the bottle of wine and fell asleep.

3pm: woke up feeling groggy and in a panic. Shit! – I needed to get myself out of the house, to replace the wine. I couldn't let Dad or Uncle Ted know that I'd drank before their working day had ended. I hastily got dressed without washing, and noted the name and make of the wine I'd drank (I had to replace the exact bottle – else they'd notice). I left, grabbing the empty bottle and placed it outside – in the neighbours bin.

* * *

Sat 10th Jul '99

Stayed in 'my' room almost all day (only came out to eat), and told Dad and Uncle Ted that I was writing. But, I've been thinking about – Past events – The Stoma – Friends and Family – Me (who am I) and thinking about emptying the bag in the outside toilet. I've been sitting, staring at the walls – lying, staring at the ceiling – and standing, staring out the window.

* * *

Sun 11th Jul '99

I've been emptying the bag in the outside toilet (apart from during the night), as Dad said I should be. I've been out in the cold as early as 5am: and as late as 12.30am. When I empty the bag during the night – in the 'sacred toilet' I've been overwhelmed with anxiety and panic. First, I open the window – then fan around me as I open the bag to let the shit out – finally I spray the air freshener – seemingly all at once. Then comes 'The Test'. I leave the bathroom and enter again to assess that I haven't got used to the odour, and there's a smell of 'fresh air' as opposed to an 'awful stench'. During the night I hope the bag won't fill up so that I don't have to empty it in the 'sacred toilet', but I always have to. I wait until the bag is completely full (risking it busting), to reduce the amount of times I empty – to reduce any 'discomfort' that Dad and Uncle Ted might experience if they smell my shit!

Going home tomorrow. I say 'home', but it doesn't feel like 'home'. I don't want to go back to 'Mum's', but I don't want to stay here either. Feels like there's nowhere for 'us' (me and the shitty stoma) to go.

* * *

Mon 12th Jul '99

9am: Dad drove me back to Mum's.

10.40am: Sharon phoned. 'Hi Sam. Can you visit a man named Terry who had a stoma formed three weeks ago? He's desperate to see someone who is living well with a stoma?' she asked. I felt like saying, 'I'm desperate to be living well with a stoma!' I took his contact details and said I would visit him. I disconnected the call wondering how I was going to show this man that I was 'living well with a stoma'. At the moment I'm trying to change the way I look at the scenery (the stoma), but 'my reality' is that 'I hate it' – I think it's disgusting – and I'm using alcohol to comfort myself. I should have told Sharon that it would be best if I didn't visit, because I'm feeling so negative. But 'I must help others'.

* * *

Wed 14th Jul '99

6.30am: woke up feeling nervous – I'm meeting Terry (the new Ostomist) today.

12.30pm: at café. 'Hi, Sam. Thanks for coming to meet me, shall we sit outside?' Terry said forcing a smile through an anxious expression. 'Yeah that would be nice,' I agreed and we sat at a table on the side walk. 'Can I get you a drink or something to eat?' he asked. 'A coffee will be fine – thanks,' I replied. 'Sam. What's it been like for you – having a stoma. I can't imagine life with one,' he shared. 'Well, I've had 'ups' and 'downs' – and it does take getting used to. But, there isn't anything I can't do – that I could do, before having a stoma. Apart from poohing from the back passage – that is,' I chuckled (trying to remain 'positive'). But his facial expression remained tense and serious. 'I hate this stoma,' he continued in a sad tone. 'Why's that then?' I asked. 'Well, it leaks and the bag has burst – I haven't been out since having it, because this could happen in public – I can't see me playing golf with it, since I usually shower in the communal area and now I'll have to go in a cubicle – people will wonder what's up – and I feel so unconfident with my partner – how can she find me attractive now – with a stoma?' he rapped.

I sat back in the metal chair, took a deep breath, and sipped my frothy coffee, to allow sometime to compose a 'positive' attitude and reply. 'Terry, I used to worry about going out in public just in case the bag leaked or burst. But I sorted out the leak problem and always carry a spare bag, just in case,' I said and continued, 'My bag has burst once, and that was because I left it too long to empty. How many times has yours burst?' I asked. 'Once, in bed. It was so embarrassing. Shit all over my abdomen and on the bed sheets.' 'So the bag has burst 'just once,' I confirmed (clarifying and emphasising that this problem had 'only happened once'). 'Yeah,' he replied with a look of bewilderment and reiterated in a low tone, 'the bag has burst just once.' 'Perhaps it was just left too long to be emptied?' I suggested. 'I don't know, but my partner acted like it meant nothing. 'Go and clean yourself, and I'll take care of the bed sheets,' she said in a calm and considerate voice, but 'I know' she was thinking, 'Yuck! And hated changing the shitty bed sheets.' I didn't comment.

I left without telling him what I really felt. When he said he knew his partner was thinking, 'Yuck! And hated cleaning up the shitty bed sheets.' I felt like saying, 'Of course she did! Who likes cleaning up shit?! And when he said, 'I hate this stoma' – I wanted to say – 'so do I'. I felt like telling him that 'life would not be the same' – 'people don't understand' – 'he'll constantly worry about where toilets are wherever he goes' – 'he won't have a decent night sleep as he gets up during the night to empty the bag' – 'having a bath or shower wouldn't give the freedom that it used to (he would have to decide whether it would be more relaxing to have a soak in the bath or shower with the plastic bag attached, or if it was more relaxing to take the bag off and have shit pour into the bath water or down his leg whilst showering) – and 'Depression' might become part of his life'. But telling him this wouldn't help. This was 'my current reality' – not every Ostomists. And, I know 'it's the way I'm looking at the scenery' that's making my current reality so 'negative'. So, I didn't tell him what I really felt – 'I want to help others'.

7.30pm: thinking about Mum's, Doreen's and Mark's trip to New York, tomorrow. They're travelling to attend our cousin's wedding. I'm not going, because if anything happens to me – those doctors don't know me. Would have been nice to go. Drank a few shots of rum and hot blackcurrant.

* * *

Thu 15th Jul '99

Joe called today – it's only been eleven days since we last spoke! I think he would have called before, but I've been at Dad's. 'So, did you enjoy your break – staying at your Dads?' he asked with interest. 'It was nice,' I lied, not wanting to talk about the awful experience (Dad's comment and the need to drink). 'I made my first Ostomist visit, yesterday. I think it went well,' I informed with excitement, changing the subject. 'I bet it did! You're a ideal role model,' Joe replied sounding equally excited. His words sounded familiar, 'ideal role model' – Sharon had said this. I wanted to tell him that I 'acted out' and 'struggled with my true feelings' – but I never.

* * *

Fri 16th Jul '99

9.30am: doctor's appointment for my repetitive strain injury. 'I could prescribe some pain relief and a course of anti inflammatory medication. You could also consider steroid injections? Resting your wrist and using a support, would help too,' she advised. 'Ummm. I'll rest my wrist and use a support – and see what happens,' I replied feeling irritated at her recommended 'unnatural remedies'. 'How's your bowels?' she asked, but didn't wait for an answer and continued, 'You'll definitely have to have more surgery due to the 'risk of cancer' in the rectum'. I was in shock. My eyes widened and my jaw dropped open – I'd never heard of such 'risk'.

I left the surgery in a panic and repeatedly hearing her words, 'You'll definitely have to have more surgery due to the risk of cancer of the rectum'. My walking increased with great speed and progressed to trotting. 'You'll definitely have to have more surgery due to the risk of cancer of the rectum'. I began crying – and starting jogging. It seemed to take a long time to get home and when I did – I bolted through the front door – rushed into the lounge and grabbed the telephone – still crying. Doreen was in the lounge and asked with concern, 'What's wrong?' I didn't have time answer – I needed to confirm if what the doctor had advised was 'true'.

I called Toni. 'Toni, my doctor said I 'will definitely have to have more surgery due to the risk of cancer of the rectum',' I blurted through sobs without any greeting and continued, 'I'm not having anymore surgery.'

I could vaguely hear Toni saying, 'Sam, Sam, calm down.' There was a silence and I forced myself to stop crying. She continued in a reassuring tone, 'That isn't strictly true. The risk of cancer is considered high if the rectum has been continually active and after ten – fifteen years. Don't worry. We'll keep an eye on you by taking biopsies.' 'Oh, okay,' I sobbed. I disconnected the call and 'sort of' felt relieved. 'The risk of cancer is considered high if the rectum has been continually active and after ten – fifteen years.' But I was also confused – 'Who was right?' the doctor – or Toni.

* * *

Wed 21st Jul '99

7.30am: woke up feeling mentally and physically drained.

9am: doctor appointment (went without washing). She prescribed – Elcon (steroid cream) for Vitiligo (skin disorder). I'm 'so confused' – I went to the doctor's?! I knew I'd be prescribed a suppressant – as a 'cure' – and orthodox medication contradicts my 'new beliefs' – 'Why did I go to the doctor?!'

10am: back at home. 'I've got so much to do' and I don't know where to start. I need to pursue writing 'novel' – write follow-up letter to Terry (patient visited) – write report on first visit for Sharon – source information about Diverticulitis – contact Multiple Sclerosis Society for Steve. And my mind has been racing regarding the meeting I had with Terry. I'm wondering if I offended him – 'Why hasn't he rung?' And I'm wondering what feedback Sharon received from him regarding the visit.

Tycho's last lecture, 'Cleansing the Colon', was extremely informative. He suggested that fruit and raw vegetables are what humans are designed to eat. He also advised us to 'Eat when hungry' – 'Sleep when tired' – and 'Drink when thirsty'. 'Feel your body's requirements!' he advocated. I want to put these ideas into practice – seem so 'natural'. But I feel distressed – I got to change so much of me – so much of my unhelpful habits – and I don't know where to start! And I'm finding the idea of all this change overwhelming. I think it's because I want to 'transform over night'. I must make a few changes at a time and not expect to adjust 'all at once'.

I realise that I've abused my body for years and in doing so, disrespected the 'Almighty Creator'. And, I've ignored my body's cry for help – and I feel sad. Sad, but not regretful – I'm thankful that I'm learning so much from this experience of 'UC' and surgery – and trust the 'Almighty Creator' won't give me more than 'I can manage'.

11.20am: I ate two bananas – a pear – a peach – and an apricot ('I've got to start putting these natural ideas into action').

12pm: abdomen felt sore. I was unsure whether this was due to fatigue or my high intake of fibre (fruit eaten earlier). I'm trying to 'Eat when hungry' – 'Sleep when tired' – and 'Drink when thirsty'. I'm trying to 'feel my body's requirements' ('I've got to start putting these natural ideas into action'). Another change I've made today is not using body lotion. I understand that lotion suppresses toxins that are trying to escape from the body. My skin looks very dry and doesn't make me feel good, but it's 'for the better'.

7pm: intended to go to Tycho's lecture, *The Power of the Subconscious*, but upon 'listening to my body' – I decided not to. I needed to honour the requirement to relax and protect my mind from more information. I've been experiencing information overload. So, I'm going to take a break from reading and thinking. Drank a flask of brandy with hot blackcurrant.

* * *

Fri 23rd Jul '99

9.30am: woke up thinking about the need to relax and have a break from seeking further information.

10.45pm: still trying to relax. Drank a few shots of brandy and felt sickly afterwards. Still it was worth it, I went to bed with a numb head and incapable of 'reading' – or 'thinking' – and feeling relaxed.

* * *

Sat 24th Jul '99

7pm: Joe called. 'Hello Samantha,' he greeted cheerfully. 'Hi Joe,' I replied in a low tone. 'Oh you don't sound happy. Are you okay?' he asked with concern. I became anxious – he'd detected my misery. 'Oh, it's 'just' that my cousin is getting married today and I regret not making the effort to travel to New York. I don't feel safe travelling, because should anything happen, I'm not sure those doctors will know what to do with me,' I reluctantly explained (not wanting to feel my sadness). 'Oh, Samantha, it's a shame you weren't able to go, but there's no point being there if you don't feel confident travelling. If you're anxious about any problems that may happen – you won't be able to relax and enjoy yourself. Aaah, there'll be another opportunity to visit your cousin. Perhaps later this year – when you feel more confident?' he consoled. Joe's words were comforting, there was 'no point in being there if [I] didn't feel confident about travelling' and '[I] probably wouldn't relax and be able to enjoy [my]self.' He was right, 'Perhaps I could visit later this year – when I felt more confident?' 'Why don't you come over to my place next Friday? I could cook for us and it would be nice to see you. Haven't seen you for over a year – I've forgotten what you look like!' he joked, changing the subject. I was struck with anxiety. 'Come over to [his] place?' And 'cook something for us?' I thought his invitation was a bit 'too intimate'. I thought about lying by saying that 'I wouldn't be around next Friday' or suggesting that 'we have a meal at a restaurant (less intimate)', but instead I replied hesitantly, 'Ummm, okay.' 'You don't have to!' Joe exclaimed, sounding offended. 'No I know. That will be nice,' I replied trying to sound grateful. 'Okay. Will seven-thirty be alright?' he asked. 'That'll be fine,' I replied in awe. 'See you then,' he said excitedly. When I disconnected the call – my anxiety increased. Joe had invited me 'over to his place' and he was going to 'cook something for us'. And, it had only been nine days since we last spoke. And, 'yet again' I had enjoyed our chat.

10.45pm: full of anxiety and excitement – I needed to relax. I drank a shot of rum and hot blackcurrant. And another. And another. And questioned, 'What was there to be scared about – Joe?'

* * *

Sun 25th Jul '99

I realise that my current friendships are based on 'sentimental attachment'. We no longer share common interests, fashion, beliefs, morals. The only thing we share is a 'history'. I need to make new friends – ones that reflect the new me. I pray for the strength to move on.

* * *

Mon 26th Jul '99

8am: woke up feeling lethargic and I knew – I needed to exercise and I needed to relax. I didn't feel like going for swim and sauna, but I forced myself to go.

12.30pm: returned from having a swim and sauna feeling relaxed. Had a nap.

2.30pm: woke up feeling energised.

7.15pm: Brendon visited and the exchange was strained. I felt uncomfortable in his presence, and agitated that he'd arrived without 'warning'. With warning (a call) I would have had time to psyche myself up, or make an excuse for him not to visit.

* * *

Tue 27th Jul '99

6.30pm: went to the Old Queen's Head Pub. It was Tricia's Birthday. I didn't want to go, but I didn't want to let her down. I've never felt so 'out of place' as I did today. I didn't find the conversations consisting of 'boyfriends/girlfriends', 'old times' or 'fashion' – stimulating. I sat feeling totally isolated and thinking 'who cares' and 'so fucking what!' On a few occasions, when I did contribute my comments seemed 'odd' and jarred with what people were saying – I could tell by the followed silence and no response when I spoke.

8.50pm: arrived home. Regretting that I'd placed myself in 'unsuitable' company. Regretting that I'd gone to the pub. Regretting drinking wine (and not listening to my body). I wish I'd done what I wanted to do – not gone. I wish I'd followed my instinct.

* * *

Thu 29th Jul '99

Feeling 'spiritually connected'. I've thought of people and they've contacted me. I've thought of events and they've happened. 'Coincidences?' I've been talking to the Almighty Creator and believe in him. He's answering my requests and needs. Even when the requests are thoughts in my head – he responds! 'I don't have to do anything'. 'I know he is looking out for me – and I love him'. I pray that he will equip me with the knowledge and strength to serve him and 'others'.

* * *

Fri 30th Jul '99

7.30am: woke up feeling very distressed – I'm going to 'Joe's place' today!

I kept watching the clock. I saw almost every hour of the day. 8.30am–9.30am–12.30pm–2.30pm–3.30pm–5.30pm. And with every hour that neared 7.30pm: my distress increased. What would I wear?! I needn't 'dress-up', but I didn't want to look a mess either.

6.30pm: I really need to be leaving, but I'm scared to go. I've thought about ringing and saying 'I can't make it' – 'silly idea'.

6.45pm: left the house in a hurry – didn't want to be 'late' – didn't want to be 'early' either.

7.40pm: arrived at Joe's (ten minutes 'late')…

* * *

Sat 31st Jul '99

2.50am: just got back from Joe's! I can't believe what a nice evening I had. He cooked a vegetable curry – we sipped wine. We spoke about our work history, being single, our experience of University, and current affairs. 'Joe do you want to see the bag?' I asked feeling the need for him to see the stoma to really appreciate what I was 'going through' and 'living with'. 'Yeah,' he replied indifferently. I began undoing the button and zip on my jeans and he looked embarrassed. 'Oh I thought the bag was in your back,' he said nervously. I laughed and asked, 'Why?' 'Well, because the operation was to do with your bottom,' he explained uneasily. I proceeded to expand the waistband on my knickers and moved it beneath the stoma. I flipped the bag over my knickers. 'Here it is – my new colon and in there's the new bum!' I said with excitement and showed him the stoma via the 'peep-hole' in the bag. 'Ohhh, I see,' he exclaimed in a long drawn out tone – and with fascination.

Joe drove me home. We hugged goodbye and he motioned to kiss me on the lips! I reacted swiftly, by turning my face. It would have been nice to kiss him but, I felt 'disgusting' – not 'sexy'.

9.30am: received a letter from Toni regarding the talk I gave on the *Patients' Perspective*. She'd attached the student's feedback. Comments included 'the talk was considered and professional' – 'great expression of how an Ostomist might feel' – 'huge insight into how coping strategies were developed' – 'would have liked double the amount of time'. This was 'unbelievable' – they appreciated 'my talk?!' Numbness prevailed – then excitement – then panic. They appreciated 'my talk?!'...

9.50am: opened a bottle of wine – and finished it.

* * *

Tue 3rd Aug '99

Mum, Doreen and Mark returned from New York. They brought back few small bottles of champagne from my cousins wedding – for me to 'celebrate'. I didn't feel like celebrating – I felt sad. Sad that I was unable to attend, and sad that I'd been considered by the gifts of champagne. I opened one of the bottles and drank it with some apple juice. I experienced a burning sensation in my stomach. Still, I kept drinking (the alcohol would soon numb the pain). Wonder why I'm getting this reaction when I sometimes drink alcohol.

* * *

Thu 5th Aug '99

6.30am: woke up feeling anxious. I'm going to a comedy show with Joan, Sharaz and Brendon.

7pm: arrived at the theatre and felt uncomfortable with the 'all black audience'. Racist stories were made about white people in the guise of humour. Joan, Sharaz and Brendon laughed heartily at the jokes, whilst I squirmed in my seat with embarrassment. And, I sat quizzing,

'Sam, have you lost your sense of humour?' I thought about Mr. Bows, Toni and Joe – 'white people' who'd shared compassion and made me realise that white people were capable of experiencing what black people could. 'That white people were like black people. 'They are – we are – human beings.'

11.15pm: arrived home. 'How was it?' Mum asked eagerly (excited that I'd ventured out with friends). 'Yeah, it was okay,' I replied in an unconvincing tone, unsure what I thought of the evening. I'd like to think I'd 'enjoyed myself' – out with friends to a comedy night – sounds 'perfect'. But I wasn't sure that I'd 'enjoyed myself' or if it was 'perfect'. I left Mum in the lounge and went into the kitchen. I switched on the kettle and took a glass out of the cupboard. I quietly unscrewed the top off the bottle of rum. I poured a large shot, added some blackcurrant, and hot water. And, crept upstairs with my alcoholic saviour – 'unbeknown to Mum'.

* * *

Fri 6th Aug '99

7.30am: it's been a week since I spoke to Joe and I've thought about him every day. I've wanted to call, but couldn't. I've got mixed feelings about this 'developing relationship'. Part of me wants to get close (my heart) – part of me wants to stay away (the stoma). Anyway, I'm going to ring him later. I've got a reason to call – he's going to Canada tomorrow and I 'need' to wish him a 'safe flight'.

7pm: rang Joe. 'Hi Joe, I'm just calling to wish you a safe flight,' I greeted nervously. 'Oh, that's nice,' he replied and continued, 'I wish I wasn't going anymore. I wish you were coming with me.' There was a silence and in this silence my heart rate increased. 'Oh, you'll enjoy yourself. And, it'll be nice to have a break from me,' I joked, nervously. 'Ummm, not sure,' he moaned. I disconnected the call and panic struck. I don't think I like the intimacy of this 'developing relationship'.

* * *

Sat 7th Aug '99

6.30am: I'm confused. I'm getting ample sleep, but feel tired? – I'm not getting ample sleep, but feel energetic?!

11am: thinking about Joe – he leaves for Canada today. And I'm already missing him? 'I don't like the intimacy of this 'developing relationship'.

7pm: myself and Steve (one friend who I can tolerate at the moment) went to a restaurant, and a white man aged about fifty remarked, 'You two are beautiful!' At first I thought, 'How strange!' But accepted the 'new' me and accepted what he said as an 'honest compliment'. He continued, 'You're both so calm – your company spoils me. I'm grateful to be in your presence.' I replied calmly, 'It's nice to meet someone who can be so honest.' 'Why aren't people honest?' he asked and then stated, 'We might as well say what we feel whilst we're alive – can't say it once we're dead!' He said he loved people and conversing. The thought cross my mind that he might be being patronising, but my instinct told me that he wasn't. And, I was reminded by his comments that 'peaceful states' offer 'peaceful auras' that are inviting.

11.30pm: at home reflecting on what the man at the restaurant had said, 'You're both so calm – your company spoils me. I'm grateful to be in your presence.' It was an 'honest compliment' (not familiar with those). Had a large shot of white rum with Guinness (Guinness, because I've been told it promotes iron – I think I'm lacking iron – I think I'm anaemic which is why I feel so tired).

* * *

Sun 8th Aug '99

> *The person who seeks to change another person in a relationship basically sets the stage for a great deal of conflict.*
>
> *I love and support you exactly as you are.*

This was the quote and message for today from Iyanla Vanzant's book *Acts of Faith: Daily Meditations for People of Color.* I reflected on my friendships – I must learn to 'accept and love them unconditionally'.

* * *

Mon 9th Aug '99

6.30am: woke up thinking about. The 'novel' – University – medication – hospital – friendships – family attitude – my behaviour and feelings (are they 'right' or 'wrong?') – gratitude (I feel so ungrateful about everything). I need some 'space' – I need a 'break' – I need to 'relax' – I wish I could 'stop thinking'. I'm withdrawing from family, just like I've been withdrawing from friends. I feel calmer when I don't interact with them. But, I can't stop interacting with family and friends – people! Avoidance won't help, but then neither will anger and frustration. Fuck! I feel insecure about everything – 'I need a break from myself!'

1.30pm: opened a bottle of wine and took it upstairs to my room. I've started keeping some of 'my drinking a secret'. I know the family are making judgments about my 'almost daily alcoholic remedy and my during the daytime drinking'. And I guess they're 'wronging' me for it. And I don't have the capacity for anymore 'wrong' – I've got too much at the moment.

* * *

Wed 11th Aug '99

1pm: planned to go to University, but couldn't find my University pass! Where could it be?! I had it yesterday! Hope I've misplaced it – and not lost it. I looked in the desk drawer – I looked in my coat pockets – I looked in my purse – I looked in the lounge – in the chairs – on the table – I looked in the kitchen – on countertop and dining table. It wasn't anywhere! Then I thought, 'Maybe I wasn't supposed to go to University today?' 'Maybe I'm not supposed to study (too stressful for me)', so the Almighty Creator is protecting me – by keeping me away. I felt like crying, but was too scared. Can't imagine not being able to go to University, one of two places (the other is Lank's Hospital) where 'I feel I belong'.

4pm: I took a chance and went to University without the pass and got in! Thank the Almighty Creator! I am supposed to be part of this place!

I entered the library and scanned the study area for a 'suitable space'. I didn't want to sit alone – I wanted to work alongside (not with) some-one else. I found a suitable space – near a woman sitting alone and sat opposite her.

10.45pm: lying in bed and feel in need of some 'male company'. 'Male?' 'Why male?' I think it's because of the developing relationship with Joe and the intimacy of it. And, shit! I've just realised it's been 'nearly a year since I had sex (16th August will make it a year)!' Perhaps, that's why male! I want some romance – and sex? But I can't visualise this – I've got a bag of shit hanging off me! When Joe tried to kiss me, it would have been nice to kiss him but, 'I felt disgusting – not sexy. I need to feel sexy'.

Tried arousing my sexual senses by masturbating – nothing?! No sensa-tion in the vaginal area – no racing heart beat – no giddy head – no – nothing! So, I reminisced and visualised on a past sexual relationship that had been 'beautiful' – still nothing! I have no mental or physical capacity for sex! I think I've, 'lost my sex drive?!' Because of the fuck-ing stoma. 'I hate this'.

11.50pm: drinking wine. 'I want some romance and sex in my life'. I know people have intimate relationships with stomas (members of IA Support Group have told me). 'I want some romance and sex in my life'...

* * *

Thu 12th Aug '99

12.35am: finished bottle of wine.

5.15am: I've got an Out-Patients appointment later. I need to ask Mr. Bows a few questions, but the burning issue is '[Will I] definitely have to have more surgery due to the risk of cancer of the rectum', as advised by doctor in July (I know Toni gave another opinion, but I need a third one).

2.30pm: Out-Patients appointment. 'Hi Sam. I think you're doing really well. Thank you for sparing the time to visit other patients. It's very kind of you. And for sharing the *Patients' Perspective* at the University', Mr. Bows said with a great sense of appreciation. I thought he was being patronising, but negated my cynical feelings and said with a smile, 'There's no need to thank me. It's very good for me.' 'No, no,' he contended, 'You're doing valuable work and we appreciate it.' I frowned at him with an expression of suspicion. 'Honestly Sam, we really appreciate what you are doing,' he sternly affirmed. I shifted uncomfortably in the seat and abruptly changed the subject. 'Mr. Bows can you tell me exactly what you removed during surgery? Do I still have all my small intestines?' Mr. Bows laughed and said, 'Yes, Sam I haven't stolen any!' 'Good,' I said with a chuckle. 'Can you also tell me why I'm experiencing period pains all over? And when I hold my urine, I get pains around the stoma?' I asked in a serious tone. 'You're probably experiencing period pains all over, because your organs have more room inside and have shifted about. And the pains around the stoma when you hold your urine are probably due to the pressure place on it by the bladder,' he explained. I left the burning concern – last, and trembling inside I queried, 'Mr. Bows, I'm confused about the issue of my rectum. Can I keep it forever? Or will I need to have surgery to reduce the risk of cancer?' he looked directly into my eyes and replied in a calm tone, 'At some point Sam you will have to have your rectal stump removed to avoid the risk of it becoming cancerous. And your rectum has been quite active which increases the risk.' I started quivering – all over. He placed his hand heavily on mine to reduce the shaking, and continued in a comforting tone, 'You wouldn't have to have surgery immediately.' I replied faintly, 'I know.' I left the hospital feeling devastated. More surgery – more invasion – more mutilation – more abnormality – more throwing away of Sam.

I travelled to the library to study – hoping that reading would distract me from my feelings of distress. But I couldn't stop thinking about the 'Possibility of needing surgery to avoid cancer'. And as I sat thinking about this 'need' – my heart began pounding. I left the library gasping for air and with my temples pounding.

When I arrived home my mind was racing with thoughts, 'Cancer – surgery – trauma – pain. Cancer – surgery – trauma – pain. I think 'I'm going to die soon'. I think 'I'm going to die from cancer of the rectum'. Because I'd rather die than have more surgery. Part of me feels distressed that I should think of death as a 'better' option than surgery. 'Rather die than have more surgery?' Death as opposed to life?' Another part of me feels comforted by the thought of death. Death the ending – of my dis-ease – and pain – and anxiety…

9.30pm: I needed to share this thought. Surely it can't be right to be thinking like this? 'Death as opposed to life?' I called Trevor. He's been consistent and continued to call even when I've been miserable and snapped. I felt relaxed as I dialled his number, but when I heard his voice – panic struck. 'Would it be fair to share such morbid feelings?' I thought about disconnecting the call, but it was too late – he'd answered. 'Hello' he said abruptly. 'Hi Trevor,' I replied sheepily. 'Sam?' he questioned, seemingly to not recognise my voice. 'Yeah,' I replied in a low tone. 'Oh, nice to hear from you,' he said with excitement. I thought he was being patronising (since I'd been miserable every time he'd called), but I didn't care whether he was or not – I desperately needed to know if my thoughts of death being a comfort were 'morbid' or even 'borderline suicidal'. 'So, how have you been?' he continued. There was a silence. 'I think I'm going to die soon,' I said flatly. There was another silence. I hurried to break it and said in a reassuring tone, 'I'm not scared though.' 'Oh… Why do you think you're going to die soon?' he asked calmly. 'Because my rectum has the risk of becoming cancerous, and I'm not having anymore surgery to remove it,' I blurted. There was another silence. He then said, 'But it doesn't have to happen – does it?' 'What doesn't have to happen?' I snapped with irritation. 'It doesn't 'have' to become cancerous.' I froze as contemplation took over – 'Of course it doesn't!' And, I repeated his words in a low voice – 'It doesn't have to become cancerous.' I raised my voice and said, 'Thanks Trevor.' 'That's okay Sam,' he replied. We said 'Goodbye' and disconnected the call. I sat for a while bewildered. 'My fear of getting cancer had gone?' I heard Trevor's words again, 'It doesn't have to become cancerous.' And my confusion and distress regarding, 'death as opposed to life' – had gone. And I felt so much better – Thanks to Trevor.

10.20pm: the thoughts of death are back! The idea that death could be the ending of my dis-ease – and pain – and anxiety. The thought that this ending would be comforting. But I'm distressed at this 'idea' – surely viewing death as comforting – can't be right?! Drank few shots of brandy and hot blackcurrant…

11.35pm: now hearing Trevor's words, 'It doesn't have to become cancerous' and finding them a great comfort. I really appreciated the relief he brought regarding 'having to have surgery' – now I didn't think I did. 'It doesn't have to become cancerous.' Saying 'Thanks Trevor' on the phone didn't feel like enough. I wanted to let him know that I really valued his reassurance. So I wrote these words for him,

An Appreciation

Sometimes your words have the most profound effect –
They are often the most simplest,
They are sometimes unspoken.
You deliver or convey them at times when I need them most,
And they are very, very comforting –

Thank you.

* * *

Fri 13th Aug '99

7.30am: woke up with thoughts of death! The idea that, death could be the ending of my dis-ease – and pain – and anxiety. And, again the thought of this ending feels comfortable. I'm meeting Lizzy so she can help me fill out a form for Uncle Solomon's Freedom Bus Pass. I wish I wasn't meeting her – I want to stay in and be alone.

11.30am: met with Lizzy at a café and we sat outside – sipping coffee. I'd told Lizzy what the Consultant had said that 'At some point Sam you will have to have your rectal stump removed to avoid the risk of it becoming cancerous.' She said she didn't think that was 'correct' and said she'd bring me something to read. She arrived with a copy of Louise Hay's book, *You can heal your life*. Lizzy was feeling distressed and needed to talk. I immediately lost my miserable, morbid, self and listened to her. She said she felt better after speaking to me, and I felt 'better' knowing I'd consoled her. I felt needed and realised 'There is a purpose for living?'

2.30pm: as I travelled home by bus I scanned a few pages of Hay's book. She explained that she had cancer, but refused to be cut, believing that if she cured her thoughts – her illness would also be healed. She refused to believe that chopping via surgery would make her well, and that this 'cutting away' could continue until there was nothing left to take. She believed that when cancer came back in certain patients, and the medical professionals advised that maybe they'd 'missed some of the cancerous tissue' that this wasn't true, but that the patient had not cured their thoughts and so dis-ease prevailed. Hay also explained that 'We are each one hundred percent responsible for our experiences. And, 'We create every so-called illness in our body'. She was diagnosed as being 'terminally ill with cancer, but cured herself?! She explained that mental patterns caused dis-ease and that an operation would not clear the mental pattern that had created it. She explains that by use of 'affirmations' – 'exercises' – and 'nutrition', we could cure ourselves –

and she had experienced this?! After six months of such practices – 'she had no trace of cancer?!' I found this hard to believe, but then why would she lie? And what she suggested 'seemed natural to Wellbeing' – and to me. I don't have to have surgery! I just need to, 'think well – exercise – and 'eat nutritional foods'.

7pm: attended Tycho's lecture. It was titled, *Death begins in the Colon* and I asked him why. He explained that 'all dis-ease's had the potential to kill and was often due to a build up of toxins in the body. 'Health of the colon determines the health of the body,' he advised and continued, 'Because the colon was the main means of elimination a poor function-ing one would begin the process of dis-ease, and a possible progression of death.' He started the lecture by quoting Bernard Jensen DC, PhD:

> *Somehow bowel wisdom got lost and it became something that no-one wanted to talk about… By putting the bowel in the closet and making believe it doesn't exist, many people have gone down the path of improper living, treating the bowel indiscriminately and reaping the sad harvest years later* (p3).

That's what I was doing 'reaping the sad harvest years later' with my mutilated body. A sharp pain advance in my heart at this realisation. Tycho continued reading,

> *No one has ever had a home nor any acreage to take care of in which they did not have to consider the elimination of waste…. Years ago it was found that many of man's diseases came from a lack of sanitation* (p4).

My dis-ease was UC – and yes, I'd not considered the importance of waste.

Tycho handed us a book depicting graphical photo's of stools – many colours and dense. There was a photo of a sticky black tar-like stool. 'Sticky black tar-like stool (like what I expelled in Jamaica last year)!' 'Tycho, this is what I expelled whilst in Jamaica!' I blurted pointing to the photo. 'What does this type of stool indicate?' 'That's a mucoid plaque and when it leaves the body it may take the form of a black tar like substance. It's old stool. The elimination of this substance should be celebrated! It's certainly no cause for worry. The worry is why it was there in the first place! The major cause of mucoid plaque is artificial foods, particularly bakery products. Certain herbs and fruits can loosen and help elimination. What foods were you eating?' he asked smiling. 'Lots of fruit – at least three grapefruits a day,' I informed. 'Oh, that's probably what started the cleansing process,' he informed. 'Cleansing process,' I repeated, and continued, 'I didn't feel better. Actually, I felt awful. I was getting severe contracting in my sides, when I opened my bowels, and it felt as though my insides were heaving, like when you vomit violently. And, I would break out in a sweat and shiver,' I retorted. 'Sounds like you overwhelmed your body. You probably needed to cut down and allow the process to take place, 'gently',' he sympathetically advised. Shit! This was a 'cleansing process?' I thought there was something wrong – that I was ill – when actually – I was getting better. He continued reading, '*So, let's operate on the problem instead of the body*' (p7). These words resonated. It was too late for me to 'operate on the problem instead of the body'. My body had already been operated on. If only, I'd, 'operate[d] on the problem'. I didn't hear the rest of what he said and thought 'If only. 'If only – fucking only.

I left feeling distressed and full of regret. 'Why hadn't I 'operated on the problem' instead of allowing them to operate on my body?' 'Shit! He was right – UC (dis-ease) does have the potential to kill and it began doing so – it was the 'death of my colon'.

10.15pm: arrived home in what felt like a timeless period (although I'd driven for at least forty-five minutes). I don't remember what route I took. All I know is that 'I arrived' – and I needed a drink. Drank few shots of rum and hot blackcurrant.

* * *

Sat 14th Aug '99

6.30am: feeling unwell (drank a lot of rum last night) and I'm feeling mentally exhausted (information overload). Yet, I want more information?! I want to know 'How I could have prevented UC overwhelming me'. And, I want to know 'How I could have prevented surgery'.

I noted some of the information that Tycho shared yesterday via Jensen,

Sick people are always tired people (p10).

People who ate a lot of bread were the ones who had the poorest colon conditions… Anyone taking bread or any refined flour products must use a fiber as found from vegetables along it… No –one should have sandwiches or have any refined carbohydrates of any kind unless they have plenty of fiber material to move it along (p24).

What disturbs proper intestinal function?… Abnormal nutrition. Nutrition is of paramount importance to the general welfare of the body (p28).

Emotional and mental strain and tension produce unfavorable conditions in the digestive and eliminative organs, causing them to become tense and underactive (p29).

When regularity is absent in the diet there is chaos in the bowel. In most cases, simply changing the diet and eating habits will alleviate many bowel problems without surgery' (p32).

Colitis is an irritable bowel condition that is highly associated with psychological distress. Few people truly realize the benefits of a calm and peaceful lifestyle. They are often unaware of the mind's ability to sink into the body's functioning ability and upset normal tissue activities. Fear, anger, depression, stress, tension, worries and obsessions can all upset delicate processes in the body, and in particular, those of digestion and elimination (p38–39).

We believe that practically everyone has bowel troubles in the civilized world today due in part to the way we are eating. We can't usually sense these things because the nerve supply to the bowel is so poor that we don't know we have a serious problem until we have pain. Any time there is pain in the bowel, it is a serious condition (p44).

Now I believe 'bowel problems and surgery can be avoided' by 'affirmations' – 'exercises' – and 'nutrition'. Louise Hay says so – Tycho Photiou says so – and Bernard Jensen says so. And, 'if only' – if only fucking only'.

* * *

Sun 15th Aug '99

8.35am: thinking about Terry (the Ostomist I met in July). I'm meeting with him on Friday and I'm wondering whether to share the information I have about UC and the prevention of surgery with him. At the moment I'm trying to be honest and I can't see anything positive about having a stoma, but how can I (a former patient with no medical knowledge) compete with orthodox medicine? Maybe I'll put off seeing him until I have the confidence to tell him the 'truth'. The 'truth' that surgery will cause more ailments, and that 'cancer of the rectum' doesn't have to happen.

10.30am: I'm aiming for the following:

To love all and not be selective,

Accept others as they are,

Do not judge or criticise others,

Be sympathetic,

To eat natural, unrefined foods,

Drink only water and herbal teas,

Stop intoxicating my body with harmful substances,

Feel and accept my emotions (and honour them)

Lose the need to be in control (gain more power)

Smile.

'I have to change – or remain dis-eased'.

9.30pm: I have to change – or remain dis-eased. My aims are racing in my mind: To love all and not be selective – accept others as they are – do not judge or criticise others – be sympathetic – to eat natural, unrefined foods – drink only water and herbal teas – stop intoxicating my body with harmful substances – feel and accept my emotions (and honour them) – lose the need to be in control (gain more power) – smile. I have a lot to change – and I'm at conflict with myself.

9.50pm: opened a bottle of wine. 'I don't want to drink'. Still, this 'problem' or 'habit' (not sure what to call it) won't last forever. I know the Almighty Creator will assist me to free myself from intoxicating my body, all I need to do is ask for his help. And, carry out 'affirmations' – 'exercises – and eat nutritional foods.

* * *

Mon 16th Aug '99

5pm: 1 year since I've had sex and I don't know how I'm going to now, with a bag of shit hanging off me. Suppose the fellow I'm having sex with presses down on it and it burst – there would be shit everywhere! Suppose the bag fills up whilst we're having sex – we'd have to stop so I could empty it! Can't imagine having sex – not in my most 'positive thoughts' – or by other 'Ostomists success stories' – or in my most 'drunken state of ecstasy'...

6.15pm: drank few shots of rum and hot blackcurrant.

* * *

Tue 17th Aug '99

7.30pm: Doreen knocked on my bedroom door and handed me the telephone. 'It's Joe,' she said. I thought 'it can't be – he's in Canada'. 'Hello' I said with query in my voice. 'Hello Samantha' was the reply – it was Joe! 'Hi, Joe. What are you doing calling me all the way from Canada?' I asked feeling overwhelmed at his contact. 'I'm calling to wish you 'Good Luck' for tomorrow – when you go to the University Open Day.' I was in shock – he'd remembered and actually rang all the way from Canada to wish me 'good luck'. 'Thanks Joe. I can't believe you've called all the way from Canada. Enjoy your trip and I'll speak to you when you return,' I concluded in a harsh tone (overcome with happiness and needing to reduce my excitement). It felt scary that someone could have such an effect on me. I felt awful after I disconnected the call. I snapped at Joe and he didn't deserve it. Shit! 'All' he'd done was remembered me – taken time out to let me know – and shown an interest. I sat consumed with 'guilt and misery. Opened a bottle of wine – and finished it...

149

9.30pm: retired with feelings of guilt and misery.

* * *

Wed 18th Aug '99

5.45am: woke up feeling excited about going to the University Open Day...

6.15am: wish I could go back to sleep. I don't have to leave until 12.30pm.

12.30pm: been up all morning and it's dragged.

1.45pm: arrived at University. My feelings of 'excitement' shifted to feelings of 'anxiety'. The hall was packed with people and I couldn't see a 'Health Studies' stand. I stood in a daze and then spotted it. I made my way over to the stand and waited for one of the women to finish talking to another attendee. 'Hi. I'm interested in studying Health Studies,' I said to the woman nervously. She handed me a leaflet titled, *Studying Health Studies at Middlesex*. 'This leaflet explains how a degree course is structured at Middlesex,' she said with a smile. 'Thanks. I'm aware of the structure, since I studied English Literary Studies with Race and Culture (RAC) during year 1997–1998,' I explained. 'Oh,' she remarked with a look of concern and continued 'Why do you no longer want to pursue that course?' 'I've become interested in Health since having major surgery last year,' I informed. 'Well you look very well,' she commented and smiled. 'I'm a lot better,' I replied and continued, 'Now, I consider knowledge of health to be invaluable awareness, cause without your health you can't do much!' 'Well, with that enthusiasm – I think you'll enjoy the course and do really well,' she concluded. I left the University feeling very confident. Studying wasn't going to be 'distressing'. This course was going to be therapeutic – and the commence date can't come soon enough!

* * *

Thu 19th Aug '99

6.35am: woke up wondering 'Why do we continually try to prolong life in this world, when we don't know what's in the next?' And, if we truly had 'faith' – would we have fear, and struggle to cling to this existence?' I don't think having faith includes opting for surgery and throwing pieces of oneself into the lab or incinerator...

I thanked the Almighty Creator for this reflection – for most of today.

8.30pm: opened a bottle of wine and finished it.

* * *

Fri 20th Aug '99

1pm: met with Terry (new Ostomist) as he wanted me to share my thoughts regarding pouch surgery. He reminded me of the 'old me' ignorant with the ideas of orthodox medicine and totally faithful to 'what the doctors say'. My thoughts were contradictory to conventional ideas. What was I to do? I didn't want 'my truth' to cause distress – nor did I want to lie. An ethic of healthcare came to mind 'non-maleficence', which is 'one ought not to do harm'. Terry was adamant that he couldn't live with the stoma, and so pouch surgery (having small intestines attached to rectum and utilising anus again) was the 'best thing' for him. I thought about sharing Louise Hay, Tycho Photiou and Bernard Jensen's ideas, but considered the information would be 'harmful'. Terry's priority was to 'correct his body image' – not 'improve his Wellbeing'. So I kept my beliefs to myself and wished him the best with his decision – to have 'further surgery'.

3.30pm: spoke to Lizzy and realised I've got ambivalent feelings about surgery and cancer. I'm 'adamant' that I don't have to have my rectum removed to reduce the risk of cancer, but I've noted my last exam date to inform Mr. Bows and Toni when I'd be available for surgery?! Maybe Louise Hay was 'lucky'? I've not heard of many people curing themselves of cancer – but I've heard of loads of people dying from it.

11.15pm: reviewed my journal to remind myself what Louise Hay had written. My notes reminded me that I must carry out 'affirmations' – 'exercises' – and 'eat nutritional foods'. And, 'I don't have to have surgery.' And, I remembered Trevor's words, 'It doesn't have to become cancerous.' I thanked the Almighty creator for this information to confirm my thoughts and rid of the confusion. I'm not going to have anymore surgery unless a 'crisis' arises. That is, if 'I'm to die within hours and don't feel ready to'. No more confusion – just need to 'relax'…

11.55pm: drank rum and hot blackcurrant until I felt 'relaxed'. Until my thoughts were 'numb' – and until my body was 'limp'.

* * *

Sat 21st Aug '99

5.10pm: feeling tired and heavy with thoughts of 'Cancer – surgery – trauma – pain'. Yesterday, I was sure that I'd only have surgery if 'I'm to die within hours and don't feel ready to'. Yesterday, I was sure that 'It doesn't have to become cancerous.' Now, I don't want to be 'within hours of death' to have surgery. Now, I'm scared of getting cancer. Now, I'm afraid to die.

Toni advised that they would keep me 'under close surveillance' (once every three months) to 'keep an eye on my rectum'. Don't like the idea of having my back passage examined this often. And I don't think the removal of my rectum is necessary? And if it is – it's not urgent? I feel less anxious about surgery? It's only surgery? And surgery has helped many – Surgery saved my life. And, I'm wondering about the idea of 'prevention' and 'luck' – I'm so confused.

Today I asked the Almighty Creator to continue assisting me, by providing the necessary information (and 'will') for me to make the right decisions. I don't want this body that has been provided to serve my spirit, to undergo more suffering. I have endured and learnt enough through 'suffering'. Enough to know that I only need to carry out 'affirmations' – 'exercises' – and eat nutritional foods. And, to love all and not be selective – accept others as they are – do not judge or criticise others – be sympathetic – to eat natural, unrefined foods – drink only water and herbal teas – stop intoxicating my body with harmful substances – feel and accept my emotions (honour them) – lose control (gain more power) – keep smiling. But 'I don't know how to do these'. And my thoughts are so negative. And I will develop cancer if I continue like this. I'm sitting with palpitations in my chest and thumping temples – and sobbing. Back to fucking square one! Very distressed – and totally confused.

* * *

Déjà vu?

6.30pm: at Grandma's and experienced severe abdominal cramps. I was rolling around in agony on her bed and she snapped, 'Haven't you and the doctors sorted that sore out yet? That supposed to have cleared up by now. I thought that operation was going to make you better?' her words sounded familiar – so did I think, the 'operation was going to make me better'. Obviously, she didn't realise that the stoma – that she called a 'sore' was a permanent fixture, and I didn't have the energy to explain – I was in too much pain.

10pm: cramping pains ceased and small amounts of stool expelling. The stoma started working. Thank the Almighty Creator.

* * *

Wed 25th Aug '99

11.30am: went to University. The course doesn't start until September, but I want to start reading and viewing material to understand the subject – 'now'. I want to be ahead, so I don't get overwhelmed with 'reading' and 'learning'. I watched videos relating to the course. Some of the documentaries were about Inflammatory Bowel Diseases and I learnt more about the scientific aspects of UC – and enjoyed watching them!

7.30pm: at home and expelled pinky discharge. Looks like the start of a flare-up. I desperately need to relax…

9.30pm: drank a bottle of wine.

* * *

Thu 26th Aug '99

Expelled pinky discharge three times. 'I need to relax'.

* * *

Fri 27th Aug '99

Went to the library and scanned Deepak Chopra's book *Ageless Body – Timeless Mind*, and noted the following,

> 'When we don't maintain the continuity of our awareness, all of us fall into gaps of one kind or another. Vast areas of our bodily existence go out control, leading to sickness, again and death.'

Too true (in relation to my eating)! No wonder my rectum is 'playing up'. I'm aware of what is necessary to eat – yet I 'cheat' – and dismiss the power of my subconscious (where I think awareness resides?). 'Today' I refrain from eating 'bad' foods (the consequences are too heavy). A diseased body – and guilty mind – both totally unnecessary – 'just' stop poisoning the body Sam.

7.35pm: Joe's back from Canada and I wanted to ring him, but never. Thinking about inviting him to our Bar-B-Q on Sunday, but it's a 'family affair'. Weird as I note 'family affair', because I feel closer to Joe than any 'family' member at the moment. 'What's in a name (family or friend)?' And, I'm concerned, 'How will the family respond to him – he's white?' I haven't invited a white friend home since Primary School (aged five years, before race mattered)…

8.15pm: drank a bottle of wine.

* * *

Sat 28th Aug '99

11am: Joe rang and excitedly yelled, 'I'm back!' I told him about the 'positive' change to study Health Studies – I never told him about my confusion and distress regarding surgery – cancer – and needing to change my Lifestyle (still not being totally honest).

When I realised the duration of the call (forty minutes) and how much I was enjoying speaking with Joe – I panicked. It was time to end this conversation – it was assisting to develop the intimacy of this relationship. 'Look Joe, I've got to go, I've got to do some reading for the course,' I abruptly informed, to bring an ending to the call. However, what I really wanted to do was carrying on talking – let him know that I'd missed him – and tell him that it was really nice to hear from him. Now it's no longer that 'I don't 'like' this developing 'intimate' relationship'. Now it's that 'I'm 'scared' of this developing 'intimate' relationship'. Expelled a pinky discharge with blood. 'I need to relax'.

* * *

Mon 30th Aug '99

It's been over three weeks since Mr. Bows advised that I would have to have my rectum removed to avoid cancer. 'I don't have to have more surgery.' 'Today' I don't believe Hay's experience was 'luck'. All I have to do is carry out 'affirmations' – 'exercise' – and 'eat nutritional foods'. And, to love all and not be selective – accept others as they are – do not judge or criticise others – be sympathetic – to eat natural, unrefined foods – drink only water and herbal teas – stop intoxicating my body with harmful substances – feel and accept my emotions (honour them) – lose control (gain more power) – keep smiling. And, I must.

No alcohol today – I'm fed-up of drinking?

* * *

Wed 1st Sept '99

5.55am: I've been thinking about Joe for the last four days 'constantly'. I feel 'stupid' and 'guilty'. 'Why did I 'act out' and end the call prematurely?' 'Why was I so dismissive and abrupt?' 'Why didn't I say anything 'nice' or complimentary – the 'truth'?' Why didn't I do what I really wanted to do – carrying on talking – let Joe know that I'd missed him – and tell him that it was really nice to hear from him?

3.30pm: wanted to call Joe. 'But suppose he didn't want to speak to me?' I wasn't very nice the last time we spoke. And, I'm still wondering why he's attracted to me. 'Why me with a shitty stoma?!' I really like Joe, but I'm scared of this developing 'intimate' relationship. He'd be the first partner since surgery – since having this shitty stoma. Not sure how 'partners' and 'stomas' get along...

5pm: drank a bottle and a half of wine.

* * *

Thu 2nd Sept '99

7.30am: woke up feeling very guilty about the way I'm treating Joe. And, feeling sickly – I drank too much yesterday (a bottle and a half of wine)!

10pm: Didn't drink today – I'm fed-up of drinking?

Expelled pinky discharge.

* * *

Fri 3rd Sept '99

11.30pm: thinking about having a drink. I didn't have one yesterday, or all day today. Yesterday, I was fed up of drinking, but now, I 'need' a drink? Now, I need a drink to help me sleep and stop thinking about Joe – the stoma – and Cancer. 'Need a drink to help me sleep and stop thinking?!' No I don't!...

Retired without drinking...

* * *

Sat 4th Sept '99

1.30am: still awake and thinking about Joe – the stoma – Cancer – and now having a drink...

5.30am- still haven't slept and I'm lying on my back staring at the ceiling and now thinking about 'having a drink' – Joe – the stoma – Cancer – and 'having a drink'...

6.30am: still awake and feeling exhausted and frustrated. I'm so tempted to have a drink, but I'm hoping my exhaustion will soon put me to sleep.

7.15am: now all I'm thinking about is 'having a drink'. Still I've done well – haven't had one!

10.30pm: I've been thinking about having a drink since last night, and all day, but haven't had one.

* * *

Sun 5th Sept '99

1.30pm: woke up feeling very refreshed. Expelled beige discharge with no blood! Maybe because I haven't drank alcohol for four days?

* * *

Mon 6th Sept '99

7pm: 'Well Done' – haven't had a drink for four days!...

7.15pm: drank a few shots of brandy and hot blackcurrant. Deserved one!

* * *

Wed 8th Sept '99

8am: expelled a beige discharge from back passage with blood. I think it's because I had a drink on Monday...

6.45pm: been thinking for most of the day that 'I need to stop drinking' – 'I need to find another way to relax'. 'I need to stop drinking'...

7.45pm: drank a bottle of wine.

* * *

Thu 9th Sept '99

7.30pm: tomorrow makes a year since Aunty Celia passed away. I wish,

'I had told her how much I loved her'. I wish, 'I had written the letter I thought about sending to her whilst in Jamaica'. I wish, 'I had done more to show my appreciation of her on her Birthdays, at Christmas, and on Mothers Day'. I wish, 'she hadn't died'. Large tears are rolling out of my eyes as I write this.

Expelled beige discharge from back passage with blood (again). Maybe due to dis-tress and upset of Aunty Celia? Maybe due to drink yesterday? Not sure and don't care – don't want to think…

8.25pm: drank brandy and hot blackcurrant – until I was giddy.

* * *

Fri 10th Sept '99

9.35pm: Aunty Celia passed away one year today. I've cried a lot and 'spoken' to her. And strangely felt relieved? And didn't feel distressed and in need of a drink…

Still, I expelled a beige discharge – with 'lots of blood'.

* * *

Sat 11th Sept '99

6.30pm: really wanted to call Joe. I'm feeling very miserable and he always makes me feel better, but I didn't want to bore him with my gloom.

Expelled three times with blood. Perhaps due to constantly worrying about, the developing 'intimate' relationship' between myself and Joe. And, wishing Aunty Celia wasn't dead.

* * *

Sun 12th Sept '99

11.45pm: expelled beige discharge 'twice' today – with blood.

Haven't been able to speak to anyone regarding my thoughts about, Joe – the stoma – Cancer – the death of Aunty Celia – friendships – thoughts regarding death – needing to practice affirmations – needing change my eating – needing to exercise – needing to change me. Everyone I'd like to speak to is either not available – or dead. Bob Marley – John Lennon – Tracy Chapman. Played a CD by Tracy Chapman and selected a song titled, 'For You'. I sang along to the lyrics,

> *Look at me losing control*
> *Thinking I had a hold*
> *But these feelings are strong*
> *I'm no longer the master*
> *Of my emotions.*

157

These words of wisdom 'validated my drinking'. My 'feelings are strong' – And 'I'm no longer the master, of my emotions'. I poured few shots of brandy with hot blackcurrant in a glass and took the bottle of brandy in the lounge with me. I sat slouched and cross-legged on the floor in front of the CD player, and replayed the track. I sang along to the lyrics, again – from my heart and straining my voice box. I poured myself another brandy. And another. And another...

* * *

Mon 13th Sept '99

3.30am: woke up to find the CD player on – lamp on – half a glass of brandy with cold blackcurrant on the floor – and me on the settee. I turned the CD player and lamp off, and took myself, and the half a glass of brandy upstairs to bed.

* * *

Wed 15th Sept '99

2.20pm- Out-Patient's appointment. 'Have I got my small intestines,' I asked. 'Yes, Sam. We told you this the last time we met,' Mr. Bows informed with some irritation. (But, I still 'think' they've taken more than they say). 'Is your rectum still active?' Toni asked. 'No. It's been fine,' I lied (if I told her it had been 'active' – she would have suggested a biopsy). And, 'I don't need to know what's going on' – and nor do they, because, 'I'm not having anymore surgery'.

I left the hospital remembering when I lied to Toni (in May 1998 before surgery), and she insisted on examining me. She discovered that my rectum was active – and that I'd lied. And how my lying and game playing (ignoring my body's response) had resulted in radical surgery. I must use this experience and today's knowledge to make this different. I need to heed my body's reactions. I need to respond. And, I need to remedy.

4.30pm: arrived home. I know wine is not a remedy for my rectum, but it is for my mind. So, I opened a bottle of wine, because I needed a break from the worry. The worry of continually expelling blood. The worry that if my rectum remains active – I risk getting Cancer. And, I'm worried that this is not just an 'orthodox' idea – it's also Louise Hay's, Tycho's, and Bernard Jensen – 'If we remain in a dis-eased state for too long...'. 'If I remain in a dis-eased state for too long' – I risk getting cancer...

6.20pm: finished the bottle of wine.

10.30pm: expelled beige discharge twice – with blood. The second time I expelled – I didn't put the light on, because I didn't want to see how much blood was in the pan, but I sensed there was loads.

* * *

Sun 19th Sept '99

10am- Aunty Celia's Memorial and one year later – I'm still questioning 'Aunty Celia is died?'

12pm: the service ended. I experienced severe pain below rib cage – in the centre of my chest. I thought something serious was happening. I thought I might be having a heart attack, or a problem regarding surgery. But, it went after talking with others. I expelled four times with mucus – and lots of blood.

5.30pm: at home and wanted a drink, but I'm too scared. The severe pain below rib cage – in the centre of my chest – is back. Not sure what's going on with my body. Maybe I just need to relax.

* * *

Thu 23rd Sept '99

9.30am: went to University for timetable. I have to go in three times a week.

8.15pm: rang Joe to tell him about University (good excuse/reason to call).

* * *

Fri 24th Sept '99

12pm: Abdominal pain...

2.30pm: still in pain.

6pm: stoma has stopped working and I'm in severe pain. And, I don't know how to remedy myself. I should seek medic advice, since a stoma isn't 'natural' or 'normal' – and I don't know what to do, but 'I don't want to go to hospital'.

7.30pm: wonder if this 'problem' is a result of tension. Took two Paracetamol and went to bed.

9pm: the stoma still isn't working and I'm now in excruciating pain. I reluctantly took another two Paracetamols (which are just taking the edge off pain) enabling me to groan in pain as opposed to scream out.

11.55pm: exhausted. Same situation and haven't been able to sleep. Hope it starts working soon – I've planned to go to 'World Ostomy Day' tomorrow. 'Can't arrange anything with this stoma'. 'I hate this'...

* * *

Sat 25th Sept '99

2.25am: stoma started working, but it's frighteningly swollen. I've never seen it that big – and wonder what this means. I'll have to ask the medics. Had to cut the hole in the bag a lot bigger to fit around the swollen stoma, so there's less sticking to me which means more chance of the bag leaking or easing off. When I'm not in pain – I'm worrying about leakage. 'I hate this'.

10.45am: woke up feeling refreshed and happy – I can go to World Ostomy Day as planned!

2.30pm: arrived at Northwick Park where World Ostomy Day was taking place. I met a woman who'd had a stoma for over twenty-six years. She said she'd had no problems with it – 'that it was other bits of her that were falling apart!' Which was encouraging?!

* * *

Mon 27th Sept '99

5.15am: woke up with pounding heart and shortness of breath. Today is the first day back at University. I want to interact and be part of a group, whilst at the same time – 'I want to be alone'.

9.15am: arrived at University and made my way nervously to the 'Lecture Hall'. I approached the entrance to the hall with caution and scanned the area from the doorway. It was empty, huge, and frightening. I wondered where the best place to sit would be. I sat at the end of the third row of about sixty. Perfect. Not too close to the front (where I might be called upon), or at the back (where I couldn't leave without notice), and at the end where I could leave without disturbing fellow students.

9.25am: the Lecture Hall began to feel small as people filed in and I felt like I was being swamped. Some were chatting with each other and laughing? I felt so tense and wondered – how they could be laughing on such a nerve racking event – the first day?

10.30am: I was glad the lecture was over (even though I enjoyed it). I sat most of the time hoping the stoma wouldn't make a noise. I headed straight to the toilet to 'check on the bag'.

7.30pm: thinking about Joe and want to ring him. I want to tell him about my first day at University. 'How childish?!' And, I only rang him four days ago! But, I'm not being honest. I'm supposed to be 'being honest'. If I want to ring – I should. I've thought about going to his house – a surprise visit, and using the book I'd loaned as an excuse for visiting! Perhaps I'll call Joe and arrange a date? Ring him?! Visit him?! Make a date?! I don't like this 'confusion'! And I don't like the attraction or intimacy that's developing.

10.30pm: I'm exhausted and experiencing fatigue. Expelled mucus and lots of blood. 'Dis-tress'. Wonder if this is to do with returning to University – or Joe?

* * *

Tue 28th Sept '99

6.30am: woke up feeling 'negative' and wishing to be 'positive'.

3.30pm: in the corner shop. Met a fellow student (by chance) from the Counselling course I pursued in January. 'Hi Sam. You look well,' she greeted with a glorious smile. 'I'm okay. I've resumed my studies and have a prospective partner,' I said with a chuckle. 'Wow, sounds great! Back at University and a partner in the making! No wonder you're looking so good!' she exclaimed with excitement and continued, 'All the best with your studies. And don't forget me on your Wedding Guest List!' We hugged and parted. I left being reminded of my 'Blessings'. That I needed to be thankful that I was Blessed with today. That I needed to be thankful that I had the opportunity to study. That I needed to be thankful that I had a prospective partner. And, I needed to stop being pessimistic.

8.30pm: been thinking about ringing Joe since 6pm (when he arrives home from work), but haven't been able to. 'I'll definitely ring him tomorrow'.

8.45pm: opened a bottle of wine....

9.35pm: finished it.

* * *

Wed 29th Sept '99

6.30am: expelled beige discharge – without blood. I think this is healthy. 'Beige' reflecting colour of stool – and 'without blood'.

7pm: began dialling Joe's number, but wasn't able to complete the call. 'I'll definitely ring him tomorrow'.

* * *

Thu 30th Sept '99

1.45pm: arrived at the first RAC lecture – late! 'How could I? It started at 1.30pm?!' And, I couldn't keep up with the lecture and never heard what was being said. I left the lecture with notes that didn't make sense and 'feeling useless' – and I rushed straight to the toilet. I expelled mucus with lots of blood. As I sat on the toilet I remembered what the

University Health Advisor had said – I needed to 're-think resuming study, if I didn't want to become ill again'. Perhaps she was right? But 'I can't give up University'. All the way home I thought, 'I'm not going to cope with study – but I can't give up University'.

4pm: arrived home. 'Hey Sis! How was your second day at uni?' Sidiki immediately shouted with excitement from her bedroom. I burst out crying as I made my way to her room, and her two friends (Bankoo and Nadola), and herself bolted out of her room. They were all saying at once and repeating, 'What's the matter?' I blurted out, 'I'm not going to be able study – I'm not going to cope.' 'Of course you will. You just need to get back into it. Remember, you've had a years break. It's like starting again,' reassured Bankoo. 'Babe, you've done a year of study before, and didn't you get decent grades? Course you'll do it,' Nadola added, giving me a hug. I dragged my notes out of my bag and said piti-fully, 'Look at these notes, they don't make sense.' Sidiki replied, 'Are they supposed to?!' And we all burst out laughing.

They were right – not the Health Advisor. I just needed 'to get back into it' and I had got 'decent grades' in the year that I'd studied. 'I wouldn't become ill again' – 'something' inside told me'.

* * *

Fri 1st Oct '99

9.30pm: still 'thinking' about ringing Joe. I told myself (on Wednesday) I'd definitely ring him 'tomorrow' – still haven't managed to call. I re-ally wanted to call him yesterday, and share my distress at not being able to keep up with the lecture (he always makes me feel better). And, it would have been a 'reason to ring', but I 'just wasn't able to'.

* * *

Sat 2nd Oct '99

9.30am: rang Joe (five days after wanting to!). 'Hi Joe. Just thought I'd call to let you know how my first lecture went. It was a disaster! I couldn't keep up with the lecturer and left with notes that didn't make any sense,' I told him with a chuckle. 'Oh, Sam! I can count on one hand how many times I've left lectures with notes that made sense! Mine often weren't legible, or they were pictures of matchstick men and dogs!' he said with a hearty laugh. I wanted to invite him to World Ostomy Day (today) at Chase Farm Hospital, but I remembered Sharaz's response – when she sarcastically replied 'Great' when I said I was going to an IA meeting. So, I didn't ask him. Would have been nice to have someone to travel with – would have been nice to share my experience of a 'social with a stoma'. I 'know' Joe would have liked to have been invited, but I couldn't bear it if he'd said he didn't want to, and I'm scared of this developing 'intimate' relationship.

7pm: returned home from World Ostomy event. I met two people about my age, who had stomas, and understood what it's like to be 'shitting out of your abdomen' etc. I've found meeting with people who share similar health challenges really helpful.

* * *

Sun 3rd Oct '99

I've been expelling mucus with blood for over a week now. I'm worried about 'dis-ease' – I'm worried about – 'Can-cer'.

* * *

Mon 4th Oct '99

5.45am: one year since being admitted to hospital for serious problems with 'UC'.

6.30am: expelled discharge with blood. This flare-up doesn't seem to be calming down.

7.40pm: Joe rang to tell me about his cold! He used his cold as an excuse to ring?! Pathetic! And 'we only spoke two days ago!' And, I told him I'd ring on Wednesday to tell him how the talk went 'Why couldn't he wait until Wednesday? What's going on?!' I'm feeling very anxious about this developing 'intimate' relationship. And, 'I'm not sure how 'partners' and 'stomas' get along....

8.15pm: opened and drank a bottle of wine. In seemingly 'no time'.

* * *

Tue 5th Oct '99

4.30am: thinking about Joe and the talk I'm to give at City University tomorrow (Toni has invited me as a Guest Speaker again).

9.30pm: haven't had a drink today – although 'I desperately needed to relax'.

10.15pm: still thinking about Joe and the talk I'm to give at the University tomorrow...

Expelled mucus with blood four times today. 'I need to relax'.

* * *

Wed 6th Oct '99

11.30am: talked about the *Patients' Perspective* at City University for an hour. Yet again, I received a rapturous applaud and left feeling overwhelmed with joy.

6pm: thinking about Joe. I told him I'd ring today – to let him know how the talk went, but I'm feeling 'scared'. And, 'We only spoke two days ago'. And, I'm trying to be honest (for my sake and others), but I'm being dishonest, because I want to ring – but I'm not going to! 'I'll definitely ring him tomorrow'. But 'tomorrow may not come'. 'How do I know I'll be blessed with another day?' And, I don't like this developing 'intimate' relationship. And, 'me' in a 'interracial relationship?' And, 'me' and the shitty stoma in a relationship?! And, I'm not sure how 'partners' and 'stomas' get along – And, 'my thoughts' about this relationship are so 'negative' – yet everything 'feels' so 'positive'. I hate this…

11.45pm: drank few shots of brandy with hot blackcurrant. 'I needed to stop thinking' – 'I needed to sleep' – I've 'got to' go to University tomorrow.

* * *

Thu 7th Oct '99

7.30pm: psyched myself up and rang Joe. I said it was 'a quick call to see how his cold was'. 'Pathetic!' I didn't mention the talk (didn't feel 'comfortable'), but he asked – he remembered! I'm trying to be honest (for my sake and others), but I'm being dishonest. I wanted to mention the talk, but I didn't. 'I don't like this developing intimate' relationship'. And, 'me' in an interracial relationship? – 'Me' and the shitty stoma in a relationship?! – And I'm not sure how 'partners' and 'stomas' get along – And, my thoughts about this relationship are so 'negative' – yet everything feels so 'positive'.

Expelled mucus and blood five times.

* * *

Fri 8th Oct '99

11.30pm: in bed and feeling very tense. I've drank quite a lot of brandy with hot blackcurrant (hoping to relax), but it hasn't helped. Tension prevails in my head – in my jaw – in my stomach. I'm perplexed by the developing 'intimate' relationship with Joe – I'm anxious with regards to University – I'm concerned about my lack of friendships – I'm worried about dis-ease…

* * *

Sat 9th Oct '99

12.20am: drank more brandy and hot blackcurrant. Still not helping – still experiencing tension. It feels like no matter how much I drink – it's not going to relax me, and this 'remedy' is beginning to cause nausea.

12.30am: I thought about ringing Joe (it's late, still it's Saturday), but I didn't. I didn't want to risk being 'too honest' under the influence of drink. 'Too honest?' – What a pathetic idea!

12.45am: expelled a lot of blood. Still feeling tense – 'I don't like this developing intimate relationship'.

2.20am: desperate to rid of tension – I ignored nausea feeling and drank more brandy with hot blackcurrant.

2.55am: feeling very sickly – fell asleep.

5.30am: woke up with the urge to vomit and did – loads of brandy and blackcurrant. Fell asleep feeling better and exhausted.

7.45am: woke up with same tension, and feeling angry, and sad. I want to 'flow with life', but negative thoughts won't allow me. I need to erase the negative thoughts – 'I need to move on'.

9.30pm: I wish it wasn't Saturday. I wish I was at University, because when I'm studying – I don't have time to think about, Joe – the stoma – Cancer – the death of Aunty Celia – friendships – thoughts regarding death – needing to change my eating – needing to change me. Still my greatest antagonism is 'Joe'. Me liking Joe – Joe liking me – and Me and Joe and the stoma.

11.15pm: reluctantly drank bandy and hot blackcurrant (still experiencing nausea), but in desperate need of a break from 'the thoughts' – and 'it's the weekend'. Only drank a small shot of brandy and felt drunk – I guess I still had brandy in blood stream.

Expelled mucus with blood.

* * *

Sun 10th Oct '99

5.30am: woke up feeling hung-over. I went to the kitchen for some water and glimpsed the brandy bottle. Shit! 'I'd drank about a third of a bottle!' Mum knew I'd opened the bottle last night. The amount I'd drank was 'shameful'. 'A third of a bottle of brandy?!' I walked upstairs in shock – 'I'd drunk a third of a bottle of brandy?'

7.30am: lying in bed thinking about the amount I'd drank. 'A third of a bottle of brandy?!' There was no way I could let Mum know I'd drank that much – she'd be disgusted. Don't know 'where the idea came from', but I went downstairs and poured some water into the brandy bottle. Now she'd never know. But I did – 'a third of a bottle of brandy?!'

8pm: to the Fridge Bar to celebrate Trevor's Birthday (second time out clubbing with a stoma) and had a nice time. Enjoyed just a few brandy's and coke – had to be sober enough to look after stoma.

11.55pm: arrived home and darted to toilet – expelled a lot of 'fresh' blood and wind.

* * *

Tue 12th Oct '99

5pm: feels like I haven't spoken to Joe for a long-time, but we only spoke five days ago. 'Five days ago!'

7.30pm: drank two glasses of wine.

9.30pm: feeling quite relaxed and tired.

Expelled loads of beige 'healthy' discharge – no blood. Flare-up seems to be settling down.

* * *

Fri 15th Oct '99

9.30pm: it's been over a week since I spoke to Joe. I really wanted to speak to him – and I really wanted to be honest – so, I ran him! 'Hi Joe – it's Sam,' I greeted him nervously. 'Hello Samantha!' he replied with excitement. 'It's nice to hear from you. How's week three at University been?' he asked with interest. I was in shock and couldn't speak for a moment – he knew how many weeks I'd been at University! He was always involved in what was going on with me. I raced to break a longer than acceptable silence. 'Oh, it was good. I'm really enjoying Health Studies,' I rapped and continued with a pounding heart, 'Joe, would you like to come over for dinner on Sunday? You could meet my bonkers family,' I chuckled. 'Oh, that would be lovely,' he said excitedly. 'What would? Dinner or meeting my bonkers family?' I jested. He laughed and said, 'Both.' 'I'll see you on Sunday, 'bout 2pm?' I concluded. I disconnected the call in bewilderment. 'Did I really just invite Joe for dinner?!'

9.50pm: drank few shots of brandy and hot blackcurrant. 'I'd just invited Joe for dinner!'

* * *

Sun 17th Oct '99

1.50pm: Joe arrived for dinner – ten minutes early! We sat at the table (myself, Joe, Mum, Sidiki, Doreen and Mark) and I was feeling very nervous, hoping that they (the family) wouldn't say anything 'wrong'. We had a 'traditional' West Indian dinner – jerked chicken, rice and peas, fried plantain, roasted sweet potatoes, and coleslaw. I was worried that Joe might not like West Indian cooking, and was relieved when he had a second serving and complimented, 'That was delicious – same time next week?!'

3.30pm: we finished eating and I panicked – 'What was I going to do with Joe now?!' I made myself busy – clearing the table and began washing the dishes. My heart was pounding, 'What was I going to do with Joe now?!' Family filed out of the kitchen and into the lounge and Joe disappeared along with them! I could hear him talking with everyone – and they were laughing?! It seemed like he'd gone for a long time when he returned in the kitchen. He walked over to me, kissed me on the cheek and hugged me, as I washed-up at the sink. I froze – it didn't feel right – 'romance with a stoma' – and 'what if the family saw?' My heart beat began to race and I immediately squeezed myself from his hug and began to move the remaining dishes from the dining table to the sideboard. He stood in the same position for a while – with a vacant space where I was. He then turned to face me and said, 'Your family are really nice. You'll have to come and met mine. Perhaps next weekend?' 'Yeah, maybe,' I replied, reluctant to make any commitment.

10pm: when Joe announced that he was leaving, I thought, 'Oh, already (not realising that it was 10pm)!' And the old adage sprung to mind, 'Time flies when you're having fun'. I escorted him to the front door and we kissed and hugged 'Goodbye.' I closed the front door with a smile. It had been a lovely day, evening, and night! I went into the lounge. 'He's nice, Sam. He made me laugh,' Mum said with a smile. 'He's alright,' added Mark with a chuckle. 'He'll do!' Sidiki jested. 'Glad you all like him,' I replied and concluded, 'I'm off to bed.'

11pm: lying thinking about the comments from the family. They liked him? 'They liked Joe?!' Even though he's 'white' and 'my partner'. It seemed okay. We (the family) aren't racist – we just 'preferred' black friends and partners. 'Funny' (I thought) – 'when our behaviour and attitudes change – it encourages others to do the same?'

* * *

Mon 18th Oct '99

7am- woke up feeling great! I think it's because I had a nice evening with Joe yesterday. And, I feel more relaxed about this developing 'intimate' relationship.

8.30pm: expelled minimum amount of mucus and blood. I think I'm 'de- stressing?'

* * *

Tue 19th Oct '99

Expelled beige mucus – no blood.

* * *

Sun 24th Oct '99

'No blood expelled for six days – just healthy beige mucus!' I think talking to Joe about the death of Aunty Celia – friendships – thoughts regarding death – needing to change my eating – needing to change 'me', has really helped. I've spoken to him almost everyday for the past week. I think the saying 'a problem shared is a problem halved' is definitely true. I don't feel stressed and my body tells me so. No blood expelled for six days – just healthy beige mucus!' And I think I 'like' our developing 'intimate' relationship?! And, I haven't drank any alcohol for the last six days – I think Joe is a good remedy!

* * *

Mon 25th Oct '99

The stoma is becoming a hindrance and problem 'again'. After lectures at University I'm shooting off to the toilet to empty the bag, whilst everyone else is shooting off for a coffee! And, I'm thinking about the developing 'intimate' relationship between myself and Joe and I'm anxious about the prospect of a sexual encounter. 'Sex with a stoma? Sex with shit pouring from my abdomen?' I'm contemplating having pouch surgery. Even though I know 'surgery isn't useful'. Even though I've been saying, 'I'm not having anymore surgery' – I want to look normal and be attractive – again – I want to feel sexy. I need to stop speaking to Joe – I'm getting too close to him – and thinking of carrying out stupid ideas. Shit! I'm thinking about having surgery?! Because of Joe – because of this 'developing intimate relationship'. I hate this...

8.30pm: drank loads of brandy.

* * *

Tue 26th Oct '99

7.30pm: thinking about Joe. I feel so close to him, yet I'm not being honest. I haven't shared with him how I feel about the stoma. I want to, but I don't want to bore him with my concerns regarding the stoma. And I don't want him to see me as a 'problem', 'miserable', and no longer find 'me attractive'. So, I think it's best to 'pretend the stoma isn't an issue'. 'Wonder if he's doing the same?' 'Pretending the stoma isn't an issue'. Or it could be that he actually doesn't think it is? Shit! Yesterday, I was sure I needed to stop speaking to Joe – today, I don't think I can.

* * *

Wed 27th Oct '99

8.30pm: visited Joe (it was a 'surprise' visit)! I used the book I'd loaned as an excuse. When I arrived I stood outside the building to his flat for about five minutes contemplating whether I should carry out the visit. I decided that I should – I needed to be honest. I took another five minutes psyching myself up for 'the meeting'. My heart was beating – double time and I felt dizzy. Part of me didn't want him to be in?! My hand shook and finger trembled as I pressed his buzzer. And, when I pressed it – my heart beat seemed to triple as I waited for a response. 'Hello,' Joe said in a questioning voice via the intercom. 'Hi Joe – it's me – Sam,' I replied tensely into the speaker on the wall. 'Samantha! Come in,' he shrieked and activated entry. As I made my way to his door my heart beat felt like it quadrupled. When I got to Joe's flat he was standing with the door wide open, and posing a beaming smile. 'What have I done to deserve this pleasure?' he asked as we hugged. 'I'm delivering your book,' I replied. 'Oh I thought it was because you wanted to see me,' he said laughing. 'Well, that as well,' I struggled to say – sharing some honesty...

* * *

Thu 28th Oct '99

2.20am: just returned from Joe's! Shit! I only planned to stay for a couple of hours, because I had University work to do, but didn't leave till 1.45am!

We ended up kissing and fondling. One minute – we were listening to music and chatting – the next – we were laid out on the futon caressing! And, my body remembered it had lips! And, my body remembered it had breasts! And, my body remembered it had a clitoris! And 'all my sexual senses – woke up'. We said we would 'take it slow'.

Joe leaves for Vancouver later. 'I don't want to go to Vancouver anymore. I'm going to miss you,' he said when we parted. But I'm glad he's going – I need a break and time to cool off!

Expelled small amount of blood. Surprised because I feel very happy. Perhaps overwhelming eustress.

* * *

Sat 30th Oct '99

9.30am: I've thought about Joe everyday since he left and I can't wait for him to return?!

10pm: Joe telephoned from Vancouver (he's only been gone since Thursday)! And I'm glad he called – and I wish he hadn't?! 'Joe, I won't be able to see you, because of study,' I told him. There was a silence. I continued, 'I'll talk to you when you get back.' Another silence. 'Okay. I'll call you before I leave Vancouver,' he informed in a croaky voice.

169

'Take care, Joe,' I replied in a harsh, concluding tone. 'I will,' he said sadly. We disconnected the call.

I sat feeling guilty and extremely scared again about this developing 'intimate' relationship. I told Joe I wouldn't be seeing him because of study – I said I'd speak to him when he got back. He said he'd call again before leaving – he sounded so sad. 'I'm completely mixed-up'. Why do I feel so scared about this developing 'intimate' relationship? 'Is it because of the stoma?' 'Or because I've never had such an understanding and caring partner?

9.30pm: drank a bottle of wine. My emotions are, 'confusing' – 'overwhelming' and distressing.

* * *

Sun 31st Oct '99

7.30am: woke up thinking about Joe. I feel calmer about 'us' today and I think I miss him?

7pm: phoned Karen (a student from University) and updated her with all my fears and happenings with Joe. 'Karen, I stayed at his place till gone two in the morning, and ended up kissing and fondling with him – he called on Saturday and I really miss him!' I rapped without taking a breath and with excitement. 'Oh! Sounds like Luv,' she exclaimed joyfully. 'So you're seeing him now?' she asked in a calm tone. There was a silence – I didn't know what to say. Didn't seem 'real' – 'me having a stoma and 'seeing someone'?' But I replied in a blasé manner, 'I suppose so.'

* * *

Tue 2nd Nov '99

9.30am: aqua aerobics and sauna.

2pm: feeling relaxed and sleepy (always do after sauna). Had a nap.

3.10pm: woke up feeling very refreshed, calm and happy.

10.30pm: retired to bed feeling very relaxed – 'without alcohol'.

Expelled pinky mucus with blood twice today – eustress – I guess.

* * *

Wed 3rd Nov '99

6.30am: woke up wondering if 'I'm only with Joe because I'm desperate?' And perhaps Joe is only with me, because he feels sorry for me?…

9.30pm: drank a bottle of wine.

* * *

Thu 4th Nov '99

6.30am: Woke up with dull pains in rectum and feeling exhausted. Expelled mucus with blood – I think I'm missing Joe…

* * *

Fri 5th Nov '99

3.10am: expelled lots of blood! I've had radical surgery and I'm still getting flare-ups! What was the point of having surgery? And, 'I've got a fucking stoma'.

3.50am: wide awake and thinking about the 'stoma' – 'surgery' – 'Joe'. I needed to sleep – drank a few shots of brandy with hot blackcurrant.

* * *

Sat 6th Nov '99

7pm: working on essay (which is due in less than two weeks time).

Joe is back tomorrow and I'm feeling stressed. Expelled blood again today – lots.

* * *

Sun 7th Nov '99

10.30pm: feeling tired and stressed – working on essay – and 'Joe returns at 11pm'.

* * *

Mon 8th Nov '99

8pm: Doreen entered my room with the telephone and said, 'It's Joe.' As I took the handset from her my heart began to pound and my mouth went dry. 'Hi Joe,' I greeted in a croaky voice. 'Hello, Samantha. I'm back. I really missed you!' he blurted with excitement. 'How have you been?' he asked in a calmer tone. 'Fine,' I snapped and continued in an insincere tone, 'How was your trip?' 'Oh, it was….,' I interrupted, 'Joe, I really can't talk right now, I'm preparing a presentation to deliver in two days time and an essay to complete in less than two weeks. Can I call you once I've handed in the essay?' I asked in a commanding voice. There was a silence. 'Yeah, no problem. I'll talk to you then,' he replied in a submissive tone. I disconnected the call and feelings of guilt immediately filled the whole of me. Why was I so defensive? Joe didn't deserve to be treated like that. My emotions are so contradictory – and my moods. On Thursday, I was missing Joe and couldn't wait for him to come back. Today, I wish he hadn't?

8.45pm: opened and drank a bottle of wine. 'Joe didn't deserve to be treated like that'.

Expelled lots of mucus – with blood.

* * *

Tue 9th Nov '99

3pm: I'm lying in bed – feeling physically 'strange'. My head doesn't feel right. I haven't got a headache, but it feels 'heavy' and 'dense'. Experienced an inward pulling sensation in rectum. Felt strange and 'unbelievable' – like my anus wanted to suck something in?! An 'inward pulling sensation?' I've never experienced that before. Wonder if this is some 'new symptom' or reaction due to surgery. 'I hate this'.

* * *

Wed 10th Nov '99

7.30am: a year since having surgery?! Feels like I had the stoma formed just yesterday – feels like I've had the stoma forever.

6pm: Sidiki sang 'Happy Birthday' to the stoma, whilst Mum and Dad went over what happened a year ago. We sat chatting for some time with equally sad and happy reflections. Sad – that I'd had surgery – Happy – that I was 'better'.

9.30pm: in my room thinking about, surgery – the stoma – and my health. I regret not listening to my body – I'm glad I feel physically better. I regret that I'm shitting out of my abdomen – I'm glad I've had surgery (I appreciate 'life' a bit more now). I've been crying, but I don't know if I was shedding tears of sadness or tears of joy. I don't know how I feel – 'Happy' or 'sad'. 'My moods and emotions are so contradictory'.

I thought I would have drunk alcohol today, to 'commiserate' or 'celebrate', but I couldn't motivate myself. And, it felt like, if I did drink – I wouldn't be able to stop. No amount of alcohol would 'calm my over-excited happiness' or 'drown my endless feelings of sadness'.

11.30pm: expelled a watery, bloody mucus, and my abdomen was very concaved at the passing. 'I hate this'.

* * *

Thu 11th Nov '99

2.30pm: delivered presentation at University (I don't think it went well) and I'm glad it's over. I feel shattered mentally and physically.

4.30pm: expelled mucus with blood.

* * *

Fri 19th Nov '99

8.15pm: all day I've been thinking 'I should ring Joe'. I've handed in my essay and I told him I'd call him once I'd done that. But I don't want to call him?

8.45pm: drank a few shots of rum and hot blackcurrant. 'Why can't I 'just ring Joe?'

10.55pm: feeling perturbed and still drinking. 'Just ring him?!'

11.40pm: expelled lots of bright red blood – no mucus. 'I hate this'.

* * *

Mon 22nd Nov '99

Received a letter from Toni stating that most students feedback had stated that the *Patients' Perspective* talk had been the most beneficial session of the whole course?! I'd asked Toni if I was considered disabled and in the letter she informed that I wasn't. But I feel disabled – I have no control over my bowel. Doesn't make sense. And, the *Patients' Perspectives* talk had been the most beneficial session of the whole course?'...

8.15pm: opened a bottle of wine...

9.20pm: finished the wine and topped up with a shot of brandy and hot blackcurrant.

* * *

Tue 23rd Nov '99

6.30am: woke up thinking about my cousin who lives in New York (NY) who got married this year. It would be nice to see her and her new baby. And I'm not worried about what might happen if there's a problem with the stoma abroad. 'What will be – will be' – I'm going to visit them!

9.30am: called travel agents. 'Right, that's the flights booked. Would you like to take out insurance?' she asked. 'Yes,' I replied. She asked a series of questions. 'Do you have any medical conditions?' 'Well, I had surgery and a stoma formed for Ulcerative Colitis,' I explained. 'When was that?' she asked. 'Last November,' I replied. 'Have you received medical care, treatment or advice in the last six months due to this?' she continued to probe. 'Yes,' I answered beginning to feel irritated. 'Well, that's classed as a 'pre-existing medical condition.' The insurance won't cover for that,' she informed. 'A pre-existing medical condition' – what does that mean?' I asked abruptly. I heard her shuffle sheets of paper. 'A pre-existing medical condition is one for which an individual actually received care, treatment or medical advice during the six month period,' she read. 'Oh. Sooo, what am I supposed to do regarding insurance?' I asked in a calm tone, trying to suppress my rising anger. 'You'll need to find an insurer that will cover 'pre-existing medical conditions.' And, I warn you – it will cost you more,' she advised in a sympathetic tone. I disconnected the call in disbelief. A new experience of 'discrimination' – based on 'disability'?

10.40am: contacted the Ileostomy and Internal Pouch Support Group (IA) to confirm that what I'd been told by the adviser was true. That what 'I had' was classed as a 'pre-existing medical condition', and that the insurance would cost me more. The advisor at IA confirmed that the information I'd been given was correct! He recommended a 'specialist' insurance company that covered people with 'pre-existing medical conditions'. The cost was more expensive than standard insurance – an extra £15! The benefits of having a stoma. 'I hate this'.

* * *

Wed 24th Nov '99

9.10pm: Joe called and I asked him to call back at 10pm, as I was watching a documentary – *Embarrassing Illnesses*. He said he would and that he'd watch it. As I sat watching this programme with Mum, tears rolled out of my eyes. A man aged twenty-seven years expressed his fear of relationships and body image, and I immediately tapped into mine. I knew I was fearful of relationships and no longer liked my body, but I never thought my feelings were justified. Other people with stomas had formed relationships and seemed confident with their body image. 'So what was my problem?!' After all 'it's only a stoma'. I thought I was being stupid and the 'only one' with such fears. And, a woman expressed, 'It's all very nice that her husband has accepted the stoma, but it's 'her' body that's been altered and 'she' doesn't feel attractive.' I knew exactly how she felt, I'd written about it during the Writing course in February – 'A rosy apple with a rotten core'. When the programme finished Mum looked at me with sad eyes. I didn't need to say anything – the interviewees had said enough. I was glad Mum had seen the documentary and hoped she'd gained some insight to what I was going through.

10.05pm: Joe called. I told him that I knew exactly what the man meant regarding relationships and body image, and now it was easy to explain to Joe how I felt – someone else had validated my feelings. 'Sam, you needn't be scared – it's only me,' Joe chuckled, but I remained silent. He then said in a serious tone, 'You having a stoma means nothing to me.' I tried to appreciate what he offered – his comfort and reassurance. However, it did little to console my insecurity. As the female Ostomist explained 'it's very nice that her husband accepts the stoma, but it's her body.' How Joe feels about the stoma is irrelevant – I'm the one who's fucking got it!

I think this documentary was 'sent from the Almighty Creator'. A great insight that will encourage development and understanding. The Almighty Creator only does what's best for me – what's 'best for us'.

11.55pm: I'm experiencing severe pain and am wondering if this is a blockage. And, I'm too exhausted mentally and physically to bear the pain – so I've reluctantly taken two Paracetamols.

* * *

Thu 25th Nov '99

7pm: out for a meal with Sharaz and Petrinella. I experienced cramps in abdomen. I'm not sure if the cramps were due to what I ate or being 'stressed out'. I'm pondering whether to organising a party for Dad's fiftieth Birthday – which is tomorrow!

* * *

Fri 26th Nov '99

7.30am: decided that I would definitely arrange a Surprise Party on Saturday to celebrate Dad's Birthday.

9.45am: rang fifty-eight guests and about fifty said they'd be able to come! I also invited Joe! 'I invited Joe!' 'How will family members and friends respond to him being white?!' And 'being my partner?'...

11am: arranged to hire a van for the night to house sofas in.

1.30pm: to the market for chicken and fish.

3.30pm: to the supermarket for foods.

6.30pm: to the off license for drinks.

7.30pm: made a sandwich and ate.

7.45pm: unpacked shopping.

11.30pm: myself and Mum prepared chicken and fish for cooking...

* * *

Sat 29th Nov '99

1.30am: to bed and absolutely shattered which isn't surprising considering all what I done yesterday.

1.40am: lying with cramps in abdomen, still although the pain was severe – exhaustion dominated and I fell asleep almost immediately.

7.30pm: Partytime! Guests began to arrive. Everything about the party was 'perfect'. The mix of music, the food, the reunion with friends and family after many years, Joe's presence, and Dad was pleasantly surprised…

* * *

Sun 30th Nov '99

3.30am: as we danced Joe showed that he wasn't rhythmic and jerked about like a turkey! I felt slightly embarrassed thinking, 'Whoops! Joe's reinforcing a typical stereotype – white people haven't got any rhythm', but then I noticed Dad was doing the same! They were doing some kind of Turkey Jive! I was nervous about how friends and family would respond to Joe, but everyone seemed to like him. Welcoming him with conversation, offering food, or dancing with him. Wonder if they were being honest?…

5.25am: we had to encourage remaining twenty guests to go!

6.10am: went home with Joe! We sat kissing and cuddling in the lounge for about twenty minutes. Then Joe suddenly grasped my hand and said in a commanding voice, 'Sam, I'm tired. Lets go to bed.' My heart gave a deep pound that felt final, and my whole body froze as if it didn't want to work. I wanted to 'go to bed' – and I didn't. I allowed him to 'lead me into the bedroom'. We got into bed and began cuddling and caressing. Joe began kissing my body – down to my abdomen. I froze. He was too close to the stoma – he was too close to the shit! I guided his head up towards mine and we kissed. This ended the heated caressing and we cuddled in silence. I could 'hear' us both thinking. After about fifteen minutes Joe fell asleep. But, I lay for at least an hour in a state of tension and feeling sure that, 'I'd never have sex again'.

12.30pm: woke up in Joe's bed with him sitting beside me reading a newspaper! 'Morning, Samantha,' he said with a beaming smile, and bent down and kissed me. 'What do you want for breakfast? I've been waiting for you to wake-up.'

I spent the day with Joe at his home. He cooked us a traditional English Breakfast of eggs, beans, bacon, sausages, and toast. We talked about favourite foods, artists, places of interests, goals in life, and 'everything' and 'nothing'! We danced to music. We cuddled and kissed. We cooked dinner. 'I felt Content, Relaxed and Loved'.

9pm: arrived home and immediately poured a few shots of rum and hot blackcurrant. I'd enjoyed my day with Joe – and I didn't want to come 'home'.

* * *

DÉJÀ VU?

Tue 30th Nov '99

7.30am: woke up with severe cramping pain in abdomen and it's swollen to the point of stiffness.

10pm: stayed in bed nearly all day feeling mentally and physically drained. Luckily, I didn't have to go to University today.

* * *

Wed 1st Dec '99

6.30am: woke up with a tension headache (pain in temples and forehead). I'm thinking about our (mine and Joe's) developing 'intimate' relationship. I told him I'd call yesterday, but I didn't. I need to stop making commitments. Joe was expecting me to call – and I should have? But I couldn't? I was in pain and felt miserable most of yesterday. 'I'll definitely ring him by noon'.

8pm: still haven't rang Joe. I'd told myself, 'I'd definitely ring him by noon'. But, I didn't feel like ringing – so never (I'm trying to be honest). And I need to follow what I feel, rather than what I 'should' be doing. Guilt is a 'negative' emotion. And, 'I must stop feeling guilty'. If Joe can't accept that I didn't want to call – I can't do anything about that. I can't alter my feelings for the sake of his.

10pm: feeling under pressure regarding this new 'intimate' relationship with Joe. 'I like him too much!' Shit! On Sunday I didn't want to come home – I wanted to stay with him. I felt 'Content', 'Relaxed' and 'Loved'.

10.10pm: opened and drank a bottle of wine. 'I like Joe too much'.

* * *

Thu 2nd Dec '99

9.10pm: had a few shots of brandy and hot blackcurrant to psyche myself up to call Joe. 'Hi Joe. How are you?' I asked feeling nervous and faked a jolly voice. 'Hello Samantha. I'm fine,' he replied in his usual cheerful manner. I was going to apologise for calling two days 'late', but his tone told me he wasn't concerned about the 'delay'. 'Are you still coming to the Stoma Support Group's Christmas Party?' I asked with anxiety. 'Of course I am: I'm looking forward to it!' he said with excitement. 'Oh.... Okay,' I replied in a drawn out tone in bewilderment. 'Don't sound so happy. I don't have to come!' he chuckled nervously. 'Oh, sorry, Joe, I was distracted,' I lied and continued, 'I am happy. See you on Saturday.' I disconnected the call and sat not feeling happy – but miserable – with anxiety. Joe said he was 'Looking forward to it'. 'How could anyone without a stoma be looking forward to a Stoma Support Group Christmas Party? I was only going because I had a stoma and wanted to meet with others. I wasn't 'looking forward to it' or even thinking that I might enjoy the event. Joe was 'looking forward to it?!'

9.40pm: opened and dank a bottle of wine – feeling 'uncomfortably' 'Content, Relaxed and Loved'.

* * *

Sat 4th Dec '99

12pm: met Joe and we travelled to Northwick Park where the Christmas Party was being held. There were numerous stalls, displaying samples of ostomy bags, Christmas cards and Aromatherapy items. A game quiz was presented and the afternoon ended with an orchestra playing famous Christmas carols. I enjoyed mingling with people, playing game quiz, and the music.

As we travelled 'home' (Joe's place) I was in awe. 'I enjoyed myself and Joe at a Stoma Support Group party?!' We exited the tube station with linked arms. 'What shall we have for dinner Luv?' Joe asked. 'Fish and Chips,' I suggested.

When we arrived home we chatted about the day, shared funny stories about our time when we worked together, and ate our Fish and Chips. It was a lovely atmosphere – and 'I felt Content, Relaxed and Loved'. We cuddled in the lounge almost all night and there was 'dread' lingering in the back of my mind. I was dreading when the time would come when Joe would say, 'Lets go to bed'…

11.45pm: the moment came. 'Lets go to bed, Sam,' he suggested and took my hand. My 'content body' was saying 'okay – lets go', whilst my 'panicked mind' was 'saying', 'No! I don't want to – I'm scared.' We got into bed and began cuddling and caressing. Joe began kissing my body – down to my abdomen. And like before – I froze. 'He was too close to the stoma – he was too close to the shit'. And, like before, I guided his head up towards mine and we kissed. 'It's okay Sam. The bag doesn't bother me,' he said in a reassuring voice. I didn't say anything, but broke eye contact and hugged him, thinking, 'It doesn't bother you Joe, but it bothers me.'

* * *

Sun 5th Dec '99

3.20pm: at home sipping brandy and hot blackcurrant. I'm thinking about Joe and the Christmas Party, and how much I enjoyed myself. I'm thinking about, how I enjoyed myself so much – 'with a stoma?' I'm thinking about, Joe and how understanding he is. And, I'm drinking, because I feel 'uncomfortable happy'.

DÉJÀ VU?

* * *

Thu 9th Dec '99

Haven't written for the last few days. Nothing's changed. Still doing the same thinking.

* * *

Sat 11th Dec '99

Received letter from Toni asking me to speak at the University again – this time for an hour and a half! She wrote that most of the students feedback had expressed they 'would have liked more time to ask [me] questions!' 'Liked more time to ask [me] questions?!' I've never met anyone who has shown a genuine interest in my experience of surgery (apart from Joe and Nada's Mum). 'Wonder if she's making it up'. Still, they are students who have an interest in stomas?! 'Talk for an hour and a half?'...

7.30pm: opened and drank a bottle of wine.

* * *

Mon 13th Dec '99

9.15am: rang Toni and said I'd be able to do the talk. I asked if it was 'true' that the last students would have 'liked more time to ask [me] questions'. She said she'd send copies of the student feedback forms 'as proof'.

* * *

Wed 15th Dec '99

9.15am: rang travel agents to inform them that I still hadn't received tickets (I'm due to travel on Friday)! The agent advised that I collect them tomorrow! I said I was unable to collect them tomorrow due to having a lecture. He then said I could collect them on Friday since the flight wasn't due to depart until 4.30pm! But I was worried about 'what ifs'. 'What if there's a tube strike' – or long queue in travel agents? I've never collected my flight tickets on the same day...

7.30pm: opened and drank a bottle of wine.

* * *

Fri 17th Dec '99

7.30am: I'm really stressed out. Because I have to collect flight tickets this morning! Because I leave for New York today. Because I don't like flying. And because it's my first trip abroad with this stoma. Expelled loads of mucus and blood.

4.30pm: in flight and I'm glad the drinks are unlimited. I drank four little bottles of wine. I needed to relax. I don't like flying. And I'm travelling abroad for the first time with this stoma.

6.30pm- got up to use the toilet and stumbled knocking into a passenger seated on an aisle seat. I thought my staggering was due to turbulence, but then I realised everything in the plane was 'spinning' – and 'I felt very drunk'.

10.45pm: woken up by an air hostess tapping on my shoulder. 'Can you place your seat in the up-right position to prepare for landing?' she asked in a calm voice. I struggled to place myself and my seat in 'the upright position'. I was dehydrated – my mouth was extremely dry – my eyes felt like they had grit in them – my temples were pounding – and I had nausea. I felt like I'd only been sleeping for half an hour and I felt very rough. As we started to descend – I began to panic about being so far away from home and feeling ill.

* * *

TRAVEL JOURNAL

Sat 18th Dec '99

3.20am: local time. Arrived safely and Aunty Kitty was waiting for me. She was full of energy and excitement, but I wasn't. I was severely hung-over and desperately needed a bed.

11am: woke up feeling much better. I was home alone and enjoying the peace.

1.20pm: cousin Perene called. 'Hey Sam! You're here! How ya doin?' she asked with excitement. Fancy doin a little shoppin over at Yonkers?' I didn't. But then thought, 'isn't that why you came to NY – to spend time with family and friends?' So, I replied, 'Yeah. It'll be nice to catch-up.'

3pm: Perene collected me and I 'reluctantly went shopping'.

* * *

Sun 19th Dec '99

1am: at Joan's Party (neighbour living downstairs). 'Carefully' drank vodka and coke. I didn't want to encourage any problems with the stoma or 'UC'.

4.30am: returned from party feeling shattered.

5pm: went to New Jersey to shop with cousin Richard. I kind of enjoyed myself. Shopping took me out of my head – away from the thoughts that have followed me from London.

DÉJÀ VU?

* * *

Tue 21st Dec '99

10.30am: travelled to Harlem alone (I love that place) and really 'enjoyed being by myself'.

* * *

Wed 22nd Dec '99

11am: met with Michelle and went to Harlem again!

Haven't drank any alcohol for three days – and I'm not missing it.

* * *

Thu 23rd Dec '99

12.35am: feeling 'negative'. I'm eating foods that are toxic – and are literally hurting and burning my stomach. I'm drinking coffee like it's going out of fashion – and I'm over-eating till it's painful. I'm speaking less to the Almighty Creator. And I'm planning – (not being thankful for the day I've been Blessed with). I need to be thankful and live and enjoy today. I need to enjoy each moment and now – tomorrow may never come. I spoke to The Almighty Creator:

> 'Dear Almighty Creator, help me to recognise my wealth, which is instilled in me, you. Remind me (show me) that I'm truly Blessed and help me to be grateful and content, knowing that many others may have certain disabilities that maybe more trying, (yet still a Blessing, for great development). In short, Dear Almighty Creator assist me to be more positive, help others, and in return help myself.'

Since arriving in NY I've felt tired. Strange, I thought I would be energised coming here – I had more energy at home.

10am: Michelle phoned to confirm our planned meeting today. 'Michelle, I need to cancel. Can we meet tomorrow? It's just that I need to study,' I told her. There was silence. 'Okay. Same arrangement, but tomorrow,' she replied in a disheartened tone. Study was an excuse to cancel. 'I didn't need to study'. I needed to be alone – no – 'I wanted to be alone'. Even though yesterday, I really enjoyed myself with Michelle – 'I wanted to be alone' – 'weird'. 'I came to NY to spend time with family and friends?!'

1.30pm: feeling tired. I think this is due to feeling guilty about not wanting to spend time with family and friends. And, I'm wondering why, 'I want' to be alone – and why I'm 'enjoying my own company so much'.

181

7pm: cousin Pernice phoned. We spoke about interracial relationships (her partner's white). 'Aren't there 'difficulties'?' I asked. 'Yeah,' she replied with a chuckle, 'He leaves the bathroom seat up and the top of the toothpaste off!' Then she calmly said, 'Samantha, it doesn't matter what colour a person is. All that matters is that he treats you right.' I disconnected the call feeling 'positive' about Joe. He does, 'treat me right'.

8.35pm: went to a shop and bought a flask of brandy. When I returned, Richard said with surprise, 'I didn't know ya drink alcohol.' I didn't reply, and thought, 'Well you know nothing.' I hadn't drank for four days and as I sipped the hot brandy, I realised that I'd missed having a drink. I'd missed the numbness of not 'thinking' – and I'd missed not 'relaxing'. I drank the whole flask.

* * *

Fri 24th Dec '99

Michelle called and asked if I wanted to go to the 'Movies' tomorrow. I said I'd go since Aunty Kitty was going to work. I was surprised that Christmas Day was celebrated in such a blasé way. 'To the movies' – on Christmas Day?

* * *

Sat 25th Dec '99

Christmas Day. Met Michelle and Venette 'Down Town'. The subway was packed and so was the cinema! Manhattan was as busy as any 'normal' day. Enjoyed being with Michelle and Venette – chatting took me out of my head.

* * *

Sun 26th Dec '99

I leave for London and I'm looking forward to going home.

* * *

Mon 27th Dec '99

9.35am: back in London and now I've arrived – I'm not glad to be 'home'.

* * *

Tue 28th Dec '99

7.30am: feeling very distressed. I need to get book for Health Studies course. I need to write an essay in ten days time. And, I need to prepare a talk to be delivered at City University in eight days time!

* * *

DÉJÀ VU?

Thu 29th Dec '99

Purchased 2000 diary and wrote the same essential details.

I am an Ileostomist (had an operation – removal of whole colon).

DATE OF OPERATION:	10th Nov '98
I AM KNOWN AT:	Lank's Hospital
	Lanks Row
	London
	E26 1SS
PATIENT NO:	250172
MY SURGEON IS:	Mr. Bows
MY CONTACT IS:	Toni Helpful

Joan, Petrenilla, Sharaz and Brendon called to invite me to celebrate the New Year. The Millennium! I decline all offers. Weird (since I planned to celebrate the Millennium with friends and family at home).

* * *

Fri 31st Dec '99

10.15pm: in the lounge playing music and glad that everyone (except Mark) has made arrangements to go out. I want to be alone, but not completely and he's in his room playing his Playstation – ideal. I'm with 'family' – yet, I'm alone!

12am: I opened the front and back doors to let the New Year in – and the old one out! Ran upstairs to Mark's room and gave him a big hug. 'Happy New Year,' I cheered struggling to sound sincere. I then raced down to the kitchen and poured myself a large brandy and hot blackcurrant. I wanted to feel happy. 'It was the New Year – it was the Millennium!' I gulped a large mouthful of my 'mind remedy'. I placed a Bob Marley CD in the player and selected the track 'Three Little Birds'. I sang along to the words,

Don't worry about a thing, because every little thing, is gonna be alright.

And, I swigged my brandy and hot blackcurrant – and danced…

* * *

2000

A UNIVERSAL CREATION AKA 'SAM SHAKES'   JUNE 08

Managing 'Madness'?

Sat 1st Jan '00

3.30am: still listening to music and dancing alone. I've drank loads. And feel 'happy?' I don't care anymore that I don't want to be with friends and family. I'm 'happy' being alone – and I'm in good spirit!

8.45am: woke up feeling very miserable. Good spirits haven't lasted. I was hoping my happiness would be the start of something new – like the 'New Year'. But the only good spirit in me now is, 'excess brandy'.

* * *

Wed 5th Jan '00

10.30am: delivered the *Patients' Perspective* talk at City University. Yet again, the students looked interested. Yet again, I received a rapturous applaud.

3.20pm: at home and wondering, 'Am I really appreciated with a stoma?…

7pm: opened and drank a bottle of wine.

* * *

Fri 7th Jan '00

10.45am: handed in the last essay. Now I have just one exam to do (18th Jan.). Over the past months I've been telling friends, 'I'll be able to meet with you, once University is over. I'll be free'. But when I became 'free' today – I was struck with panic – I'm now able to 'meet with friends'. And because of this, 'I don't appreciate this freedom at all'.

12pm: Trevor called and cancelled our lunch date. I felt relieved, but, my relief was thrown into a panic, when he suggested meeting later! I swiftly thought and lied, 'I don't know where I'll be later.' 'No problem. I'll phone to see if you're at home around 7pm, anyway,' he pursued.

5.30pm: I travelled all the way to Ponders End campus – to be away from home, at the time Trevor suggested we meet. I travelled away to feel less deceitful. The 'truth' would be that I wasn't available – I wasn't

187

at home – I was in Ponders End.

9.30pm: arrived home. 'Trevor called,' Doreen informed as I entered. I walked upstairs to my room, and my body felt heavy with guilt. I'm letting people down more than ever, by breaking arrangements. I need to stop, because it spurs so much guilt, and is unfair on others. 'Today, I will stop breaking arrangements'. 'Today, I will no longer make arrangements (since I know they will not be met)'. 'Today, I stop pretending that I want to meet with people'. 'Today, whether feelings are 'positive' or 'negative' – I'll honour them (it's the resistance that is causing distress)'. Today, I won't allow 'loyalty' to dictate – 'honesty' will.

11.30pm: felt something crawling in my head – an insect, but when I tried to brush it away, 'there was nothing there?'

* * *

Sat 8th Jan '00

11am: went to University today (a Saturday)! To be away. Away from 'home' – where I can be contacted.

6.30pm: at home. I realise that University has been a great distraction. I haven't needed to accommodate my relationship with family and friends, because I had a 'priority' – I had an excuse (studying). But now I have a break – I'm forced to consider my relationships…

9.45pm: opened and drank a bottle of wine.

Twice today I've felt something crawling in my head and down the side of my face. Twice I tried to brush it away – twice nothing was there.

* * *

Mon 10th Jan '00

I saw an advert to practise Yoga at University. I've read that Yoga is good for relaxation – and I need to relax. I went to the Sports and Leisure Club and purchased membership – I could attend all classes. I know exercise will help me mentally and physically. And it would mean less time at home – less availability to meet friends.

Again, I've felt something crawling in my head – and now down the side of my face. And, again when I tried to brush the 'insect' away – 'there was nothing there'. This has happened about three times. I've also seen from the corner of my eyes 'darting figures' – like rats running? But when I turned my head to fully see them, 'there was nothing there'.

9pm: drank few shots of white rum and hot blackcurrant. I need to relax – I need to sleep.

* * *

Wed 12th Jan '00

9.30am: I've tried revising for exam today, but my head is so hazy. I'm wondering 'how I'm going to avoid friends' once this exam is over. And, I'm wondering 'why I'm getting 'crawling sensations' and 'seeing darting figures'. And, 'I'm not sleeping well'.

8.30pm: needed to clear mind of thoughts – and to relax – and to encourage sleep. Drank a bottle of wine.

10.15pm: still not feeling 'relaxed'. Drank a few shots of rum.

* * *

Fri 14th Jan '00

3.30pm: thinking about friends. I haven't had an interesting conversation with any of them in the last six months. I don't have one friend that I feel close to – not one! Feel so lonely. 'Wonder if I'm creating this isolation?' Distancing myself? 'All I want' is my family and friends to understand what I'm going through, but none of them seem able to. And I feel extremely selfish and guilty, because right now I'm unable to consider their feelings. Can't think past myself – with shit pouring out of my abdomen. It's alright for them – they're not trying to manage a shitty stoma – or struggling to keep sane.

* * *

Sat 15th Jan '00

5.45am: been awake most of this morning and feel exhausted, but can't sleep.

Over the last three months I've been prone to going into trances. They usually happen at Bond Avenue ('home'). Family try to wave me out of them and sometimes it works – most times it doesn't. And, everyday for the past five days I've been 'seeing' the darting figures, but can't make out what they are (they move so fast). As I try to see them, I'm repeatedly turning my head. I must look very odd. Glad this only happens when I'm alone.

6.30am: 'I need to sleep!' Sipping wine – and no-one knows. I'm not going to note my drinking anymore. I'm drinking every other day and I don't want to. And the more I note – the more distressed I'm becoming.

* * *

Sun 16th Jan '00

5pm: neighbours were playing a CD that I have. I thought 'they've stolen my CD'. I jumped out of bed and darted over to the CD rack.

I frantically looked 'up and down' – 'down and up' – scanning every single Disc. I couldn't see it – and thought 'they've definitely stolen it!' And my heart began pounding. 'When did they come in?!' 'How did they get in?!' No – it must be here!' I looked again – 'up and down' – 'down and up' – there it was! For a moment I felt relieved 'Of course they hadn't stolen it?' But I then thought, 'Suppose they'd taken the CD and left the case?! I grabbed the case from the rack and abruptly opened it. The CD was in there – 'of course they hadn't stolen it?'

* * *

Mon 17th Jan '00

The crawling sensations are happening more and now 'outdoors'. When I'm out, I try not to brush away what feels like an insect crawling in my head and down the side of my face, but I can't stop myself, even though I 'know' nothing's there – I 'feel' it. That sounds 'mad'. If I know there's 'nothing there' – what am I brushing away?' I've seen darting figures outdoors too. I try to ignore them, but I can't, and repeatedly turn my head to try and look at them. I 'know' there are no darting figures – but I 'see' them. That sounds 'mad' too.

* * *

Tue 18th Jan '00

12.30pm: last exam – University is over for four weeks! And, I think I'm supposed to feel a sense of relief? But, I feel fear and panic.

2pm: had a sauna. As I 'relaxed' I wondered where I could go instead of going to Bond Avenue, where I'd be accessible.

3.50pm: decided to stay at University. Checked next semesters timetable, then thought, 'Now what can I do?' I wondered around the barren campus, looking at flyers – reading flyers – collecting flyers…

4.35pm: still wondering around campus. Too early to go to Bond Avenue – with no coursework – no revision – or no presentation to prepare. 'I'd have no reason not to see friends'. I desperately considered, 'There's got to be something I can do here instead of going to Bond Avenue?' Videos! I could watch a few videos instead of going 'home'. I dashed to the library and selected three documentaries. I left the University hours later – at 8.40pm. I wouldn't arrive at Bond Avenue until after 9pm – too late to meet or visit anyone.

9.50pm: forced myself to call Sonia, (since she'd rang four days ago). I honesty told her about my feelings regarding friends – that I was only continuing contact due to loyalty. She said in a scolding tone that not telling friends how I felt was 'cruel', that I was 'stringing them along' and 'hurting their feelings'. She was 'right'. 'You're actually winding me up,' I angrily told her in an accusing tone, as if she'd said something 'wrong'. What she didn't understand was that 'I didn't want to be dishonest'. That the essence of me 'felt anxious to let go and lose my friends' and I felt 'very guilty' at the way I was treating them. Her words spurred chaotic distress. Guilt filled me from the top of my head – to the tips of my toes. I felt sick – a bitter taste surged my mouth – a sudden headache occurred – my chest became tight – and my stomach – nauseated.

10.45pm: in bed full of anxiety – scared that 'I' could be such a cruel person. My head is still aching – my chest still tight – and my stomach – still nauseated. I've been lying on my back and taking deep breaths hoping to release some of the tension and some of the guilt, but it hasn't helped. A large lump advanced in my throat indicating that my body wanted to cry, but I couldn't – my mind felt too guilty to cry. And, the way I've been treating friends – I deserve to be sad and alone – I'm supposed to feel guilty.

11.45pm: fell asleep full of fear and guilt. Fearful that I could be such a cruel person. And guilty, because of the way I've been treating friends.

* * *

Wed 19th Jan '00

7.25am: woke up with the same feelings of fear and guilt in every cell of my body, and with the added emotion of 'despair'. I feel drained – heavy – and hectic. Like something is pressing down on my head – and inside a whirlwind is stirring me off balance – upsetting my mind.

8.15am: tried to eat breakfast, but my digestive system doesn't seem to want to work – it's so tense and feels uncomfortable to eat. And, I'm finding it difficult to breath – I'm having to force myself to inhale.

9.15am: decided to write to Joan. I needed to do something to relieve my feelings of fear and guilt (they're causing too much distress). And, I needed to stop being 'cruel' and to be 'honest'. So, I wrote Joan the following letter:

Dear Joan

I hope you are well. As for me, I am confused, lonely and depressed.

Before I write anymore, I must first apologise for my intolerant behaviour that I communicated last Sunday evening. I said that 'you were actually winding me up', but the truth is, I was already 'wound up' with depression.

I have needed to say something to you with regards to our relationship for sometime now, but found the truth unbearable, but it has come to the point where I can no longer go on as if everything were 'hunky-dory', much to my dismay.

Our relationship has surpassed many, I have years of wonderful memories, shared history and experiences that many can only dream of. I have learnt so much from you and gained considerably from your support and advice in the past – you have been one of my most trusted and loyal friends.

But what do you do when friendships begin to 'struggle' like ours? I feel that our relationship has been and is becoming 'strained' and I have tried to continue as though everything is fine, but it is no longer working, the pressure is too much – I can no longer pretend.

In this letter I'm going to be honest. Honesty is something that I find extremely painful, but I think the benefits of the truth far outweigh the pain, even if at first it doesn't appear to, eventually blessing reign. Indeed it is the pain that has kept me from writing before now and whilst I thought of what I needed to express in this letter, many tears have flowed.

So… let me try and explain, just what is going on for me, so that you may attempt to understand, why I am, the way I am. I have developed considerably, at such a rate that I hardly know myself! Some aspects are negative, many are extremely positive, whilst others are sad and shocking. But whilst I journey along, it is inevitable that relationships will also change – it's a fact and this is what we are experiencing.

The operation that I had a year and two months ago has had the most profound impact on my life. It was both the physical and mental aspects of this experience that gave 'pause for thought'. Being so poorly made me realize that life is far too valuable to be played around with, (nothing profound in that you may say, maybe you already knew this, but I didn't). Many 'everyday' matters/complaints/problems that cause miserable countenances have become extremely trivial, for example the common cold, miserable weather (whatever that is, usually the rain. That horrible thing that wets us, yet lack of it causes drought and starvation), and bills. If these are problems – then I have none at all. I find such everyday 'complaints' draining.

Now, by viewing a multitude of common complaints as 'trivial' sets me apart from many people. I am not saying that the complaints 'are' trivial, (far be it from me to judge), but what I am saying is that they are trivial to 'me'. It is my shift in focus that no longer finds many of my relationships stimulating, differing interests.

This leaves topics viewed by the majority as 'deep', 'serious' or 'boring'. Labels that I suspect are currently being attached to me. Now I am prepared to be viewed as such, but what I am not prepared to do, is constantly expose myself to people who are not in tune with my way of thinking. More often than not, comments like 'deep', 'serious' and 'boring' are expressed with negative connotations, because of the lack of commonality, and this I believe is damaging. It pigeon-holes and stifles the spirit.

This realisation is extremely sad. Commonality is an important part of friendship, it's what forms the basis of a sound relationship. If you no longer have any common ground, what do you have?

Where I am is an extremely lonely place to be. I don't have any 'being' around that I can express myself freely to. It is also a frightening place to be, because although I feel so lonely, I don't actually want any company! It's contradictory, but as lonely as I am: I want to be alone, because my feelings are too 'deep' for those around me and a lack of understanding, adds to my depression, creating frustration. At the present moment, all I require is 'understanding'. No 'help' – no sympathy', just plain 'understanding'.

I appreciate that my attitude has a selfish tone, and as a result may cause pain, and feelings of rejection, but it is not my intention. My intention is to readdress and get in tune with the real me. To start living a truly productive, creative and fruitful life, instead of existing in the expectations of others, and in a shell full of limitations.

My energy is low and as you have experienced, I am finding it a challenge to maintain regular contact 'like before', but that's because I'm not like before. This means that you will be disappointed if you are expecting the old Sam to reappear – that person is disappearing rapidly. I appreciate that the new Sam that evolves may not be palatable to you and this is the key point in this letter – the sad part of development, the fact that changes may bring about incompatibility, and place a strain on the relationships, but it need not be viewed negatively.

This letter was written to let you know that you have not done anything to 'upset' me and that you are not being 'singled out' – all my relation-ships are changing. I would have preferred speaking to you about this, but couldn't foresee a 'right time', and decided after speaking to you on Sunday that you had suffered enough of my depression and that it was unfair to continue the way I was – not explaining my actions.

I reminded myself on Sunday that whilst I am depressed, the feelings of others are not immune to pain, and that no man is an island (although I feel like one!) – I must still consider the feelings of others, and this is what I have proposed to do in this letter, offer you some consideration.

I have no idea how you might be feeling at this pint – I have never received a letter like this, but I hope it has offered some sort of comfort, and light in the darkness of the unknown, and that you will not be fearful to call or write. I merely wanted to let you know what my 'absence' was all about.

193

If this letter sounds final, it is not supposed to be. Objectively analysed it is a letter of new beginnings, a letter of hope, a letter of friendship and love – I hope you can feel it.

Take good care of yourself,

Forever a Sister-Friend…

Whilst I wrote – I cried and my feelings of fear and guilt eased. It was painful to write this letter, yet ironically it was relieving so much hurt. This letter was an 'admission of my state' and a 'confirmation of change'. As I folded the letter and placed it in an envelope, my hands were shaking and my temples were pounding.

12.30pm: wondering how this 'honesty' will be received. And, wondering if I want to share – so much of me. As I began to doubt the 'plan' – to let Joan know how I was feeling, and to rid myself of guilt – I knew 'I had' to do it. I hastily put on my coat and walked hurriedly to the letter box. When I got to it – I stood for a while, pondering 'Should I post it – how will Joan receive it – I've shared too much of me'. I recognised this uncertainty as 'fear' and again knew 'I had' to post it. So, I slowly took the letter out of my bag and slid the envelope into the large black hole (the letter slot) that was keen to gulp me and my honesty (the letter). As I let go of the envelope – I wished I hadn't. My heart began racing and my temples pounding. I raced home in a panic – 'my inner thoughts were out there' in the world. I raced home, feeling totally exposed – the letter – the essence of me was out in public. I raced home 'to be safe'. When I arrived, I wanted to read my copy of the letter, but I couldn't. I knew the reflection would be too painful. My heart began racing and temples pounding again, as I wondered 'How Joan would receive this letter?' Still, I've got to sort out my relationship with friends. I've got to stop being cruel and I've got to be honest.

* * *

Thu 20th Jan '00

7pm: my physical state of tension has eased tremendously and my energy has increased. I think it's because of the letter I wrote to Joan. It was a burden being dishonest. I'm sure I've done the right thing?

* * *

Fri 21st Jan '00

6.20am: I'm concerned at my increasing lack of faith in the Almighty Creator. I'm struggling to connect with him – and I'm totally pissed off.

2pm: abdominal pains that feels like the start of a blockage. 'Perhaps, I should've taken my chances, and not had surgery – and died'…

5.40pm: Perhaps I should've taken my chances, and not had surgery – and died?…

6.10pm: Perhaps I should've taken my chances, and not had surgery – and died?…

7.45pm: Perhaps should've taken my chances, and not had surgery – and died?…

8.25pm: Perhaps I should've taken my chances, and not had surgery – and died? This thinking can't be right. And, I'm remembering what Simeon said when I told him I was fed-up being back in hospital, be-cause of my second blockage. Because of the fucking stoma! He retorted, 'Bloody hell Sam! You must expect it to get blocked sometimes, even us with bowels have problems!' He was right. 'I've got to put my thoughts into perspective.' I've got to stop viewing all incidences negatively and due to having a stoma. And, I've got to stop feeling sorry for myself. This is a contradiction to what I wrote on 7th Jan: 'Today whether feelings are 'positive' or 'negative' I will honour them. I know this is 'the best policy'. But, if I honour these feelings I'll get too angry – too sad – too depressed – and begin to question again, 'Perhaps I should've taken my chances, and not had surgery – and died?' I can't cope with this 'negativity' it's too much! But suppression of these thoughts and feelings won't make them go away. Perhaps I do need to honour them? 'Shit! – I don't know what I'm supposed to do or feel'. I'm 'sure' me not knowing what to 'do' or 'feel' has something to do with me worrying about the expectations of others. Them expecting me to be happy – now I'm 'better'. Expecting me to smile whilst I have blockages – and with shit pouring from my abdomen! Simeon isn't fucking right! Telling me I 'must expect it to get blocked sometimes' that 'even us with bowels have problems'. They can fucking fix their problems. They don't have to rely on the 'expertise' of others. They don't have a fucking mutilated and unnatural body. They don't experience pain that standard painkill-ers barely take the edge off.

8.40pm: the pains are increasing and now I feel sick. I should contact A&E, but, 'I don't want to go to hospital'.

9.10pm: rang the out-of-hours doctor. 'My stoma has stopped work-ing since 2pm, and I've got all the 'classic' symptoms of a blockage. Severe abdominal pains, swollen abdomen and nausea,' I informed the doctor. 'Well, it doesn't sound like a blockage. And you needn't go to A&E. Take some Paracetamols and rest. Observe what happens in the next twenty-four hours,' he advised. I was surprised at his advice and contended, 'You say it doesn't sound like a blockage, what do you think it might be then?' 'I'm not sure. But it's not a blockage,' he concluded.

Part of me felt relieved. He said, 'I didn't need to go to A&E,' and I was hoping that I didn't need to go to hospital, yet thought the doctor might diagnose 'something'. 'Doesn't sound like a blockage' – 'not sure' – what 'good' was that 'advice'. And, I 'knew' it was a blockage – I'd had two before. Strange that some medics think they know more than the patient – more than the experience.

11.30pm: blockage cleared – I think me massaging around the stoma helped.

* * *

Sat 22nd Jan '00

6.30am: glad the blockage cleared without me going into hospital. This was a Blessing and I need to be thankful. 'This was a blessing'. And, I've just realised that I haven't been connecting with the Almighty Creator. I need to sit and listen to the Almighty Creator via the inner voice that is located in my heart. I sat on the floor cross-legged, taking deep breaths and talking to the Almighty Creator...

'Please help me to gain confidence in you again. Help me be thankful and grateful for all the 'lessons' you send – 'positive' and 'negative'. And, please forgive me for contacting you when in despair.'

I feel like the 'old Sam' (the one that used to take life for granted) with no appreciation for spirituality, and thinking I'm in control. I must continue to have faith in the Almighty Creator. I feel more relaxed knowing that I'm not in control in this (Life). I know that all my experiences and lessons are due to his workings. And I believe that they're all invaluable lessons. And, I know that resistance, worry, or rigid planning – make living a struggle.

* * *

Sun 23rd Jan '00

I've started focusing on foods, because I know food influences dis-ease (UC). And even though I've known this, for the past few weeks I've not been eating healthily. 'I've got to start eating healthily for the sake of my body'. Still, I'm convinced that the greater influence on my body is my mind – my thoughts and suppression of them.

The reappearance of Vitiligo (skin disease) has reminded me of the power of the mind, since I believe it's a psychosomatic disease. Vitiligo suggests my 'negative' thoughts are having an impact on my body. Louise Hay suggests that the *probable cause* of Vitiligo is *Not belonging. Feeling completely outside of things. Not one of the group.* 'That's exactly how I've been thinking and feeling'.

'I must address the issue of my 'negative' thoughts and emotions'. I've lost my colon due to suppressing my anger, guilt and sadness, I can't afford to lose anything else. I need to honour my feelings. I need to honestly express myself. I need to start accepting people as they are.

I wrote to Tycho on 12th Jan to ask him if he could practise some Hypnotherapy with me, and I still haven't heard from him. So, I contacted another Hypnotherapist today, because I'm desperate to rid of these negative thoughts and uncover what is causing discontentment. The second therapist called whilst I was out and left a message with no contact number! These are 'signs'. I don't think I'm supposed to have Hypnosis – so, I'm not going to pursue this anymore.

4pm: Joan visited! I was surprised and nervous at her presence. I asked her if she was surprised by the letter – she said she wasn't. When she left I thought, 'it doesn't matter that she doesn't understand what it's like having a stoma – it only matters that she cares'. Joan's visit spurred a re-evaluation about commonality and acceptance. Even if it is 'just' that we 'friends' are human beings alike? And, 'I need to start accepting people as they are'. Before Joan's visit I was 'sure' I didn't want to celebrate my Birthday with friends. Now, I'm sure I must celebrate my Birthday! Shit! Again, 'I don't know what I'm supposed to do or feel'. 'I'm so confused'. But, I must decide by tomorrow how I will 'make merry' of my Birthday – it's just two days away.

10.30pm: the crawling sensations and darting figures are increasing – 'I need to keep busy'.

* * *

Mon 24th Jan '00

I've decided to let my emotions be my guidance. I don't want to meet up with friends to celebrate my Birthday, but, 'I always do something with my friends for my Birthday' – well not this year. 'I need to embrace change'. So, I'm not going to arrange anything.

* * *

Tue 25th Jan '00

5.30am: today is my Birthday. I'm twenty-eight years old and I'm lying on my back in bed wondering, 'Who I am?' And, 'What was I born to be?'…

8.35am: I'm home alone. Still lying on my back in bed – and still wondering, 'Who I am?' And, 'What was I born to be?' And, I think I'm supposed to feel something today? Happy, maybe? But, I feel indifferent. Part of me is enjoying being by myself – part of me is feeling sad and very lonely.

11am: doorbell rang. I went to Sidiki's room to see who was 'disturbing me'. I aggressively moved the curtain to the side of the window and banged on the glass. It was Joan! I strained a smile and groaned, 'I didn't want to see anyone.' 'Hi Jo,' I said upon opening the door. 'Hi Sam! Happy Birthday,' she bellowed and gave me a hug. I forced my arms around her to form a hug too. 'How have you been?' she asked with a smile. 'Okayish,' I replied feeling irritated by her presence. 'Oh,' she uttered as she dug in her bag and handed me a small parcel that I opened. It was a book titled, *The Little Book of Egyptian Wisdom*. In it she wrote, 'To Sam Happy 28th Birthday. Best wishes for the future. Love always, Jo'. She also gave me a letter.

11.40am: Joan left and I reluctantly began opening the letter she gave me. My heart was racing, hands shaking and palms sweating, as I wondered what she'd written. The contents of the letter expressed understanding and conveyed a lot of Love. In essence, she wrote that 'even though we were experiencing a time of incompatibility, our friendship needn't die'. I sat crying and sobbing for about twenty minutes after reading the letter. I felt relieved – relieved from the restrictions and expectations that friendships can sometimes impose. I felt guilty – because of how I've been treating friends. I felt content – about friendships.

6.45pm – 10pm: several people phoned to wish me a 'Happy Birthday'. Brendon, Joan, Sharaz, Roy, Petrinella and Dad visited and I 'enjoyed the company and being remembered'.

* * *

Wed 26th Jan '00

9.30am: lying in bed and feeling bored. Been awake since 6.30am and haven't got out of bed.

Although I appreciate how friendships can develop – I still don't want to contact any friends. And, I've been distancing myself from Joe. It's his Birthday on Friday and he's going to his family home in Essex to celebrate. He asked if I wanted to go with him. I told him I wasn't ready to meet his family. He said he understood. 'Fuck! – He always understands'. I posted him a Birthday card (didn't want to see him) – but, wished I could have visited him in person – I'm so mixed up.

* * *

Fri 28th Jan '00

11.55pm: listening to the radio (talk show). Sometimes I tune in for company. Sometimes because the night is too still – too quiet – too lonely. Most times because, the thoughts are too much.

* * *

Sat 29th Jan '00

11.30am: the last time I bathed was five days ago (my Birthday). I've been leaving the house for short trips (to the corner shop) without bathing, and now I'm going on longer journeys – I've been as far as Ponders End campus (an hour twenty minutes bus journey away). 'I don't care if I smell'. 'I don't care what I look like'. And, 'I don't care what people think'. I remember whilst in hospital Dad saying, 'Dirt naw kill you, unless it fall pun top a ya'. And, right now, I need to sort out 'my friendships', sort out my 'eating habits', and, sort out my 'negative thoughts'. Bathing is not a 'priority'.

* * *

Sun 30th Jan '00

4.30pm: a man named Ken phoned. He got my number via the IA Support Group and wanted to speak to a student who had a stoma. 'I don't think I can study. Every time I attempt – I get a flare-up,' he explained. 'What do you do for relaxation?' I asked. 'Relaxation?' he quizzed. There was a long silence. 'I don't know. I don't think I do anything,' he concluded. 'Oh. When I practice Yoga, Swim or have Saunas – I never experienced 'UC'. I find these practices relaxing and help reduce stress, which causes my dis-ease – my 'UC'. I think that's why I'm able to study,' I shared. 'Sounds like I could start doing something to relax – combat my stress,' he admitted with a sigh. 'Well, it might be useful to first identify what's causing your UC.' Mine's overwhelming stress – what's yours?' I asked. 'I've got no idea,' he remarked with bewilderment. 'Have a think and depending on what you come up with, put something in place to combat it. For example, it might be something that you're eating, your environment, or overwhelming stress. You could alter what and how you eat, change your environment – your job or home, or find a relaxation method that helps you,' I suggested.

I reflected on our exchange. He had fears of 'failing' (academically) and said he found it 'difficult to express his emotions (especially anger) – sounded familiar. Ken thanked me for listening to him and being understanding. I wanted to thank him – he'd spurred a reminder of the benefits and necessity to think well – exercise – and eat nutritional foods. And, I enjoy and gain so much satisfaction from helping others.

* * *

Mon 31st Jan '00

6.30am: woke up feeling heavy with gloom and full of tension. I'm meeting with Joe later. I think he's expecting us to have sex soon, but, I've got no feelings for sex. He might think I have, because I've been pretending to be excited for his sake. 'Pretending to be excited?'

I haven't had sex for nearly a year (I should be eager for some?!)! But, I've got no feelings for sex, and pretend to be excited. I 'pretend', because, there is no excitement – there is the fucking shitty stoma.

6.30pm: arrived at Joe's and as I assumed – he was expecting us to have sex. 'Joe, I can't do this. I can't continue like this,' I blurted. 'Like what?' he asked in an alarming tone. 'I'm pretending that I want sex and I don't. I can't see me having sex with this stoma,' I sobbed. 'Samantha, it…' I interrupted, 'Joe, I know – it doesn't bother you –but it bothers me,' I angrily retorted and concluded, 'It's best that we part.' I put my coat on and made my way to the door. 'Sam…' Joe said in a pleading tone. I glanced at him, opened the door and left.

8.15pm: at home pacing my room and howling inside. 'I'm alone again – and I don't want to be. This ending with Joe felt familiar – it was like the one with Barry. A 'forced' ending, but this time due to the stoma – not UC.

* * *

Tue 1st Feb '00

5.30am: thinking about Joe with huge tears rolling out of my eyes, and my heart feels like it wants to give in. I feel sad about us – and very angry about the situation – the forced ending – the fucking stoma!

I can't wait to return to University. It's been two weeks since the break and I feel under pressure. University is a great 'distraction' – less time to focus on stoma, friendships, family and Joe – too busy reading, studying and writing. I 'need University' – I need to 'keep busy' – I need to 'keep sane'.

For the last few months I haven't been able to go to bed without a lamp or candle on. A couple of nights ago I turned the lamp off and my heart started pounding and I couldn't breathe properly. I scrabbled to switch the lamp on, in the terrifying darkness, and haven't tried to sleep in the dark again. Wonder what's wrong with me? It's pathetic – I'm a bit 'old' to be 'scared of the dark'. And, the crawling sensations and darting figures are increasing – and so are the trances.

11.45am: reading Jackee Holders book, *Soul Purpose*. I purchased it a few months ago, but didn't feel ready to read it (wasn't ready for action). But, today I felt prepared to free myself from the shackles of the past. After reading a few pages – I felt equally distressed and refreshed at what she disclosed…

> *…we hang around and throw ourselves deeper and deeper into the negative energy, until it takes over our minds and our lives. I know – because I have been there many times. I grew resentful and frustration always magically lifted as soon as I took action to fulfil my purpose.* (p3)

I wish I knew my purpose. 'Who am I?' – 'What was I born to be?' I continued to read...

> ...*I do not spend time thinking about the house I want, or the car I desire. Right now they are not essential requirements for the journey I am taking. Jesus said, 'In my Father's house there are many mansions'. I know that my needs have already been taken care of.* (p3).

I trust that the Almighty Creator always provides us with what we need.

> ... *You may find that the inner you is very different from the person your project externally.* (p4)

'This is so true to me'. It's refreshing to know that someone else understands.

I know 'action' is necessary and this is what Holder encourages 'Action'. I've been thinking and reading – and reading and thinking. I'm exhausted by the constant storing of information and analysing – it's time to 'act!' When I attended Holders workshop she emphasised the importance of 'action' and suggested keeping a journal and writing 'honestly'. I've always kept a journal and when I read what I've written, I'm able to 'see' more clearly what I'm feeling and doing. And, writing about my thoughts and feelings alleviates 'stress'. I can 'see' the problems and the thoughts are 'out of my mind'. I reckon my mind would have collapsed if I didn't write. I read last years journal and ninety-five percent of it has expressions of 'negativity' and fear. I find it easy to write when I'm 'down' – shame I can't write when I'm feeling 'up'. Or, perhaps this is a true reflection of me – ninety-five percent 'negative' – five percent 'positive?' Shit!

7.30pm: still reading Holders book and feeling very angry. I've been recalling conversations that I've had with family and friends – I think 'they're trying to control me' and I'm fed up with 'their criticisms and their opinions.' And as I adopt a more honest approach to life, I foresee many arguments with family and friends, due to our conflicting ideas and differing values. I don't like quarrelling, but hate deception. And, I've got to be honest – 'even if it means being confrontational'. 'I realise I've been 'restricting my true self, my needs and my morals'. I've been 'living by the expectations of others'. Living in a box – and 'living a lie'.

10pm: wondering what my *Soul Purpose* is. 'Who am I' – 'What was I born to be'. Wonder if I'm supposed to be a Counsellor? I've spoken to five people over the last week offering support and they seem to benefit from my suggestions. But, who am I to offer advice?

* * *

Wed 2nd Feb '00

9.30pm: lying in bed remembering the time I expressed that I felt like a 'rosy apple with a rotten core' via the Writing course. I still feel like a 'rosy apple with a rotten core', but today it's more than physical. The stoma is still the 'rotten core' and my appearance the 'rosy apple', but today events and emotions are attached. The 'rotten core' represents the events I've experienced in my life, various abuse, insults, criticisms, and the spurred emotions of anger, fear, frustration and sadness. The 'rosy apple' is the deception of what's inside – the charade that I'm okay and managing – the 'great pretender'.

I've got vaginal thrush and the itching is 'unbearable' (very sore with broken skin that bleeds). I've been using ice to reduce the soreness – but I've been drinking tea and coffee with milk and sugar even though I think thrush thrives on milk and sugar! The 'itching is unbearable – but I've still been drinking tea and coffee – with milk and sugar?!' This must be 'stress behaviour'. I'm 'willing' to have 'unbearable soreness' rather than not drink the offending liquids! I've read that the best cure for thrush is a total 'avoidance of sugar or anything sweet', and eating lots of 'garlic' and 'onions' helps. I don't have the energy to struggle with eating healthy. I know my diet will improve once my thoughts are reduced and become more 'positive'. Seems trivial to worry about eating healthy when my mind is so sick.

* * *

Thu 3rd Feb '00

6.30am: woke up feeling full of energy and positive. I created two journals (as suggested by Holder). A 'Gratitude Journal' and a 'Loving You Journal'. In the Gratitude Journal you're supposed to spend seven minutes, writing seven things that you appreciate each day. In the Loving You Journal you're supposed to write a love letter once a month to yourself! This journal can be enhanced by adding letters of appreciation from others, thank you notes, photo's of people you love, and meaningful cards (anything that reminds you of your wonderful attributes (p47) etc. I feel a great challenge ahead – I feel excited about the future – I'm going to start 'taking action!'

4.30pm: I thought about writing a letter to Sharaz (one of a similar content as Joan's), but as I thought about what I'd write – angry thoughts consumed me. Our relationship has been based on transaction (what I've been able to do for her – rather than who I am). If I weren't going through a difficult spell, we would have spoken at least once a week, because I would have contacted her. But because I haven't been able to call her – she hasn't called me either! I decided not to write to Sharaz, because I didn't want to cause offence. And, I thought she didn't 'deserve a letter' – there was no friendship to salvage. I think 'true friendship' is a bond of support that is not broken by a change in circumstances? 'What good is a friend if they're not around in a crisis?!'

7.30pm: Joan rang. She asked me to go to the sauna with her tomorrow. I told her 'I didn't feel like it', but she pleaded with me, and so I said I'd go. Because, although, 'I don't feel like it' – I really, really do.

9.30pm: had a bath and washed my hair! And, I look and feel completely different – I look vibrant and feel energetic! Shit! There is 'someone' there – in that body! Must keep this up! Must buy some bathing sea salts and essential oils, to pamper myself.

* * *

Fri 4th Feb '00

10am: completed exercise *Finding Your Soul Purpose*, from Holders book that I found distressing. The answers to the following questions were particularly upsetting:

What did you want to become when you were eight years old?

'Noticed.'

What single thing could you do at this moment to move you closer to your Soul Purpose?

'I have no idea.'

Part of the exercise required to write a letter to an unborn child telling them how to stay in touch with their Soul Purpose. I couldn't do this exercise. I felt overwhelmed with injustices and I felt dirty – contaminated with 'wrongs'. I wanted to be pure and clean again (like an unborn child). So instead of writing a letter I wrote:

Too painful right now – a great challenge.

This task brought tears to my eyes. I wish I was an 'unborn child' – pure and clean, but most of all – I wish I was 'pain-free' – mentally and physically.

1.30pm: I feel physically tired and mentally energised. My body wants to rest, but my mind won't let me. I feel 'disconnected' and the physical symptoms are getting worse. The crawling sensations are becoming 'more real' – and there are now 'insects' instead of an 'insect' – and they feel like they are stamping instead of crawling. I couldn't identify the darting figures, but now I see them – they're definitely rats. The palpitations in my chest are so violent – they are moving my clothes. And the trances have developed 'locks'. Now when I try to break out of them by blinking and shaking my head, it doesn't help – they dictate. I don't understand this. My thoughts are 'positive', yet, 'something still doesn't feel right'.

2.20pm: I'm feeling anxious about going to the sauna this evening with Joan...

4.20pm: My anxiety is growing...

4.45pm: I have a faint headache. I needed a distraction and decided to complete *Beck Depression Inventory*. This is a tool to determine whether an individual is experiencing depression. My score was '21', which equals 'moderate – severe depression'. 'Moderate – severe depression?' Still, such tests aren't 'accurate?'...

5.50pm: maybe I am experiencing 'Moderate – severe depression?' Fuck! More problems.

6.10pm: rang the Counselling department at University and left a message. I knew no-one would be there, but I needed to make contact now – so that my message would be received early Monday. No more denying the 'strange physical sensations'. The crawling insects – the rats – the palpitations in my chest – the trances. 'No more denying – it would be detrimental to my mind. I can't afford to lose it. I can't afford to let my mind get 'sick' – it's the core of 'me'. And, I ignored physical symptoms before – when my colon was crying out for help. Now 'I've got no fucking colon and I'm shitting in a plastic bag stuck on the side of my abdomen?!'

I was overcome with panic – I need help 'now' – 'I need help now'. I frantically ran downstairs in despair and with tears streaming down my face. 'Now I've got no fucking colon and I'm shitting in a plastic bag stuck on the side of my abdomen?!' – And I'm getting 'strange physical sensations' – crawling insects – the rats – the palpitations in chest – the trances – and 'I don't know who I am'. I ran into the kitchen wailing. 'What's the matter? What's the matter?' Mum repeated in shock. I blurted, 'I need help – I'm not coping.' 'What do you mean?' she asked hugging me and giving me tissues. 'I'm losing it and I need help,' I sobbed. She repeated calmly, 'What – do – you – mean?' I forced myself to stop crying and tried to think of a way to tell her about the 'strange physical sensations' without sounding 'mad'. I started crying again and through hysterical sobs said, 'Mum, I'm getting crawling sensations in my head and from the corner of my eyes I see figures darting'. I couldn't believe what I was saying, 'I'm getting crawling sensations in my head and from the corner of my eyes I see figures darting.' There was a silence. 'Oh, Sam! It's 'just nerves.' I get crawling sensations in my head too,' she reassured and gave me a hug. I felt relieved, yet thought, 'Great, we're both 'losing' it!' She continued, 'Don't worry.

You'll be alright. But if you think you need help – make an appointment with a doctor on Monday.' Her suggestion sounded more like an order, and her tone told me, that she wasn't sure that [I would] 'be alright' – and neither was I.

6.40pm: Joan blew her car horn to notify her arrival. I left the house with red eyes, snotty nose, and lots of tissues. Mum followed me out the front door. I looked back and she was standing at the gate watching me walk to Joan's car – she had tears in her eyes. When I got into Joan's car – I burst out crying again. 'What's wrong?' Joan asked alarmingly. I explained that 'I wasn't 'coping' and that I was 'getting crawling sensations in my head' and 'seeing darting figures'. She hugged me and said, 'Don't worry Sam, it'll be alright.' I felt totally detached and numb.

9pm: returned from the sauna feeling mentally and physically relaxed and no longer had the detached and numb feeling. I felt in need of company – real company (not the radio or TV). So I took my quilt and pillow into the lounge and lay on the settee. Doreen and Mark looked at me with surprised expressions. 'You've come to join us – that's nice?' Doreen said with a smile. 'Yep,' I replied with a yawn and snuggled myself beneath the quilt. They watched TV and I fell asleep peacefully, in their company. Sauna's are great for relaxation...

* * *

Sat 5th Feb '00

1.30am: woke up lying on the settee in the lounge – in darkness – and in a panic. Where was everyone – what was the time?! I considered going to my room, but I'd be 'alone' – with the 'negative' vibes. I've spent so much time in there writing – reading – reading – writing, that haven't seemed to help. If they had, I wouldn't be getting 'strange physical sensations – the crawling insects – the rats – the palpitations in my chest – the trances. I 'couldn't' go to my room – I needed a break from it, so I switched on the TV and remained in the lounge. The TV was good – it provided light as well as people.

6.15am: woke up under the quilt hearing strange voices! I lay like a statue wondering what to do. 'Should I flee from the burglars, rapists, or murderers?' Or should I confront and attack them?' I lay with my heart racing – and eyes wide in terror, under the protection of the quilt for a few minutes, listening intently. At first I couldn't understand what they were saying, but then realised the strange voices were on the TV (forgot I was sleeping in the lounge)! There were no 'burglars', 'rapists' or 'murderers'. There was just 'Rodney and Del' from the series 'Only Fools and Horses'.

11am: went to the Counselling department at University. I knew no one would be there, but 'I needed to do something'. No one had contacted me in response to the message I left on Friday (that they would have received early Monday – yesterday). 'Maybe they never received it – maybe it never recorded?' So, 'I needed to do something'. I wrote my name and telephone number on a piece of paper and slipped it under the door – now they couldn't say they hadn't got my details.

2pm: in my room. I feel like screaming – I feel hysterical inside – 'I don't know who I am!' Perhaps I am 'moderate – severely' depressed as the *Beck Depression Inventory* suggests? Perhaps, I'm not losing my mind – just 'moderate – severely' depressed (even though, I'm getting 'strange physical sensations').

I've been trying to stop hearing my thoughts by playing music, but this distraction hasn't worked. I hear half of the first track, but the thoughts conquer. Sometimes, I play the music loud (to win), and this works, but when the thoughts get less intense – I realise the music is blearing.

8.30pm: spoke to Joan and Brendon and expressed my disappointment and anger, at Sharaz not being in contact. They both asked why I hadn't rang her. 'I haven't been able to contact anyone. Me not calling Sharaz hasn't been a 'choice'. Under normal circumstances I would have spoken to Sharaz nearly everyday, because I would have rang,' I retorted angrily. However, they both implied I was being selfish and suggested I should contact her! I don't have the capacity to nurture anyone else's insecurity. Don't they fucking understand – I'm on the verge of losing my mind?!

* * *

Sun 6th Feb '00

9.30pm: just returned from Mickayla's (cousin) for dinner. I wish I never went. I wish I'd followed my instinct and stayed home – alone. 'Well, at least me naw Mickayla can bake – you can't mek Apple Crumble,' Dad said (without reason) as we sat eating. Everyone laughed – everyone except me. 'What's your point?' I asked sternly. He never answered, and the roars of laughter stopped. I got up and walked into the lounge – to get away from them. I paced the lounge and a surge of panic prevailed – Dizziness – pounding temples – tightness in my chest – and shortness of breath. And a hysterical howling was fighting to get out. I'm struggling to maintain my sanity and he's concerned that I can't bake an Apple Crumble. 'Can't mek Apple Crumble' – for fuck sake!

As Dad drove us home I had few surges of panic. I was sitting at the back of the car staring out the window that was half open. I had my face close to the opening, taking advantage of the air rushing in – hoping it would help my breathing. The panic? I was too close to family members. I needed to get out of the car. I needed to get away from them.

As soon as we arrived home – I dashed out of the car – placed the key in the front door – and went straight to my room – to get some relief. But it never came – I could hear them laughing. And I knew they were laughing at me (like they were at Mickayla's). And, the more I heard them laughing – the greater the panic and physical sensations. The dizziness – the pounding temples – the tightness in my chest – the shortness of breath. I sat at the edge of my bed trying to regulate my breathing, but I couldn't. I climbed into bed and covered my head with the quilt – hoping to drown out their laughter (if I couldn't hear them – I'd be able to breathe better). But covering my head with the quilt never helped – I could hear their laughter even more. I felt like running away. Away from them. And, away from myself. I wanted to run away from their comments, and away from my thoughts that are always there 'nagging' – 'confusing' – 'questioning' – 'draining' – and 'demanding'. I feel like running away – but where to run to? And, how can I detach 'me' from my mind?

* * *

Mon 7th Feb '00

6.30am: woke up with Sharaz on my mind and feeling very angry, because of her lack of communication. I need to contact her. I need to tell her exactly how I feel. But I need to do this when I feel more in control and calmer. I thought she was a good friend, but this 'friendship' seems a bit one-sided – 'me being a friend and she not'.

9.30am: rang doctor's surgery to arrange an 'Emergency Appointment' (I needed help – now) and was given one for today at 10.45am.

10.45am: I was sitting in the waiting area and was startled out of a trance by the doctor shouting, 'Samantha Shakes – Samantha Shakes.' I leaped from the chair and I sensed an irritation in her voice, when she looked at me and repeated in a questioning tone, 'Samantha Shakes?' I answered 'Yes,' wondering how many times she'd called, before I'd heard her. I followed her to her room feeling anxious and wondering, 'How I was going to make it clear that I needed help now?' As we entered the room she asked, 'Right Samantha, what can I do to help?' I immediately began crying and blurted, 'I need help. I'm not coping.' She passed me a tissue and asked, 'What do you mean?' 'I'm losing it and I need help,' I sobbed. She calmly repeated, 'What do you mean?' It was like deja-vu (the same situation with Mum). I forced myself to stop crying and tried to think of a way to tell her about the 'strange physical sensations' without sounding 'mad'. Through sobs I said, 'I've been getting crawling sensations in my head, and from the corner of my eyes – I've been seeing figures darting.' 'Oh,' she replied calmly. 'How long have you been getting these symptoms?' There was a silence as I struggled to remember. 'About four weeks, I think,' I replied with uncertainty. 'Is there any particular time when you get the crawling sensations?' she queried with concern. 'No they come anytime,' I replied. 'And what about seeing the darting figures?' she continued. 'No they come anytime as well,' I informed. 'Are they getting worse or more frequent?' she questioned. 'Yes,' I said with a deep sigh and huge tears streaming down my face. 'Are you anxious or worried about anything?' she questioned. 'No, not really. But, I feel a bit angry that friends don't understand what it's like to have a stoma, but I can't blame them... And, sometimes, I hate the stoma, but I'm really getting used to it,' I said trying to convince myself and her. 'How's your sleep?' she continued. 'I don't get much, and it doesn't matter what time I fall asleep – I'm usually up by 6.30am. And I have to get up about five times during the night to empty the bag and urinate. So I'm not getting much sleep at all,' I pitifully explained. 'I think it might be useful for you to take a mild anti-depressant,' she suggested. My heart felt like it wanted to stop working and her words resonated in my mind, 'take a mild anti-depressant'. Her suggestion horrified me as I remembered my experience of anti-inflammatory tablets – 'suppressing rather than curing'. There was no way I was going to do that again. I frowned and said, 'I would prefer Counselling.' 'I can make a referral to a Clinical Psychologist, but this appointment could take up to eight weeks. I think a mild anti-depressant might be useful until you get some Talking Therapy. I think you need something now,' she advised with a voice of concern. There was a silence as I sat thinking, 'she's right, I do 'need something now', but not a 'mild anti-depressant'. And, 'there's no way I could wait for eight weeks'. I felt distressed – 'What was I going to do now?' I rose from the chair and said, 'Thanks. I'll wait for the appointment.' She looked disappointed and replied, 'Okay. I appreciate your situation and you're welcome to book another appointment for a chat,' she encouraged. I trotted most of the way home. I'd said that 'I'll wait for the appointment' – but there's no way I can wait for eight weeks – 'I need help now.'

11.20am: arrived home and bolted through the door. 'I needed help now'. I grabbed the Thompson Local and Yellow Pages and searched for 'Counsellors'. I rang eight public and private services. Most had waiting lists of at least six weeks – 'six weeks!' 'I need help now'. I left a message at MIND (mental health charity) via an ansaphone. I sat with the telephone directories on my lap, rocking and crying hysterically. 'Where was the help I needed now?' And, 'Why hadn't the Counsellor from the University rang?' There was no-one – there was 'nothing'. 'Just me' and 'emptiness'. I went to bed with the quilt over my head, and curled up in the foetus position. 'I needed help now'. And, 'I needed taking care of'.

12.45pm: heard the phone ringing and ringing. I was ignoring it, but then thought 'it might be the University Counsellor!' I dashed out of bed and ran downstairs to answer the call. 'Hello. Can I speak to Sam Shakes?' A voice calmly requested. I knew it was the Counsellor and hastily replied, 'Speaking.' 'Oh, hi. My name's Eunice. I'm one of the Counsellors at University. I received your message and wondered if you might like to come and see me today at 2.30pm, if this is okay with you?' she invited. I thought, 'of course 'it's okay with me!' 'Yes, yes, it's okay with me,' I excitedly replied with a great sense of relief.

4.30pm: back from Counselling session and feeling distressed. When I arrived Eunice discretely scanned me from head to toe. 'Come in and take a seat,' she coldly said with a fake smile, pointing to an arm-chair in the corner of the room, and didn't take her eyes off me as she seated herself in a chair opposite. She was holding a notepad and pen and asked in a demanding voice, 'Right, would you like to tell me a bit about yourself?' 'Well, I had a stoma formed just over a year ago and sometimes it bothers me – sometimes it doesn't,' I explained. She looked puzzled. 'Do you know what a stoma is?' I asked. 'No, can you tell me, please?' she answered. I explained 'UC' and what a stoma was. 'Oh, sounds like you've been through a lot in the last couple of years. How are you managing? Do you like the stoma?' she probed. I thought 'what a fucking stupid question'. I told her 'it bothers me', and explained that I was shitting out of my abdomen. Wasn't she listening? How could I 'like it!' 'No I don't 'like the stoma' – I just get on with it,' I retorted. She shifted uncomfortably in her seat and wrote in her notepad. 'How do you cope with not liking it?' 'Well, when it bothers me – I have a drink,' I disclosed without shame. She continued, 'Does it bother you often?' 'Every other day,' I replied. 'Oh, so you drink every other day?' she 'cleverly' calculated with an expression of worry. 'Yes,' I agreed. 'Can you tell me a bit about your past? Your childhood?' she asked with inquisitive eyes. 'My childhood,' I quizzed with a frown, and my heart began to beat faster. I shifted in my seat – I didn't want to talk about my 'dreaded childhood'. What did my 'childhood' have to do with how I felt now, and why I was getting 'strange physical sensa-tions?' 'What did my 'childhood' have to do with my shattered beliefs and value system?' 'My childhood?' I slowly repeated. 'Yes, what was it like growing up? Were your parents married?' she continued to probe. 'Yes, my parents were married. My Mum wasn't much of a talker and my Dad used to drink alcohol to manage his distress,' I replied defen-sively hoping she would change the subject, but she never. Instead she continued, 'And how did you feel about this?' I began feeling angry and reluctantly answered through gritted teeth, and a stern tone, 'Well it was difficult – I guess. Anyway, I don't see much point in going into the past and blaming others. I want to change my negative thoughts into positive ones and get back to the 'Old Sam,' I sternly informed. 'Oh,' she exclaimed, leant forward, made eye contact and continued, 'What was the 'old Sam' like then?' 'I was happy, relaxed, friendly, sociable and confident. But I was also too accommodating for others, disregarded my morals and I judged my success by what everyone else thought success was. I don't want that 'old Sam' back,' I explained. 'So what do you want to do?' she quizzed. 'I don't know – I don't know,' I cried with my head bent and left hand on my temple. I continued through violent sobbing, 'I don't know, because I don't know who I am, or what I want to be. I feel lost.' There was a silence and she handed me a tissue. 'And, 'I've been getting crawling sensations in my head and see from the corner of my eyes figures darting. Feels like insects crawling down my head and the side of my face – sometimes I try to flick them away. And the darting figures disappear before I can identify them, but I think they're rats. And, I get palpitations in my chest, and go into trances. Why do you think this is happening?' I ranted. There was another silence. I continued, 'I know there are no insects or rats, but I 'feel' and 'see' them.' She looked shocked and sat upright in her chair. 'It sounds like you're asking me if you're going mad,' she suggested in a fluster, as she wrote in her notebook, again. I forced a chuckle and said, 'Yes, I guess that is what I'm asking.' She closed her book – got up from her seat, and replied, 'We'll talk about that next week.' Her reply and reaction scared me. 'What did these symptoms mean?' And, I thought 'I can't wait till next week.' 'I need to know if I'm 'going mad now' – and what I can do about it. As she made her way to the door, she asked, 'Is there anyone else you can talk to?' 'No, there isn't,' I replied with annoyance, and I thought 'if there was anyone else – did she think I would have contacted her'. 'It's best that we work as a multi-disciplinary team. So if other health professionals such as your Stoma Care Nurse, Consultant, and Doctors are able to offer support it would be useful,' she informed. 'Useful' – for who?' I quizzed silently. 'The Stoma Care Nurse could address issues regarding any problems you're having with the management of the stoma, the Consultant could deal with any physiological aspects, and your Doctor could help by perhaps prescribing medication to rid you of the sensations you are getting,' she said in a voice of authority, closing our meeting. 'Oh,' I sighed as I walked out of the room. I felt like she wanted me to expose my 'self' to the whole world. 'Stoma Care Nurse' – 'Consultant' – 'Doctor'. I don't need more than one 'professional'. All I need to do is talk. I left the session questioning the ability of this 'Counsellor'. It was obvious that she wasn't equipped to deal with problems as 'severe' as mine. It was shown via her shocked expression and her sitting upright in her chair when I told her about the strange physical sensations I've been getting, and by her suggestion to gain support from other health professionals. No, this woman wasn't equipped to deal with problems as 'severe' as mine. Even in my confused and desperate states – I know this woman will not be useful.

4.55pm: arrived home feeling more desperate than when I left and that 'can't be good'. I need to start trusting my instinct – 'Eunice will not be useful – I'm not going back'. Still, 'I need help now'. I reluctantly rang Toni, on Eunice's suggestion that, 'it's best that [they] work as a multi-disciplinary team'. I got her ansaphone and abruptly disconnected the call. Ansaphone – 'I need help now!' I sat for a while violently sobbing with tears streaming down my face. I redialled and left a message with no indication of what I wanted to talk about. I didn't want to inform her of my distress and desperation – Toni thinks I'm doing well, because I give talks at the University, and visit patients pre- or post- operatively. If I tell her how I'm feeling – that I'm not coping, she probably won't arrange anymore visits – and I'll be useless again.

I didn't think contacting Toni would be useful, but, 'I needed to do something'. My distress isn't about having a stoma. My distress is about 'strange physical sensations' and 'not knowing who I am'. I've accepted and overcome the concerns surrounding the stoma? I've been through the 'What ifs?' 'What if the bag leaks?' 'What if shit goes all over my clothes?' 'What if there's no toilet to empty?' 'What if the bag fills up and people see it?' 'What if the clip undoes?' Now I need to deal with having lived a nonsense. Now I need to deal with 'getting rid of their ideas' and implementing mine. 'They' told me 'success' is measured by gaining qualifications – by securing a job with a 'big' salary – by purchasing property – by having a partner – by having children – by the commodities I acquire. And, I need to forgive those that taught me this nonsense. Parents – Grandparents – Aunts – Uncles – Friends – and Teachers.

8pm: feeling distressed about friendships again. I needed to desperately talk to someone. I rang Aunty Bernice. 'Hi Aunty Bernice,' I greeted in a low tone. 'Oh, hi Samantha. How are you?' she asked in a cheerful voice. 'Not bad,' I lied. 'How's your health been?' she continued. 'Oh, that's been good. It's just that... It's just that... I've been wondering why people are so selfish?' I said hesitantly. 'What do you mean?' she asked. 'Well, they just don't seem to consider other people. Most of my friends don't seem to think about me, and the experience I've had. It's always about them,' I explained, swallowing to keep the 'crying lump' down in my throat. 'Unfortunately Sam, there are 'Givers' and 'Takers' in this world – you're a 'Giver' and you need to accept this,' she said sadly. 'I can't always be giving – why can't we share?' I blurted and started crying. There was a silence. 'We can't share, because you're a 'carer' and people need caring for, and that's what they like about you. It doesn't necessarily mean they are 'bad' friends,' she advised. I didn't want to hear this. So they wasn't to blame – they wasn't 'bad people' or 'selfish' – so I must be?! 'Oh,' I sighed feeling hopeless and angry. We concluded the call.

8.55pm: what Aunty Bernice said is repeating in my mind. 'We can't share, because you're a 'carer' and people need caring for and that's what they like about you.' And, I'm questioning 'what happens when I can't 'care' – who fucking takes care of me?!' No, this can't be right – it has to work both ways.

* * *

Tue 8th Feb '00

6.40 am: woke up with palpitations. I dreamt I was shouting at Aunty Susan. 'I was hysterical' – 'I was out of control' – and 'I was very angry' – I called her a fucking bitch! The anger that I experienced in the dream reminded me of the passion I felt regarding Nathan in Jan '99 (when bile filled my stomach – bile that physically burnt). This dream made 'sense'. I've always felt that whatever I do in her eyes is never good enough. 'What didn't make 'sense' was the intensity of my anger'.

9.30am: haven't been able to bathe for some time, but today I had a long soak in the bath with Table Salt (same as bath salts – not as expensive). I considered taking my clock in the bathroom, but remembered reading in Holder's book that baths are therapeutic – relaxes both the body and mind, so it wouldn't be useful to be considering time – when trying to relax. I'd always considered a bath just for hygiene purposes, but today I left the bath feeling refreshed and relaxed.

10.30am: Gwyn from MIND returned my call. She said I would be assessed next week. 'Next week' seemed like a long time, but I felt a sense of relief.

I'm feeling 'scared to go outdoors again'. I leave Bond Avenue – and immediately want to get back. And, before I leave I calculate how long the trips should take. Seven minutes to walk to bus stop – ten minutes waiting for the bus – twenty minutes journey to destination – twenty minutes activity. Whilst out I constantly check the time and, if walking takes longer – I quicken my pace. If the bus journey takes longer – I consider getting off and trotting. And, I rush to complete the twenty minutes activity and I've started to feel scared to be in my room – alone. So I've been spending more time in the communal areas with family. That space (my room) feels like it's pulling at all my limbs and sometimes it feels like the ceiling wants to crush me. I've off-loaded so much negativity in that room that it doesn't feel like a safe haven anymore, but a 'danger zone'.

9.30pm: haven't been noting my drinking, but today it's necessary. I'd been drinking almost every other day, sometimes once every three days, which was an improvement to my daily habit. However, the daily habit is returning. Sunday, I drank two glasses of wine at Mickayla's. Monday at '10.30am' – I drank four shots of vodka with hot blackcurrant (I don't even like vodka, but there was no brandy or wine). The longer I stay sober – the thoughts become more intense. They're always there 'Nagging' – 'Confusing' – 'Questioning' – 'Draining' – and 'Demanding'. I need a break from them. But, I don't want to use alcohol anymore – I need to exercise some control – I'm out of control of my mind – I can't afford to also be out of control of what I ingest.

So, tonight, I resisted the temptation of 'relaxation'. And, I resisted the 'pleasure of numbness' – I didn't have my alcoholic remedy. Instead, I decorated my Gratitude Journal and became engrossed with my drawings. It was a challenge, and the thoughts were still there, with added thoughts of 'needing a break from thinking' – and 'just a little bit of alcohol would help'. I went downstairs for a fruit and was nearly defeated when I saw the bottle of vodka on the sideboard. So easy to access – staring at me – and begging to be drunk. But with the support of the Almighty Creator – I didn't indulge.

* * *

Wed 9th Feb '00

8.20am: woke up with the experience of being in hospital and having surgery on my mind – and feeling angry. 'Why didn't I have anyone to depend on whilst in hospital?' 'Why did I have to ask questions like, 'What was the medication for?' 'How long will I have to take it?' 'What's the alternative?' I had to ask all the questions – address all the concerns – whilst being so ill. Even when I was ill – I still had to fucking take care of myself! Dad asked to see the doctors once and made enquires, but I was in hospital for seven and a half weeks, and there were a lot of questions and procedures that needed challenging. I feel especially angry with Mum. I don't remember her asking any questions, or being concerned with how I felt about the whole experience – she's my Mum – she's supposed to take fucking care of me! But, I realise the Almighty Creator was (and is) always with me, giving me the strength to ask questions and the knowledge to make useful decisions. Fell asleep…

10am: woke up with palpitations recalling a dream. I was looking for Barnet Hospital and got lost. I could see the street, but I was in a maze and couldn't get to it. The terrain was hilly – wet, muddy and dark.

As I trod down a hill, it revealed a housing estate and two black men came out of a flat. Their faces were harsh and ugly. They were hiding something that I instinctively knew was a weapon. I ran in the opposite direction, back up the hill and met a white woman who was running as well. I caught up with her and she screamed, 'Run they're rapists.' My fear increased – my pace quickened. I became unaware whether the men were still pursuing us, yet my fright and knowledge of their evil intention, kept me running. Eventually, I managed to seize a look behind – the rapists were nowhere to be seen.

I've been having a lot of dreams and they seem to be based on my thoughts. I've been feeling nervous about travelling to Barnet Hospital (due to go on Saturday), because of the two hour long bus journey, and worried that it is an area that I've never been to before (not sure how safe it is). And, I've been scared to go outside (doesn't feel safe out there – might have an accident – might be attacked). I'm not getting any let up from the thoughts. Even when I'm trying to sleep – they are in my dreams! 'Nagging' – 'Confusing' – 'Questioning' – 'Draining' – 'Demanding' and causing 'Panic'. I read in James Redfield's book *The Celestine Prophecy* that dreams are significant and they are trying to tell us something. The dreams I've been having are usually distressing and mainly about me being attacked, arguing with someone, or falling from heights. 'Wonder what my dreams are trying to tell me?

10.45am: outdoors looks bright and inviting. I want to go out, but I don't feel like it. I might force myself? And, I'm wondering what time I'll be back. I heard Sidiki getting ready to go to college and thought I could travel with her (bit safer) to Holloway and do some shopping. So I did. I panicked when Sidiki said, 'Right this is my stop,' kissed me goodbye and got off the bus. I was out there alone. I thought about going back home. But, I decided to pursue my plan – to go shopping, because I needed a distraction from the thoughts, and I needed to stop 'being scared of going outside'.

It was difficult to enjoy this shopping trip. I felt a million miles away from home – from 'safety'. Whenever I went into the shops – the assistants stared at me (I think they thought I was a shoplifter). Most people were in couples, or more, and laughing (I'm sure some of them were laughing at me). And people who weren't shopping looked like they might be murderers, kidnappers, or rapists (they had evil facial expressions, or they posed fake smiles). It felt disturbing being out with so many people around. I knew they could see me, because they were staring or laughing at me, or giving me a fake smile, but I still wondered 'if people could actually 'see' me'. I felt like a ghost – some people 'noticing' me, but not 'seeing me', and although they could attack, kidnap, or rape me – part of me felt 'unable to be reached'. I felt isolated – yet exposed. Whilst out I experienced five strange spells. I went dizzy and lost my balance. I thought it might be because I was hungry (although I didn't feel hungry) and ate a sandwich. But even after eating, 'I still experienced these strange spells'. I was supposed to buy anything I wanted to treat myself, but I couldn't see anything I liked or wanted. No CD – no clothing – no artefact. So I returned home with nothing.

1.35pm: at home. I don't want to be alone, but I don't want to be in company. I don't want to be alone with my thoughts – they're too intense. It feels like my head is going to explode. I've just looked in the mirror and my temples are bulging! Shit – blood vessels might burst and cause haemorrhaging. 'My thoughts are too intense. And, 'Alone is not good'. Still I never am, the Almighty Creator is always with me.

8.25pm: I cried a lot today and realised that no work – no amount of crying – sadness – or anger is too much to experience. I deserve all the energy – and all the time that it takes to be healed. I've been wounded in many ways – for many years.

* * *

Thu 10th Feb '00

6.40am: woke up remembering two dreams. I dreamt Carol and Sharaz had come to see me in hospital – in a psychiatric ward. I shouted, 'Now you come – when it's too fucking late – when I'm at rock bottom!' They 'defended' themselves by saying, 'You never called.' I hysterically retorted, 'I was fucking sick'!' I also dreamt that I was on the top deck of a bus with Brendon and although there was no exchange – I felt animosity between us. I sat next to a black male who had no face. He was surrounded by a thick cloud of smoke and was drinking beer. He was perceptive and expressed (through silent cursing) an understanding of disloyal 'friends' and the pain it causes. He was angry – very angry on my behalf and I liked him – he was on my side. It's been a long time since anyone has been on 'my side'. More dreams that appear so 'real' – reflecting my reality – the experiences and thoughts I'm having. Sometimes, I only know I've had a 'dream' by the event. I know I haven't been admitted to a hospital via psychiatry, but then I'm not sure, I may have been on a bus with Brendon and met the stranger who was on my side? Sometimes, it's as though my 'dreams and reality are one'. Bit weird, and disturbing. Fell asleep.

7.45am: woke up and went back to bed.

10.20am: disturbed and woke up – went back to bed.

2.45pm: woke up! Stayed in bed...

3.25pm: still in bed – still feel tired!

Yesterday, I planned to go out to buy some bath salts and essential oils, but haven't. I'll go tomorrow (after visiting the doctor) – I'll already be out.

Received a copy of Tycho's issue of *The National Society for Personal Growth*. It had some interesting and relevant information. In particular, a quote referred well to my reality it read:

> *Disease is, in essence, the result of conflict between soul and mind. So long as our souls and personalities are in harmony all is joy and peace, happiness and health. It is when our personalities are led astray from the path laid down by the soul, either by our own worldly desires or by the persuasion of others, that conflict arises.* Dr. Edward Bach

This is my belief – this is my current state of being – in conflict.

3.40pm: Dad called. 'Hellow Sa-man-ta. How ya do?' he greeted in a cheerful voice. 'Oh, hi Dad, I don't feel well – mentally,' I replied in a low tone. 'Wat?!' he snapped in a voice of disbelief. I slowly repeated, 'I don't feel well mentally,' and rapped, 'I've been getting weird physical sensations. Crawling feelings in my head, and see from the corner of my eyes figures darting. Feels like insects crawling down my head and the side of my face. And, the darting figures disappear before I can see them, but I think they're rats. And, I keep going into trances'. 'Look, diss is all to do wid de operation and ya diet – de way ya a eat. Ya need fe eat beta, and you will feel beta,' he said in a voice of authority and panic. 'Do you think so?' I asked in an apathetic tone. 'Yeah,' he replied abruptly and continued in a stern tone, 'You naw know wat you eat affects ya mood? I tink you beta call dat doctor at de hospital – de surgeon, and tell him bout dis. Ask him wat you can do bout ya eating, now you have dis stoma ting. And, I tink you beta go an see a 'Harley Street' specialist bout ya mind.' 'I've already got an appointment with MIND, so…' Dad interrupted, 'An appointment wid MIND – a who dat?' he asked abruptly. 'It's a charity that helps people with mental health problems,' I said in a low tone. 'Oh. Well, if dem mess you bout, you juss mek an appointment with someone at Harley Street. Ya mind naw fee be messed wid,' he sternly concluded. I disconnected the call feeling sad, and guilty.

Our conversation was enlightening and it confirmed what I really felt. 'De operation' and 'ya diet' were the catalyst of what was bound to happen after years of suppression, and un-useful habits. This result (me feeling mentally unstable) wasn't based on a recent occurrence – it was based in my life history and adoption of conventional ideas (now I understand why Eunice asked, 'Can you tell me a bit about your past? Your childhood.'). The reason why I'm experiencing mental health challenges is because of 'their' (Parents – Grandparents – Aunts – Uncles – Friends – Teachers) ideas and habits. 'They' told me 'success' is measured – by gaining qualifications – by securing a job with a 'big' salary – by purchasing property – by having a partner – by having children – by the commodities I acquired. But I couldn't tell Dad this – I couldn't tell him that some of his influences were partly to blame for my mental health challenges – it would hurt his feelings. And, his intention is always so clear – 'he loves me and wants the best for me' – it's 'just' that his conventional ideas stop him carrying out his purpose. Dad was recommending that I continue to practise the orthodox approach when he suggested that '[I] beta call dat doctor at de hospital – de surgeon… Ask him what you can do about ya eating, … And … you beta go to see a 'Harley Street' specialist bout ya mind.' But conventional practises and ideas have assisted my state of ill health – mentally and physically. And, I now need to disregard most orthodox practices, and ideas – for the sake of my Wellbeing.

7.30pm: speaking to Dad has made me think about my eating habits. 'You naw know wat you eat affects ya mood?' he'd said. It's really weird – I've got no appetite, yet I'm constantly hungry – and eating, but losing weight?! I wonder if it's 'hunger', because I have no appetite, and it feels more like a 'discomfort'. I've had this feeling most of my life and have always thought 'I must be hungry'. Perhaps, this 'discomfort' expressed by my body is not hunger for food, but for something else? Maybe this discomfort is my body's way of expressing that it needs some mental attention and/or nutrients? And, I might be causing a problem when I eat with no appetite?

10.45pm: went to bed singing Diana Ross's 'I'm Coming Out' with words:

> *I want the world to know-*
> *Got to let it show*
> *There's a new me coming out –*
> *And I just have to live*
> *And I wanna give – I'm completely positive.*
> *I think this time around,*
> *I am gonna do it*
> *Like you never knew it,*
> *Oh, I'll make it through,*
> *The time has come for me to break out of the shell,*
> *I have to shout*
> *That I am coming out…*

As I sung, huge tears rolled out of my eyes and down my face. The words conveyed exactly what I aspire to do, and be. I want to let people know that, *'there's a new me coming out – And I just have to live… 'The time has come for me to break out the shell'.'*

* * *

Fri 11th Feb '00

9.40am: sitting in doctor's surgery. Another appointment (the last one was four days ago!). I didn't want to visit the doctor, but I needed to let her know that I was getting worse. And, 'I needed to do something'. As I waited to be called my mouth went dry and I had to take deep breaths to regulate my breathing. How was I going to tell her that, 'Things are getting worse?' 'That I'm now experiencing unbearable anger' – 'having very unhelpful thoughts' – 'a panic of going outdoors' – and the 'physical sensations were becoming more intense and frequent?' It sounded like the doctor bellowed, 'Samantha Shakes' as I sat waiting to be called. My heart began pounding and I went dizzy as I walked to her room. 'Take a seat Samantha. Now what can I do for you?' she asked with a smile, when we entered the room. 'Things are getting worse,' I blurted and started crying. She handed me a tissue and asked, 'What's getting worse?' 'I'm consumed with anger – with everything and everyone – even in my dreams – and I don't want to go outdoors – I'm scared – and the thoughts are always there nagging – draining – demanding – and the physical sensations are more frequent and intense,' I rapped between sobs. 'Samantha these are normal signs of Depression. It's good that you have come back and updated me,' she reassured. She looked at my notes, 'Right, I see I've made a referral for you to see a Clinical Psychologist. Let's hope it comes through soon. When do you resume study?' she asked with a smile. 'This Tuesday,' I informed. 'Oh, just four days away. Keep yourself busy until then. Perhaps, by doing some reading to prepare yourself for the return?' she suggested and continued, 'I think attending University will help improve your Depression. Studying, being with people, and getting out will help. Sometimes, when we have nothing to motivate us – it can encourage Depression,' she advised and rubbed my shoulder. 'Yes, I think so, and thanks,' I replied in a sad tone.

I left the surgery feeling sort of relieved. I think she was right about the attendance of University, studying, being with people, and getting out will help to improve my 'Depression'. 'Depression?' She said my symptoms were 'normal signs of Depression'. At least there is some 'normality' about me. But, 'Depression?'

11.25am- back at home and feeling relieved (glad to be back at home 'safer' than outdoors).

11.50am: bathed and felt very relaxed.

12.25pm: ate lunch and went to bed.

3.15pm: woke up thinking that I will die soon. When I'm about thirty years old (I'm twenty-eight years now – so not long). And that I will kill myself not violently, but in an unconscious state, slowly with unhelpful thoughts – my diet and un-useful eating habits, causing dis-ease and then death. I don't want to kill myself – I want a long life – full of happiness. It's my conflicting thoughts, idea's and habits that's causing dis-ease (mental and physical) and I'm finding it difficult to reduce the conflict.

* * *

Sat 12th Feb '00

8pm: woke up full of energy. I'm going to Barnet Hospital for a IA Support Group meeting. The distance is far (two hours bus ride), but it's for a 'good' reason – I need to meet people like me – people who have a stoma – people who understand what it's like to have one.

1pm: at Barnet Hospital. Met two people (Kevin and Ann) aged twenty-five and nineteen years. 'I find it really difficult to be with friends. They still think I'm normal,' Kevin said. 'Well we're not abnormal,' I replied with a chuckle. 'Naw, but I know what he means,' Ann added and continued, 'Friends seem to want us to do all the things we used to do before the operation.' 'Well, we can – can't we,' I quizzed with slight irritation. 'Yeah, I suppose we can, but it's different. We have to think about whether there are toilets when we go out, and have a 'Plan B' for accidents like leakages, or the clip undoing,' Ann explained. 'Oh, I see what you mean,' I agreed. 'And it irritates me when they say things like, 'He looks like your type and he's smiling at you. Why don't you ask for his number?!' They don't realise that 'no-one' is 'my type' anymore. I don't think any man will be attracted to me once they know I've got a stoma,' she continued. 'Yeah! I can relate to that,' I said in an almost rejoicing tone. 'Me too, I've lost confidence in relationships. Wouldn't dream of chatting up any girl – even if she looked like the 'back of a bus!' Kevin shared and we all laughed. Ann added, 'And, there's the issue of clothes. Can't wear 'anything'. Got to consider if the stoma will show, and if the waistband will rub against it, causing soreness'. 'Do you think it would be useful to form a 'Young IA Support Group? It's been good talking – I feel like a 'human-being' – with a stoma! Not an alien with a case of the missing body part!' I joked and we all laughed. There was a silence and Ann broke it. 'I think forming a Young IA Group is a good idea.' 'What would we do in the group?' Kevin asked. 'Support each other,' Ann said in an assuming tone. 'What do you mean 'support,' Kevin asked looking at Ann who didn't respond. 'Well, perhaps we could share problems, offer solutions and arrange social events,' I suggested. 'Yeah, at least we wouldn't have to deal with insensitive questions like 'you're so fussy when it comes to food', 'you're always tired', or 'you need to use the toilet – again!'

We wouldn't have to explain ourselves', we just be out enjoying,' Ann said with a sigh and added with a chuckle, 'Imagine that – out enjoying ourselves with a stoma!' 'Gosh, this feels exciting,' I shrieked. 'What are you two into?' I asked. 'Oh you know the usual. Stoma bags, paste, wipes and adhesive sprays!' Kevin replied sarcastically. 'Urgh, very funny,' I responded, whilst Ann said nothing. 'Naw, cinema, pubs, visiting places of interest,' he concluded. We exchanged contact details and departed. I left thinking, 'I might have just made two new 'friends'.

5.30pm: arrived home feeling happy – it was good meeting Kevin and Ann. 'New friends?' Meeting with Tricia at 8pm for a meal – feeling bit anxious – 'Old' friend'...

* * *

Sun 13th Feb '00

12.30am: arrived back from having a meal with Tricia! I really enjoyed meeting with her. This time she listened to me – to my experience of surgery – to my feelings about friends and family – and to my feelings of Depression. We arrived at the restaurant at 8.10pm and left at 11.50pm! And we only departed because the restaurant was closing! I told her I was going to have a sauna on Monday and she invited herself. At first I thought 'great' and was looking forward to the company, but then, I felt swamped – out of control – and fearful of this display of intimacy. And I worried about the 'what ifs'. 'What if, she didn't make it?' 'What if, she'd heard enough today?' 'What if, she couldn't listen to me again?' No – I'd prefer to go alone.

6.40am: woke up with a cold. I'm sure this is due to my body being full of toxins and unhelpful thoughts draining the system. So I'm going to eat 'clean' foods (fruit and vegetables), drink loads of water, and St. John's Wort tea (herb good for the mind) to help rid of the toxins. All efforts and success will be due to the Almighty Creator. He's always with me – even when I don't 'feel' him.

7.15am: drank the juice of a lemon (got to start cleansing this body).

8.30am: lying thinking about jogging. I've read in Holder's book that jogging is beneficial to alleviate tension, energise the body, and helps rid the body of toxins. 'I should' go jogging for ten minutes in the park, but I don't have the correct footwear, or a decent jogging suit and I'm fearful of being attacked... But, 'does it matter if I don't wear the correct footwear on one occasion?' 'Does it matter what I wear to jog in?' And, as for being attacked – this could happen anywhere – at anytime...

9.45am: arrived back from a fifteen minute jog! I 'had' to go. I needed to alleviate tension. I needed to energise the body. And I needed to help my body rid itself of toxins. My body is 'showing' and 'telling' me it's 'time to clean-up'. I've got blackheads in my nose – pus spots and boils – and a cold! I had a salt bath with essential oils to help rid of some of the toxins via the skin – and to relax.

4pm: called Trevor and Tricia (psyched myself up with few shots of brandy). Trevor wasn't home and I felt relieved. I spoke to Tricia for about forty minutes. 'Hi, Tricia – it's me, Sam,' I said in a low voice. 'Oh, Sam nice to hear from you. How have you been?' she replied cheerfully. 'Well not too bad – not too good,' I told her. 'Oh, what's been happening – she asked in a voice of concern. Well, I've been experiencing symptoms of tightness in my chest and dizzy spells that seem to happen mainly when I go outdoors. And it's putting me off going out – it's so hard going outdoors at the moment,' I said trying not to cry. 'Sounds like Panic Attacks, Sam. And, they can get worse if you stay in. People who stay in can experience Panic Attacks just by looking out the window. But, the more you go out – the attacks gradually reduce. It'll be useful for you go out every day, to reduce them. I can come out with you, if you think it will help?' she offered. Although I assumed I might be having 'Panic Attacks' it was shocking to hear. 'Me – having that much 'fear' to invoke physical symptoms of panic?' I thought about telling her about the other physical symptoms. The crawling sensations – the darting figures – and the trances, but these symptoms were 'too weird'. She'd think I was 'going mad' – I think I'm going 'mad'.

6pm: thinking about calling Brendon, but he hasn't been welcoming, and if this is his response today – it will upset me. And, I'm not prepared to be upset by others (I cause enough upset by myself). But he might be more in need than me? Perhaps this is why he's unable to listen? I'm being selfish. 'I'll call him later'.

7.30pm: the telephone rang and I hoped it wasn't for me. I've been doing this for months – hoping not to get calls – not to be 'disturbed'. I've noticed that my reaction isn't as intense. I'm not getting a tightness in my chest and dizzy spells (panic attacks), anymore. Still, I'm holding my breath to listen to what's being said, and desperately hoping not to hear, 'I'll just get her', and footsteps making their way to my room.

8.45pm: I was out on the landing looking at myself in the mirror and Mum joined me. 'Look at me. I look like a skeleton,' I exclaimed with horror. 'I think you're worrying the weight off,' she suggested with telling eyes. I never replied, and returned to my room. I sat thinking about what Mum had said, 'I think you're worrying the weight off.' I forgot that 'stress' could be a factor to losing weight, and it could also contribute to my 'loss of appetite' and 'constant hunger' (symptoms of Depression).

10.45pm: just finished eating! Recently, I've been eating at night even when I don't feel hungry – it seems to get rid of that discomfort, and it also helps me to relax by making me tired, but 'I'm eating until it's painful'. And, I'm eating at night (when my body definitely doesn't need food). Surely, 'my physical ill health must be related in some way to my diet and eating patterns in the past – and indeed still in the present?' Few doctors (and research) inform that UC has little to do with diet and eating habits, but this can't be true? 'Eating when not hungry' – 'Eating at night' – 'Eating refined, unnatural foods' would appear to be a recipe for digestive problems? 'I need to adjust my diet and eating habits'.

11.30pm: just realised that I haven't rang Brendon and it's too late now (oops and thank goodness).

* * *

Mon 14th Feb '00

6.30am: woke up feeling distressed. Thinking about, 'Past events' – the stoma – 'friends' and family – 'Me (who I am)' – 'needing to adjust my diet and eating habits' – and 'I'm starting University tomorrow'.

9.30am: still thinking and desperate to speak to someone. I called Toni. 'Morning Toni,' I said in a low tone. 'Oh, Morning Sam. How are you?' she responded lively and with surprise. 'I don't know,' I whined and continued, 'I'm back at University tomorrow and part of me feels happy and yet another part feels distressed. I only enjoy University because it offers escapism – a break from my thoughts'. 'I think you might enjoy University because you meet with like-minded people and enjoy the learning. It's not necessarily about escapism, Sam. And, most students are anxious about returning to study after the summer break – it's actually quite normal,' she reassured. 'Oh, I don't know,' I responded with uncertainty, and there was a silence. I then blurted, 'Toni. I don't know who I am anymore, or what I believe. Everything I've been taught is a lie and nonsense. I'm so flipping confused'. Toni adopted a very calm tone and said, 'You're questioning your fundamental beliefs. You're now an adult and have been spurred by a traumatic experience to question those beliefs. I think you know exactly who you are,' she affirmed. I replied in an unconvincing tone, 'I don't know Toni – I don't know.' We disconnected the call and I immediately started crying. 'You know exactly who you are' – Toni said. And somewhere, I know I do. It's 'just' that I'm scared of 'who I am' (in need of protecting, sensitive, and loving) – and that I will be taken advantage of – and that I won't be accepted.

11.35am: thinking about Counselling session booked at University to-day. I don't want to go – can't remember anything useful about the last one. I do remember Eunice's fearful facial expression when I disclosed my strange physical sensations. And her belittling question, 'it sounds like you're asking me if you're going mad'. And her insecurity (the need to involve other 'health professionals'). But 'I'm desperate to talk', so I'm going to go. And, I need to go now – else I'll be late (session starts at 12.30pm)…

11.40am: I really don't think I should go to this session – the last one wasn't helpful…

11.45am: or perhaps I should? 'I really need to talk'….

11.50am: I truly don't think I should go – I left feeling more desperate than when I arrived after the last one….

11.55am: decided not to go. I rang Eunice. 'Hi Eunice, it's Sam,' I nervously greeted. 'Oh, hi Sam, I'm expecting you at 12.30pm. Is everything alright?' she asked sounding concerned. 'No, not really. I'm not going to make this week's session,' I sheepishly told her, hoping she wouldn't ask why. She sounded shocked and in a scolding tone said, 'Oh! You seem all over the place and you really should keep attending.' I felt guilty and replied in a low tone, 'I'll come next week.' When I disconnected the call – her words resonated in my mind 'You seem all over the place' and they pierced my heart. I felt 'all over the place' – and I felt despair. I sat slumped and thinking, 'you should have gone – you need Counselling' and I regretted cancelling. Still the prevailing emotion was guilt. Eunice sounded disappointed and I think she felt rejected. I should have given her another chance. My temples began pounding and my chest felt tight. 'Maybe it was me?' – 'Maybe I was being over-sensitive?' – 'Maybe I was viewing the session as 'un-useful' when it wasn't?'…

12.10pm: my pounding temples and tightness in my chest were intensifying, causing dizziness. I needed to do something to reduce this stress – I decided to go and have a sauna.

3pm: had a sauna at University campus and felt a lot more relaxed, and pleased that I had gone. It was not only reducing my stress, but helping to eliminate toxins – and I had 'gone out'.

5pm: went to the student bar (didn't want to go home) and was approached by two students studying Psychology. They asked if I would complete a questionnaire for research. One of the questions was 'If there was a tablet that you could take and know it would result in a pain-free death would you take it?' I answered, 'Yes.' The students looked at each other in shock. I was in 'shock' – not at my answer, but at my confidence.

7pm- rang Brendon. 'Happy Valentines Day,' he wished. I'd forgotten about this day to celebrate 'Romantic Love' (no point in remembering – romance is so far removed from my life). He talked as if he'd been gagged for a lifetime! He said he didn't contact anyone, because people often misunderstood him, or never really listened. Sounded familiar. I listened to Brendon – for over an hour. He thanked me – I felt appreciated and useful. I was being the 'Giver' – he the 'Taker'. I think it's okay to be a 'Giver' – just not all the time.

11.45pm: experienced pulling sensation and pain in the rectum and expelled blood and mucus...

* * *

Tue 15th Feb '00

12.30am: finding it difficult to sleep – thinking about starting University later.

Had the urgency to expel from the back passage and dashed to the toilet – expelled lots of blood and mucus.

6.30am: woken up with the urgency to expel and a pounding heart. Expelled lots of – blood – mucus – pain (again). My pounding heart was evoked by a dream. I dreamt a man my fathers' age was fondling with me whilst I was asleep, and aroused me. His wife thought I was the perpetrator and was going to stab me. I was petrified. The whole event was misunderstood – 'I was the victim – not the doer'. Dreams and their significance. I must feel 'completely misunderstood' and 'a victim' according to most of my dreams? Actually, I do.

7.30pm: arrived back from University (first day of second semester). I found it hard to concentrate (I could see the lecturer talking, but never heard what she was saying). It was the same when students were talking to me – I could hear the thoughts in my head – not them. On a few occasions the students were frustrated when I responded to what they were saying by asking, 'Can you repeat what you just said please, my mind went off?'

9.30pm: I've passed bloody mucus from the back passage six times today. I'm hoping this flare-up – this stress will ease once I have the MIND assessment (on Thursday) and start practising Yoga again.

9.50pm: I've just expelled bloody mucus again and the thoughts are back. 'Past events' – 'the stoma' – 'Friends' and family – 'Me (who I am)' – 'need to adjust diet and eating habits' – and an added thought 'perhaps study is too much?'

10.10pm: rang Trevor and told him about the 'crawling sensations in my head', 'seeing darting figures' and that 'I felt suicidal'. He listened intently and didn't appear to be alarmed by what I'd told him...

* * *

Wed 16th Feb '00

12.20am: expelled blood and mucus with pain.

1.30am: up again to expel more – blood and mucus with pain.

7.45am: I feel exhausted and I'm 'trying' to sleep.

10.50am: just woken up – I didn't intend on sleeping this long! I'm supposed to be at a local Stoma Support Group meeting for 12.30pm. I can't go now! I'd be rushing and that would cause stress. But 'I should rush' – 'I should go' – 'I need to get out' – or 'the thoughts will consume me' – and 'I need to get out to reduce the Panic Attacks'.

2pm: decided not to rush, but needed to 'get out', so I went shopping for clothes. The experience was the same as last weeks outing. Whenever I went into the shops – the assistants stared at me – most shoppers were laughing at me – and people who weren't shopping looked like they might be murderers, kidnappers, or rapists. And, I experienced the strange dizzy spells and lost my balance. I couldn't decide what clothes suited me – I couldn't decide whether I liked the design – and I couldn't decide if I liked the colour. So, again I returned home with nothing.

4.30pm: arrived home and there was a note on my door. It read:

> *4pm*
> *George called.*
> *Please call him back.*
> *020 8222 *****

George called? He was Trevor's friend and had never contacted me before. I took the note from my door. 'George called? Wonder what he wants'. Then I remembered that he works with people experiencing mental health challenges. He's ringing me because Trevor has told him about me! About the 'crawling sensations in my head' – about me 'seeing darting figures' – and about me 'feeling suicidal'. What a fucking cheek! I wish people would stop discussing me. I don't want everyone to know about this. This is why I don't talk to anyone – can't trust them. I felt frantic, and contained my feelings of hysteria – by not screaming, but ripped the note up in what seemed like a thousand pieces, and threw them at the wall.

* * *

Changing 'Bad' Behaviour

Thu 17th Feb '00

2pm: arrived at MIND for assessment. I immediately felt like crying when I met Gwen (the assessor) and entered the room. She had a friendly, welcoming, and sincere expression – and the room was too quiet – too still – too calm. There were two comfy yellow chairs, a small table with a box of tissues on top, and a picture with a white circle and yellow background. Gwen's aura was sympathetic – and the room had nothing to distract the thoughts – it was a perfect environment to cry – and as soon as I sat down – I did. There was a silence. Then looking at the floor and rubbing my temples, I blurted in a desperate voice, 'I'm going mad – I'm losing it – I'm out of control'. There was another silence, and Gwen asked calmly, 'And what will happen to you if you 'lose it'?' There was a longer silence as I thought, 'I don't know'. But then replied, 'I'll end up in a psychiatric ward and I won't be able to help myself.' She replied, 'Others will help you.' I shook my head and said in a whisper, 'I can't rely on others. And I'm getting crawling sensations in my head and see from the corner of my eyes figures darting – and nothings there! I'm having panic attacks, drinking too much alcohol, and not getting good sleep,' I continued, no longer whispering, but almost screaming with huge tears streaming down my face. She handed me the box of tissues and I took a few to mop up my tears. 'You're soul searching and I sense that you're frightened of knowing your true self. You've diverted your focus on the crawling sensations, the darting figures, and the panic attacks. These are natural reactions to what's going on. You're not 'going mad'.' You'll be fine Samantha. You just need to shed some layers and ease the overload,' she said in a reassuring voice. As I got ready to leave Gwen rubbed my shoulder and concluded, 'You've already done a lot of work on yourself. You just need some support. And, if you 'lose it' – if you go 'mad' – by your definition – you'll find yourself again, and you'll be stronger and freer.'

Gwen highlighted the points that were identified from the assessment. She explained that 'conflict with self', 'fear', and 'fear of insanity or going insane' had been recognised. I left with tears in my eyes. After speaking with Gwen, I felt relieved, empowered, and hopeful of my future – even if it did include 'going mad'. And, as I walked to the bus stop to go to University, Gwen's words resonated, 'And, if you 'lose it' – if you go 'insane' – 'you'll find yourself again, and you'll be stronger and freer.'

4.30pm: arrived at University to practice Yoga. I fell asleep during the relaxation period (can't remember feeling so relaxed). I felt 'light' and 'peaceful' – completely different to how I felt this morning – 'heavy' and 'disturbed'. Feeling 'light and peaceful' – Thanks to Gwen – Yoga – and the Almighty Creator.

10.30pm: lying wondering what results I got (exam marks are published tomorrow). Still feeling 'light' and 'peaceful'. Retired.

* * *

Fri 18th Feb '00

6.30am: woke up feeling refreshed.

3.30pm: back from University and pacing the house in shock. I received First Class grades for both Health Studies exams! I had to return to the notice board twice to confirm these results belonged to me?! First Class grades?! I stared at the results and at my student number. Yep! The grades were definitely under my number – First Class grades – Sam Shakes?! As I walked to the bus stop I cheered out loud! People looked at me with puzzled and frightened faces – I assumed they thought I was 'mad'. I didn't care. I didn't mind 'losing it' or going 'mad' in this capacity. This kind of 'madness' was for a good reason!

4pm: expelled bloody mucus. Strange, because I don't feel distressed – I feel happy (so eustressed). Seems like any 'overwhelming stress' causes 'problems (flare-ups)'.

4.30pm: Doreen and Mark arrived home and I was sitting in the lounge. 'Guess what?' I asked in an intriguing tone. 'What?' they both replied with enthusiasm. 'I got two First Class grades for my Health Studies exams.' 'Oh, that's good Sam,' Doreen said with excitement. 'Oh is that it?' Mark chuckled, sounding disappointed.

6.30pm: Mum arrived home and I immediately burst out of my room and darted downstairs. 'Mum! I got First Class grades for my Health Studies exams!' I yelled. 'First Class – First Class! Yeah! Yeah! Well done! You deserve them. You've worked hard,' she cheered waving her hands in the air, and then hugged me. When I returned to my room I questioned Mum's comment 'worked hard'. I don't remember having 'worked hard'. I remember thinking about – 'past events' – 'the stoma' – 'friends' and family' – questioning 'who I am' – and 'the need to adjust eating habits'. And having 'panic attacks' – 'crawling sensations' – 'seeing darting figures' – and 'drinking alcohol'. And, I don't know how I received First Class grades – but I did?!

10.15pm: expelled loads of mucus and blood. I'm still overwhelmed with shock and excitement of gaining two First Class grades! Would have liked to share my excitement with few 'friends', but couldn't think of anyone who would be interested. So, I celebrated alone, by playing music in my room and drank two bottles of wine (as opposed to one). Two bottles today – we always drink more when celebrating.

* * *

Sat 19th Feb '00

5.15am: woke up feeling nauseated (drank too much wine) and expelled what felt like loads of fresh blood (too dark to see and I didn't want to).

7am: expelled loads of mucus and blood.

8.30am: woke up feeling energized and 'good'.

9.30am: decided to go shopping for clothes 'again'.

4.10pm: just returned from shopping – after six and a half hours (I haven't been out on a leisure trip for that long since surgery)! I purchased two tops, a skirt and two pairs of trousers – I needed them! I enjoyed this trip – and I felt more relaxed. Still, whenever I went into the shops – the assistants stared at me (only 'some' thinking I was a shoplifter), and other shoppers were laughing at me (but not all of them). And people who weren't shopping looked like they might be murderers, kidnappers, or rapists (but they weren't necessarily going to attack me). And I never experienced the strange dizzy spells and lost my balance. Tricia was right when she suggested that going out may reduce Panic Attacks. This has been my experience. Sometimes it's good to talk and share experiences.

6.15pm: expelled loads of mucus and blood.

8pm: would like to celebrate my grades, but who with?...

9.30pm: the excitement is going (they're 'just' grades) and feeling bored and sad. Opened and drank a bottle of wine.

* * *

Sun 20th Feb '00

7.30am: woke up feeling refreshed.

11.30am: been working on presentation and part of me wants to scream 'I'm not getting anywhere.' Yet I'm remembering the Almighty Creator and the belief that 'nothing need be a struggle'. So, I'm trying to relax and work, and affirming that 'studying needn't cause distress'.

3.30pm: time is ticking away and I'm getting little done. I feel anxious about how the presentation will go on Tuesday, but I don't feel stressed. 'Nothing need be a struggle' and 'Studying needn't cause distress'. Hope my First Class results aren't encouraging complacency.

7.30pm: Joan called. I told her I was feeling better, but part of me that wanted to say, 'I'm alright now, but what I'll be like tomorrow is another story.' It feels strange, and for no apparent reason – no change in circumstances or events, I can feel so happy in one moment – and so sad in the next.

8.10pm: rang Kevin (the man I met at the IA Support Group). I wanted to call before today, but felt scared – a 'new friend?' 'Hi Kevin – it's Sam, we met last Saturday at the support group,' I said nervously. 'Oh, hi Sam. How have you been?' he asked sounding surprised. 'Fine. Did you want to meet up – to talk about forming a support group?' I continued with uneasiness. 'Yeah. Definitely,' he replied enthusiastically. 'What's a good day, time, and place for you?' I rapped. 'Next Saturday, Marble Arch, 1pm,' he answered confidently. 'Okay. I'll ring Ann and hopefully, she can make it too. If you don't hear from me – assume this is date!' I eagerly confirmed. 'Hi Ann it's'… 'I know – Sam,' she interrupted excitedly and continued, 'Nice to hear from you.' 'Ann, I've just spoken to Kevin and we hope you'll be able to meet with us for lunch and talk about forming the support group?' I continued 'Yeah! Where – what time – when?' she shrieked. I gave her the details and we disconnected the call. I felt happy – I think this is going to be the start of two 'new and refreshing friendships'.

* * *

Mon 21st Feb '00

6.30am: woke up with the presentation on my mind. I'm going to work on it all day.

11.45pm: although I worked on the presentation on Sunday, and all of today, it still needs editing! I haven't worked hard or long enough – I've had too many breaks. I thought of the quote *Fail to prepare – prepare to fail*. So, I'll get what I deserve by the grace of the Almighty Creator.

I feel relaxed, but my rectum doesn't say I am. I've expelled blood and mucus four times today.

* * *

Tue 22nd Feb '00

6.10am: woke up thinking about the presentation and feeling physically tired.

6.30am: started working on the presentation – I had to show it at 11.30am! I worked continuously for three hours, but I still felt 'I hadn't read enough' – 'I'm not prepared' – and 'the work isn't good enough'. Anyway, I feel confident that the Almighty Creator has already graded my work – the outcome is in his hands – not mine.

11.30am: the presentation was greatly appreciated by both students and lecturer. They commented that it was informative and asked for copies of the bibliography?!

9pm: rang Brendon. I've been wanting to speak to him for the last few days. I got his ansaphone and left a message...

* * *

Wed 23rd Feb '00

12.20am: called Brendon again. I wondered if he'd received my message, because he hadn't called. This time his phone rang, but he never answered the call! My heart began racing and my temples were pounding as I thought, 'He recognised my number (by the number display) and he didn't want to talk to me! He was fine to talk the last time – when he wanted to – the 'Selfish Bastard'. I poured a large rum with hot blackcurrant. I went to my room and lit a candle for light, and put the radio on for company. I sat in bed with an angry head and sad heart. 'Why are people so selfish? Take – take – fucking take!' I gulped the hot rum and blackcurrant. My angry head soon became calm, but my sad heart got sadder. I sat hearing the voices on the radio babbling, and staring at the flickering candle flame – with huge tears rolling out of my eyes.

7.25am: woke up feeling physically tired and with the thoughts on my mind. 'Past events' – 'the stoma' – 'Friends' and family – 'Me (who I am)' – 'need to adjust diet and eating habits' – 'perhaps study is too much' – and an added one – 'I need to relieve false friendships'. 'I need to cut my friendship with Brendon and Sharaz – they're so selfish'.

11.15pm: I've felt tired all day. I'm aiming to be lying down to sleep (as opposed to sitting up thinking), by midnight (an 'early' night).

* * *

Thu 24th Feb '00

6.45am: woke up with a tight chest and thinking about Sharaz. I'm hoping it won't be long before I talk to her. I'm looking forward to the relief I'll get from 'telling the truth' and getting the thought of 'needing to tell her' – out of my mind. I've been rehearsing what I'll say, and how I'll say it. I've got to say it 'right', and 'with compassion'. I need to practise more, because at the moment it's coming out very offence.

5.30pm: back from University. I wasn't sure if I felt exhausted or relaxed. I practised Yoga at 12.30pm and felt like this since. I had a lecture at 2.30pm and I found it difficult to concentrate and sit up! My brain felt like it wanted to shutdown and my body felt like it wanted to lay down! Fell asleep…

9.30pm: woke up from a deep sleep! Not a cell in my body feels tired – or tense – and I look so refreshed. I guess I was exhausted mentally and physically. Yoga – relaxed my mind – allowing me to sleep and rest my exhausted body.

* * *

Fri 25th Feb '00

6.30pm: practised Yoga.

10.30pm: feeling very relaxed – retired.

I've been expelling blood and mucus four times per day, for the past few days, but I only expelled three times today. Stress must be reducing.

* * *

Sat 26th Feb '00

7am: woke up refreshed and thinking about my eating. I'm worried that I'm not fuelling my body with foods for vitality (fruit, vegetables, and fish). Instead, I'm eating white bread, lots of fried foods, drinking about five cups of coffee a day and too much alcohol (urgh!). White bread irritates the stomach and digestive system – fried foods and drinking alcohol seem to worsen flare-ups – and coffee encourages 'mood swings (irritability)'. I'm a 'Health Studies' student learning (and know) that foods can prevent and cause illness and disease. I understand that foods assist to dis-ease or 'ease' the body. My body is telling me that it's diseased, since I've been expelling blood and mucus for the last week (three times a day). Still, I eat foods that are not conducive to health! I must honour my body by fuelling it with ideal foods, and if I don't – I 'deserve to be sick'.

9.30am: ordered Hemp Seed Oil. I've read that 'Hemp seeds contain the most balanced and richest natural source of essential oils for human consumption, and that they help to restore wasting bodies and improve damaged immune systems'. I believe my body needs restoring. Apparently, UC is an 'auto-immune disease' (the body attacks its own cells), so I assume my immune system is 'damaged' and in need of repair.

1pm: met Kevin and Ann to discuss the formation of a support group. We ate at a small café and talked about our experiences of surgery (treatment, medics attitude, feelings about having a stoma) and what we were currently doing (studying and claiming Incapacity Benefit).

3.30pm: as we departed, I realised that we hadn't spoken about the support group! 'Oops! We haven't spoken about forming the support group,' I stated with a chuckle. 'Oh, yeah,' Kevin replied in a long drawn out tone. 'I think we just had our first one!' Ann said and we laughed.

As I travelled home – I reflected on our lunch date. I felt like I'd known these two people for years and really enjoyed their company. I think it was because of the clear understanding, acceptance of our challenges, and empathy that made our meeting so intimate. 'This was 'definitely' the start of two new friendships'.

* * *

Sun 27th Feb '00

2am: retiring to bed.

7am: woke up feeling energized (with just five hours sleep) and thinking about Sharaz again. I really need to talk to her, but I need to be able to speak rationally and 'with compassion'. I'm still getting so angry when I think of how she's let me down – and I want to upset her – and I want to make her feel guilty. I've endured so much pain – she must suffer too (can't believe I've written that 'she must suffer too'). I hate feeling this angry – and I feel wicked – and I'm crying as I write – and trembling with fear of my feelings of revenge. And, I'm trying to believe the affirmation that,

> My anger is disappointment,
> My disappointment was due to an expectation,
> And my expectation a creation of my 'self'.

I expelled blood and mucus from back passage – just once today.

* * *

Mon 28th Feb '00

8am: woke up feeling lethargic and with Sharaz on my mind 'again' (this thinking of Sharaz is becoming obsessive). However, my anger towards her is reducing as I appreciate the part I've played in this 'sad' affair. I chose her as a friend – and I had expectations – and I hid my true 'self'. So, much of the anger needs directing at me and at those who instilled me with foolish ideas (ideas based on transaction) in relation building friendships.

8.30am: needed to stop thinking – so, I'm reading.

10am: feeling tired and losing interest in reading, but I don't want to think.

10.30am: continued to force myself to read.

11am: forcing myself to read – what a waste of energy. I can't recall any of what I've 'read' (the thoughts of Sharaz dictating) and I'm feeling very tired (retired to bed).

12.30pm: woke up and thought I'd only slept for about forty minutes, but it was actually an hour and a half, and I still felt tired!

I was supposed to practice Yoga after the lecture today, but I couldn't motivate myself and felt too tired. The thoughts of Sharaz seem to hinder not only the activity of my mind, but also of my body.

* * *

Wed 1st Mar '00

9.30pm: I spent most of today lying in bed staring at the walls and ceiling and thinking about Brendon and Sharaz. Feeling lethargic – and unable to carry out activities, or concentrate to read.

* * *

Thu 2nd Mar '00

8am: woke up sexually aroused. Dreamt I was kissing and fondling with my husband whose face I never saw.

7pm: Lynn (Sharaz's sister) visited – without warning! I felt 'disturbed' and angry. Whilst she was here, Sharaz called her, on her mobile phone. 'I'm at Sam's!' Lynn announced excitedly and handed the phone to me. My heart began racing and my mouth went dry. 'Hi Sharaz. I haven't been well,' I impatiently informed without hearing her greeting. 'Oh, have you been to University?' she asked in a flat tone. 'Yeah, but it's been a struggle,' I answered. 'Oh,' she uttered, and there was a moment of silence. 'I need to speak to you, but I don't have the capacity right now,' I nervously informed. 'I know, we've both been busy studying and working – that's the way it goes!' she stated. 'Yeah'... How have you been?' I asked insincerely. 'I've been fine,' she answered. 'Oh. Good. Take care until the next time,' I concluded and handed the phone to Lynn. I was confused. Didn't Sharaz hear me say that I 'haven't been well' and that University had 'been a struggle'?' she stated that 'we've both been busy', but I never said I'd 'been busy'. It was obvious that she either wasn't listening, or she didn't want to feel guilty about not contacting me – so she made up that I'd been 'busy'. And, my chest began to pound and my temples ache as Sharaz's comment, 'I've been fine' resounded in my mind. She'd 'been fine' – I'd 'been suffering'.

* * *

Fri 3rd Mar '00

7pm: felt like socialising and thought I'd ring a friend to go out with. I searched my address book. A... B... C... D... E... F... G... H... I... J... K... L... M... N... O... P... Q... R... S... T... U... V... W... X... Y... Z! I came to the end of the book and there didn't seem to be anyone 'fit' to socialise with? I scanned the book again and once more – I came to the end with no 'suitable' friend to contact. I sat for a moment and suddenly a feeling of panic overwhelmed me as I thought 'I haven't got any friends'.

8.10pm: Joan called. 'Hi Sam, fancy coming out for a drink?' she asked cheerfully. 'Oh, thanks Joan, but I really don't feel like going out,' I replied and we disconnected the call. Sitting wondering why I 'lied' – why did I say 'I don't feel like going out'? It was just an hour ago that I thought I wanted to socialise.

8.45pm: Steve called. 'Hello Sam, do you want to go out for a meal with me?' he invited. 'Steve, that's really nice, but I don't feel like going out,' I replied. Again, I'm sitting wondering why I lied – why did I say 'I didn't feel like going out'?' This is ridiculous. I've decline two invitations to go out – I thought I wanted to socialise?! I'm confused – something's wrong with me.

* * *

Sat 4th Mar '00

5.30am: woke up feeling dis-eased (physically and mentally detached) and thinking about Sharaz. I can still hear her comment 'I've been fine.' The people I've chosen as 'friends' are so selfish. Brendon still hasn't called – he doesn't care. Sharaz has no time to call – she's 'busy working' – and when I asked Trevor if he'd like to come to Camden with me he replied, 'Yeah, I haven't been to Camden for a while.' Wonder what his response would have been if he'd been to Camden recently? Selfish – Selfish – Selfish.

* * *

Sun 5th Mar '00

7.45pm: Brendon called and my heart began racing and temples pounding as I tried to contain my anger. 'How was I going to tell him how selfish he was – 'with compassion'?' But, I also I felt guilty – he was calling me. Perhaps he did care? Still, the prevailing emotion was anger.

'Hi Sam, how have you been?' he asked in a calm tone. 'Not good,' I snapped. 'Oh, why's that?' he asked sounding concerned. 'I haven't got any friends,' I blurted. 'What are you talking about – stop being silly,' he asserted. 'I'm not being 'silly' Brendon – and people are so selfish,' I retorted. 'What do you mean – people are so selfish?' he asked defensively. 'This operation – I know you're probably thinking 'that was a long time ago', but this operation has changed everything, and I don't know what I'm supposed to do,' I desperately explained trying not to cry. 'I know, I know Sam, and I don't know what to say or do, to help you,' he pitifully replied. There was a silence. My anger decreased and my guilt increased. 'I thought you didn't care,' I said sadly. 'Of course I care,' he answered in a comforting tone.

After speaking to Brendon I felt sad. I felt sad, because 'the operation' wasn't 'our' fault'. And, my guilty feelings intensified. I felt guilty that I'd accused him of being selfish, uncaring and considering his actions 'unfriendly'. I've been misjudging and expecting too much from friends – and family – they aren't doing anything 'wrong'! As Brendon explained, 'it's just that they 'don't know what to say or do, to help'. It's amazing what honest communication, understanding, and acceptance can do. And I thought, 'Sam, you do have a friend.' Actually, now, I think I have many.

* * *

Mon 6th Mar '00

6.35am: woke up sexually aroused spurred by another dream that I was kissing and fondling a man!

11am: feeling distressed and in need to talk to someone, but couldn't think of anyone, and I realised that I need to find an alternative (can't rely on others to relieve my distress). But, 'What to do?' Have a Drink (but I'm desperately trying to reduce my alcohol intake) – Read (but I'm finding it difficult to concentrate) – Jog (but I'm feeling really tired and anxious to jog alone) – Yoga! I could practise Yoga! There's a class at 6.30pm today – plenty of time to psyche myself up.

6.30pm: practised Yoga.

10.15pm: in bed and feeling very relaxed (mentally and physically).

* * *

Tue 7th Mar '00

5am: awake and feeling refreshed.

11pm: all day I've felt 'balanced' – not experiencing 'distress' or 'eustress'. Yoga is amazing.

* * *

Wed 8th Mar '00

7.30am: woke up feeling indifferent – remembering a dream. I dreamt Aunty Celia asked me to return her ring (it was given to me, because she had died. She didn't ask for it with a malicious approach). Her presence implied that she was alive again! I was so happy – Aunty Celia was alive again – 'Aunty Celia was alive!' But my happiness was shattered when I woke up and realised that I was only dreaming – Aunty Celia was still dead'.

10am: dreaming of Aunty Celia spurred reminisce about the wonderful times and relationship I had with her. Huge tears are rolling out of my eyes – I'm really missing Aunty Celia. She would have listened to my sorrows and understood. She would have made everything feel better. A lost friendship…

Expelled blood with mucus.

* * *

Thu 9th Mar '00

7.30am: woke up from dreaming I was in bed with Trevor. I didn't see us in bed, but my aroused feelings indicated that we had 'made love'. This is the third dream I've had in the past seven days, and woken up 'sexually aroused'. I've been worrying about romantic relationships – wondering if I'll meet someone suitable for 'me and the stoma'. And I've agonised when I'd tell the prospective partner that I have a stoma. At the first meeting? – After we start dating? – When we're about to have sex? I want to be honest, but I don't want to scare him off.

9.30am: feeling very 'tired' and examined the bottom of my eye sockets to 'see' if they looked healthy. They were a pale pink (not the red they're supposed to be). I diagnosed 'lack iron – anaemia' and prescribed and drank 15ml (5ml extra of recommended dosage) of a liquid iron supplement. I'm sure some of my tiredness is due to anaemia – it can't all be psychological.

* * *

Fri 10th Mar '00

6.20pm: Joan called. 'We're all set to go! Me, you, Anthony and Brendon. We're going out for a drink tomorrow,' she informed with excitement. I was thrown into a state of panic and replied, 'Oh, Joan, I've got reading to do. I can't go out tomorrow.' 'Oh… Okay. I'll tell Anthony and Brendon not to bother then,' she retorted with disappointment, and ended the call. I sat feeling guilty. My friends were trying to please me, and I was rejecting their kindness and invitations – now who's being selfish, uncaring and unfriendly?

6.35pm: my guilt took lead and I called Joan. 'Joan you sounded so disappointed,' I said indifferently. 'Yeah, well, I haven't seen you for a while and thought it'd be nice for us to meet up,' she replied sadly. 'You're right. It has been a while, and it would be nice to meet up. I'll come out tomorrow,' I replied.

After we disconnected the call I sat with part of me feeling like 'I'd been bullied', whilst another part of me felt like the 'old Sam' (honouring others feelings and neglecting her own). But then I contemplated, 'It can't be 'bad' to accept an invitation and go out with friends – can it?!' I was thinking they weren't friends because they didn't consider me, and now they were – I was feeling 'bullied?!' And, how could I feel like I was 'neglecting my feelings' when I've wanted to socialise for over three weeks now?!

'Friends' or 'not friends?' – Socialise or be a recluse? I'm confused – 'something's wrong with me'.

* * *

Sat 11th Mar '00

10am: I've been drinking more water (two litres a day as part of my healthier diet). I've noticed that I don't feel as lethargic, minor aches/ pains are disappearing, and my skin looks radiant! I must keep this up. Apparently, we are eighty percent water and drinking water is essential for vitality – no wonder I'm looking and feeling good!

12.00pm: Joan called. 'Hi Sam. Just wanted to know what would be a good time to come and get you. I was thinking about 9pm or 10pm?' she asked excitedly. I felt irritated, and wished I hadn't 'given in' and said, 'I'd go.' I couldn't decide what would be a 'good time' to go, be- cause I didn't want to (my moods changing from one moment to the next). 'I thought you were sorting this out?' I snapped. 'I am, but I just wanted to know what time would be good for you,' she retorted. 'Anytime. Right now, I'm reading,' I abruptly replied. 'Oh sorry. We'll come for 10pm,' she rapped apologetically.

I disconnected the call feeling guilty 'again'. Joan wasn't giving up on me – even with me turning down previous offers, and my awful at- titude. And Brendon was going to be joining us – even after me tell- ing him that I had 'no friends' and 'people were selfish'. 'No friends?' 'What else could Joan and Brendon be, but 'friends?'

2.10pm: the doorbell rang and I sat in my room hoping it wasn't anyone visiting me. I'm trying to read – I don't want to be disturbed! I listened intently. 'Oh, hi Sharaz. Come in – I'll call her', I heard Doreen say. Shit – it was Sharaz! My heart began racing and my mouth went dry. I didn't know how to feel – 'happy' or 'angry'. 'Happy' – I do exist and I am worthy of a visit. 'Angry' – why has it taken her so long to contact – I don't want to see her. 'Sam, it's Sharaz,' Doreen shouted from the bottom of the stairs. I lay for a while – I needed to compose myself. I took a few deep breaths, looked up at the ceiling and said to the Almighty Creator, 'Thank you for sending her.' I got up from lying and slowly proceeded downstairs, and with every step – my heart raced faster and my dry mouth – became drier. I entered the lounge and Sharaz leapt from the settee and hugged me. 'Hi girl! How ya been? It's been a long time,' she said excitedly. 'Hi Sharaz. It's been a bit rough,' I gloomily informed. 'Oh, what's been happening – I'm all ears,' she said calmly and sat back in her seat. 'I've been feeling so pissed off, and it feels like I haven't got any friends. I don't think you lot really understand what I've been going through since this operation. It's changed everything,' I retorted. 'Oh. I still see you as 'Sam' – the girl that can handle anything. I know the operation was a lot to manage, but I thought you were coping – getting along with it,' she replied. 'Yeah, well I'm trying, but since the operation, I've began viewing life in a different way. So much of what I've been taught and believed are contradictory to what I think now,' I explained. 'What do you mean?' she asked with enquiring eyes. 'I don't care about fashion, clubbing, having a job with a large salary, having a 'nice car, watching TV, or knowing the latest news. All that doesn't matter anymore, because as far as I can see, these don't help us live better,' I explained. 'Oh. So having the operation has made you question your values?' she clarified. 'Yep. And I don't even know who I am most times and I'm so confused and angry… And I've got no-one to talk to,' I exploded. There was a silence and I calmly continued, 'Anyway, I've contacted MIND for Counselling.' 'That sounds good. You must help yourself,' she encouraged. 'Sam, you can call me. The reason why I haven't called is because I thought you were busy studying,' she explained. 'Oh,' I sighed and sadly expressed, 'There is a contradiction going on… I want to be alone to reflect, but I don't want to be forgotten.' She got up and hugged me, 'Sam, how can I forget you? We go back too far,' she said in a comforting tone. I began crying and so did she. I went into the kitchen for a napkin to dry our tears. 'Oh, bet I look like I've been punched in both eyes now – mascara everywhere,' she joked and we both laughed.

3.25pm: Sharaz left and I felt so relived. She understood more than I thought. Again, I realised that I've been expecting too much from friends and family. I accused Sharaz of being selfish – she isn't selfish. So what if friends and family don't know what it's like to have a stoma. It's cruel to expect people to do what they are not capable of. And, I must remember that, 'We are all doing the best that we can, with the knowledge and experience we have'. Ironically, the acceptance and understanding that I want – I've been unable to express. I've been harshly judgemental. And, the adage *Live and let Live*, comes to mind.

4pm: I'm trying to read, but I'm unable to concentrate. I'm recalling the comment Sharaz made when I told her that I'd 'contacted MIND for Counselling'. 'That sounds good. You must help yourself,' she'd said and was so 'right'. '[We] must help [ourselves]'. Others can assist us 'Family' – 'Friends' – 'Professionals', but the best person to help us – is us.

8pm: reluctantly got into the bath with pounding temples. Getting ready to 'go out' with Joan, Anthony and Brendon. Even though I know 'it's for the best' – I still wish I never said 'I'd go'.

8.30pm: finished soaking in the bath and my temples had stopped pounding.

8.45pm: flicking through wardrobe. What to wear?! No tops seemed to compliment any skirt, trousers, or jeans. Should I wear trousers or a skirt? And, what footwear – trainers, shoes, or boots?!

9.45pm: eventually found something to put on.

10pm: sitting in my room 'waiting' and wondering, 'Where are they? – Joan said '10pm.'

10.20pm: feeling agitated. 'Where are they? – Joan said '10pm.'

10.45pm: 'Where the fuck are they?!' My temples are beginning to pound and if they don't come soon – I'm not going. I feel so angry – I need to relax – 'I need a drink' (else I'm going to be miserable all night). I drank a few shots of brandy. I was feeling 'relaxed' when they arrived – at 10.55pm!...

* * *

Sun 12th Mar '00

1am: arrived home from Bar with Joan and Brendon. We sat in the lounge debating ideas regarding slavery, racism, the British political system and relationships. I drank about half a bottle of brandy whilst we talked.

4am: Joan and Brendon left. The house appeared empty in their absence (everyone else sleeping), and I found it difficult to relax – and I felt scared. I poured myself some brandy and hot blackcurrant, topping my intake to about a bottle since I started drinking yesterday – yet I didn't feel drunk. I went up stairs to my room and took the quilt from my bed. I returned to the lounge, turned on the TV, and lay on the settee snuggled under the quilt. 'I really enjoyed last night/this morning – 'Old' Friends'.

* * *

Mon 13th Mar '00

Received a letter from MIND confirming Counselling sessions are to start on 29th March. 'Counselling?' It was only on Saturday I thought I needed Counselling, but do I really? I'm sort of managing now, and I'm altering my unhelpful thoughts, changing my behaviour, and eating healthier. 'Counselling?'

Over the past week I've been experiencing dizziness and having blackouts (can't remember activities or conversations) 'again'. It's so embarrassing when people ask me to recall activities or conversations, and I confidently deny having had them (so sure they didn't happen). But when there's more than one person present, and they both say, 'Oh, I remember you saying or doing that' I think 'they must be right'. Then I desperately try to recall the conversation or activity – sometimes I remember – mostly I don't. Wonder why this is happening?

* * *

Tue 14th Mar '00

6.30am: woke up feeling very refreshed, yet with an achy hip (perhaps spurred by the relaxation of practising Yoga yesterday. Some advise that relaxation allows body symptoms to manifest (as tension can sometimes suppress). I looked up 'Hip Problems' in Louise Hays book. She suggests that the probable cause is *Fear of going forward in major decisions. Nothing to move forward to.* This is so true to me! I'm fearful of making new decisions and change at the moment. And I don't have any goals/aims to move forward to.

* * *

Wed 15th Mar '00

7.30am: woke up with palpitations in my chest spurred by a dream. I was in a relationship, but hadn't told my partner about the stoma. He was lovingly stroking my abdomen, and with every stroke – the more tensed I became. I started crying – didn't see his response. I told him I had a stoma – didn't hear his reaction. 'Dreams' and my 'reality' of having an intimate relationship.

Today I'm fully aware that 'our bodies speak to us'. I've been feeling more relaxed and healthy (due to Yoga and diet), and for the past few days, I've been passing a normal brown discharge with no blood.

6pm: visited Uncle Solomon to wish him a 'Happy Birthday'.

* * *

Thu 16th Mar '00

5.30am: woke up feeling 'physically energised' and 'mentally drained'

– 'detached from myself and from reality'. One moment I'm 'up' – and the next I'm 'down'.

5.30pm: feeling very tired, but forced myself to attend a meeting 'The Met On Trial', which was about injustices (deaths in custody and framed imprisonment's) carried out by the Metropolitan Police. The meeting enlightened me to the 'real issues' and an 'appreciation of life'. Life is precious – Life is 'Here and Now'. And, I must help people in need for the duration of my life.

* * *

Fri 17th Mar '00

12pm: decided to go to University to study, to be in a more 'comfortable environment', and to be active.

8.30pm: arrived home feeling 'happy', pleased that I'd ventured out and studied, and it was 'Friday' – the weekend. To honour the happiness and the weekend – I had a drink of brandy and hot blackcurrant.

* * *

Sat 18th Mar '00

7.30am: woke up feeling very hungry (I didn't eat an evening meal yesterday). I ate two fried eggs, half a can of baked beans and chips, and immediately felt guilty after eating. 'I'd poisoned my body with toxic food'. So I planned to eat fruit for the rest of the day – to flush the poisons out – to cleanse my body. I wish I could rid of these guilty feelings after eating 'poisons' – I'm sure these foods are not as damaging as the negative thoughts. And, if I flush the toxins out – they can't cause dis-ease. I think the resistance to eating and thinking might be more dis-easing than the actual foods, and the adage comes to mind, *A little bit of what you fancy does you good.*

7.30pm: Trevor called and I immediately felt defensive. I thought about him discussing me with George (as a 'mental case') and I didn't want to disclose anything with him. 'What's been going on?' he asked in a blasé tone. I thought 'here he goes – wanting information so he can discuss me with George again', so I cautiously replied, 'Loads, but my memory fails me.' He continued to probe, 'So how you been feeling?' 'Fine,' I replied trying to sound relaxed. 'What about the physical symptoms you were getting – have they stopped?' he hassled. 'I said I was fine – didn't I?' I snapped, hoping to cease his interrogation, but he continued, 'Have you heard from MIND?' There was a silence as I deliberated whether to tell him the truth – that the sessions were to start. But, I didn't want him pestering me with his interest in the future, so I lied and replied, 'No, I haven't, and I don't think I'm going to have Counselling anymore.' 'But...' I interrupted him and concluded in a stern tone, 'I don't want to talk about it.' We spoke for about three minutes. I found his 'interest' annoying – not caring. All his questions were about my mental state – I don't want to discuss my 'madness'. I need to focus on other subjects – 'I'm always focusing on – and in my head'.

* * *

Sun 19th Mar '00

12.45am: visited the lounge feeling restless. I left my room to watch TV – to get a break from my thoughts, but this distraction didn't work. I was 'looking' at the figures on the screen, but couldn't 'see' them, and I saw mouths moving, but couldn't hear the voices – the 'thoughts dictating'. So, I poured a few shots of vodka (don't like vodka, but it was the only alcoholic drink in house) with hot apple and barley.

1.15am: the thoughts pursued. Poured myself a few more shots...

2am: the thoughts are drowning, and actually, vodka doesn't taste that bad...

2.45am: thoughts were still nagging – topped up my nearly empty glass with small amount of vodka...

3.15am: the thoughts have drowned, and actually vodka tastes nice!

6.30am: woke up confused. I was in the lounge? – Fully dressed? – With half a glass of vodka, and apple and barley? I went up to my room feeling very sick.

9.40am: woke up still feeling sick and my head felt like it was going to explode. Weird – I didn't have a 'headache' like a hangover. I think this 'head dis-ease' is due to thoughts/feelings (tension). I drank two glasses of water to hydrate, which helped, and a cup of St. John's Wort tea (it's supposed to be good for the mind).

* * *

Mon 20th Mar '00

Today it was 'confirmed' – I am scared to establish new friendships. Whilst having lunch I was telling a student the benefits of Yoga and she invited herself to the next class! She said, 'I'd love to join you.' I panicked and 'lied' in an insincere tone, 'Oh. That would be nice.'

5pm: practised Yoga. At the end of the class one of the participants approached me. 'If you lived nearby I'd invite you to do Yoga at my home,' she informed. Again I panicked, and again I 'lied' in an insincere tone, 'Oh. That would be nice.' These invitations feel, 'too friendly' – 'too intimate' – and 'too sincere'. And, on both occasions – I couldn't wait to flee from these women. Shit – do I want friends or not! Socialise or be a recluse? I'm confused – 'something's wrong with me'.

11.10pm: I'm going to have a good night's sleep. I feel very relaxed (always do after Yoga). And, I'm going to watch a comedy before going to bed. Laughter is part of my 'therapy'. I need to laugh – I need to strike a balance.

* * *

Tue 21st Mar '00

6.30am: woke up feeling refreshed.

5pm: reading notes via a module 'Stress and Health'. I never realised the affects of extreme stress (distress and eustress) on the body. Tensed muscles – Dizziness – High Blood Pressure – Pain – Inflammation (any 'Chronic Condition' ending with 'tis'). I'm convinced my imbalance and extremes of stress caused my 'UC' (via my analytical mind). I think 'UC' is partly psychosomatic – I think all 'dis-eases' are.

* * *

Wed 22nd Mar '00

2.10am: at home watching documentary about suicide rates of men. The house is so quiet and I feel scared. Scared that someone will attack me by entering from the garden door – I'm scared to go in the kitchen. And, I'm scared that someone will throw something through the window as I sit watching the TV (I keep looking at the window and the entrance to the lounge). And, I'm scared of the fear and insecurity that I'm feeling at home. I have thought I'll meet a violent death out in the street – not at home where it's supposed to be safe. 'There's no security anywhere'.

12.30pm: ate a jacket potato with coleslaw in University café, and experienced an uncomfortable throbbing afterwards. I hoped the ache wasn't the start of a possible blockage, however, as time passed I began getting abdominal pains.

1.05pm: Mina (fellow student) approached me as I sat dining. 'Can you help me distribute these flyers opposing the closure of the Halls of Residence. I haven't got anyone to help me?' she asked. 'Yeah,' I offered – then immediately developed a 'bad mood'. 'Why did I say I'd help when I was in pain?' I scolded myself, silently.

2.15pm: finished traipsing around the Halls of Residence and was in extreme pain.

2.30pm: travelled home by bus and groaned out loud throughout the whole journey. People looked at me with puzzled and concerned expressions. I felt embarrassed, but I couldn't contain my groaning.

3.40pm: arrived home and headed straight to the cupboard for Paracetamols – gulped two, and struggled upstairs to bed.

5.40pm: still in severe pain.

6.05pm: Lizzy phoned. She was in hospital and wanted me to visit her. I was still in severe pain, but I 'had' to go and see her...

6.50pm: arrived at the psychiatric ward. 'Hi, can you tell me where I'll find Lizzy?' I asked a nurse seated behind the desk. 'In bed Four,' she replied without looking at me. I headed hastily to 'bed Four'. When Lizzy saw me she displayed a grand smile – and gave me a tight hug. 'Let's go to the Day Room,' she said ushering me down the corridor. As soon as we entered the Day Room – she slammed the door behind us and burst out crying?! I was in shock. It was only moments ago that she'd displayed a grand smile, and we'd hugged. 'I can't let them see me cry,' she sobbed and continued, 'They'll keep me in here longer – they'll say that I'm not well – I know how they think. I just need to have a good cry and talk'. I didn't reply, and hugged her. 'I'll be alright Sam,' she reassured.

I left the hospital feeling very sad. Lizzy had to restrain her emotions in an environment that was supposed to 'care' and encourage 'Wellbeing'. I was still in extreme pain, but 'Life is here and now'. And I've got to help people for the duration of my life.

9.30pm: back at home and took another two Paracetamols. Retired hoping that sleep would relax my muscles and allow this suspected blockage to pass...

* * *

Thu 23rd Mar '00

3.10am: the stoma stopped working.

4.35am: in severe pain and vomiting. Woke Mum up. 'Mum I've got to go to hospital,' I told her. She dialled '999' and packed the familiar hospital bag.

5.20am: arrived at A&E via ambulance.

8.35am: still in A&E (been waiting over three hours) and hadn't been seen by a doctor! Decided to go and see Toni (hoping she would diagnose the problem). I hobbled in pain to her office and she examined me. 'Sam, I think your bowel is partially blocked and will probably clear itself,' she advised. I instantly felt better?! This sounded like 'permission' to go home – nothing serious. 'It will probably clear itself'. I think Toni detected my thoughts, because she continued, 'But I'd advise you return to A&E and have x-rays taken, to be sure.' 'I'm going home Toni,' I said hoping for her agreement, but instead she replied in a disapproving tone, 'It's up to you Sam.'

I returned to A&E and entered the cubicle I was in. 'Mum, come on let's go,' I said. I feel better and Toni thinks my 'bowel is partially blocked and will clear itself'. Mum looked surprised. 'Are you sure?' she quizzed in a stern voice. 'Yep! Let's get out of here,' I said enthusiastically, struggling to ignore the severe pain.

9.10am: back at home in bed and still experiencing pain. Mum asked if she should stay with me. I told her I'd be okay – that she should go to work (I'm fed up disrupting others lives, because of this stoma).

9.25am: vomited green bile.

11.20am: feeling dehydrated. Drank some water and vomited – and the pain is getting worse (I should have stayed in A&E).

11.50am: in severe pain – I desperately need some relief, but 'I don't want to go to A&E'. So, I called the doctor's surgery and requested a Home Visit. I thought Pethidine pain-killer might help reduce the pain, and relax me (and my bowels) which might encourage the blockage to clear.

1.30pm: Mum called. 'Hi Samantha. How are you now?' she asked. 'I'm still the same, but no worse,' I lied. 'Oh. Okay,' she responded in a low tone. I never told her I'd requested a 'Home Visit' – I didn't want to alarm her, and I didn't want her to make a 'fuss'.

3pm: the doctor arrived. 'Have you vomited, Samantha?' she asked as she examined my abdomen. 'No,' I lied (I didn't want her to refer me to hospital). 'Right, okay. Perhaps some pain relief and rest might help'. She administered Pethidine and I fell asleep almost immediately.

6.15pm: Mum arrived home. When she entered my room I was groaning. 'You're still in pain!' she exclaimed with shock. I think you better go back to hospital. You're not getting any better,' she scolded. 'I will. Just let me see what happens in a little while,' I whispered, feeling very weak. 'You've been doing that since yesterday,' she retorted angrily. She was right – I should 'go back to hospital', but I hate being in there.

9.30pm: still in pain. Every time I've tried to lie down – the pain intensified. So, I've been sitting up in bed. I feel exhausted and I really need to lie down – I desperately need to sleep. I feel like crying, but I'm too weak – and crying won't 'help'. I'm pleading with 'no-one' to 'help me sleep'...

11.10pm: 'I thought this operation was supposed to make me better?' And now, huge tears are rolling out of my eyes – without effort. Can't feel any energy in any part of my body. I feel limp – completely exhausted – sick – and in severe pain – and death feels preferable...

* * *

Fri 24th Mar '00

1.25am: woke up with a fever and experienced a severe pain that felt like a single stab in my abdomen and I 'saw silver glitters'. I felt as if I wanted to vomit, and panicked – scared that something fatal might happen. I didn't want to be alone, so I hobbled as quickly as I could to Sidiki's room shivering – sweating – reaching. I nudged Sidiki awake and rapped in a panic, 'Sidiki, I'm going to be sick! I'm going to be sick!' And struggled to hurry to the toilet. I reached, and a small amount of saliva came out and I felt a burning sensation in my chest. Sidiki was rubbing my back. 'I'll get you some water,' she said. I was too weak to reply, but nodded with approval. I sipped the water and the burning sensation in my chest returned, but the urge to vomit ceased. We retired to bed...

3.40am: woke Sidiki up again! Vomited green bile and experienced the terrible burning sensation again, but this time it was so intense that my chest was shaking. Again, I felt scared, but still 'not frightened enough to go to A&E'.

5.35am: woke up in a panic and needing to vomit. Again, I didn't want to be alone, but I didn't wake Sidiki (it would be the third time disturbing her). If I feel in need of 'supervision' – 'I should go to A&E'.

7.10am: air-called Toni, because this 'blockage' is not like the ones I've experienced before. I've been vomiting, and experiencing severe abdominal pains, but the stoma was still working (expelling watery output). I felt guilty calling her at this time, but I was desperate to know what was happening to me. 'Hi Sam. What can I do for you?' she asked cheerfully. 'Oh, Toni. I haven't stopped vomiting and the pains are getting worse. I'm baffled, because the stoma is working. It's expelling loads of liquid,' I groaned. 'Sounds like you might have Gastroenteritis. And since this has been going on for over twenty-four hours I suggest you go to A&E. You're probably dehydrated and in need of intravenous fluids,' she advised. 'Gastroenteritis?' I repeated with disbelief. 'Yes Sam. Symptoms are vomiting and diarrhoea which is what you have. Now get yourself to A&E to check it out,' she said in an equally commanding and friendly tone. 'Okay, I will,' I reluctantly agreed.

'Gastroenteritis?' 'I'm sure this problem is related to the stoma and surgery'. 'Gastroenteritis?' Still, she might be right, because the stoma is working. But if it's just 'Gastroenteritis' – I don't need to go to A&E? 'Gastroenteritis' doesn't warrant hospitalisation – and dehydration won't kill me? 'I'll drink some water and see what happens in an hour or so'.

7.35pm: tried drinking water, but could only manage a few sips that caused the burning sensation in my chest again, and spurred me to vomit. 'I had to return to A&E' – and inconvenience Mum who dialled 999 and packed the hospital bag.

9.20am: arrived at A&E. X-rays and blood tests taken. The examination and tests didn't disclose 'anything serious', but they couldn't say what was happening to me! I was left undiagnosed and admitted for 'observation'.

11.20am: taken to Cut Up ward where intravenous fluids and pain relief (Pethidine) was administered. Feeling miserable and bored with the situation. 'This is so boring! Backwards and forwards to hospital. I hate this,' I blurted to Mum with tears in my eyes. She rubbed my hand and comforted, 'This won't last forever.' And 'somewhere inside' – I thought the same.

2.40pm: woke up? I must have fallen asleep almost instantly once fluids and Pethidine were administered. Mum was sitting beside the bed, smiling. 'How are you feeling?' she asked in a calm voice. 'Still sleepy, but much better,' I replied forcing a smile, and nodding (the fluids and nap had really helped).

2.55pm: I lay thinking, 'I don't need to be here anymore'. I still felt very sore, but I didn't need 'medical attention'. I looked at Mum and whispered calmly, 'Mum I feel much better. I'm going to go home.' 'Samantha, why are you rushing?' she asked with displeasing eyes. 'You've just woken up and they said they want to observe you.' 'But I feel so much better. All I need now is a good sleep in my own bed... And I hate being in here,' I persisted. Mum frowned and didn't reply. There was a silence and I knew one way to 'prove' that I felt better was to eat or drink something. I didn't feel well enough to eat, but thought I could manage a drink. 'Mum have you got anything to drink? I'm starving, but I don't want to force things,' I lied to convince her that I was being realistic about me 'feeling better' – and not unreasonable about wanting to leave. 'I've got this,' she said and took out a small carton of apple juice from her bag. 'But I thought I heard them say you were to let your stomach and bowels rest?' she affirmed. 'Oh Mum, they say a lot of things. They don't even know what's wrong with me!' I exclaimed with a chuckle. She sighed heavily and reluctantly passed the carton to me. I sucked on the straw and the juice created a burning sensation when it reached my stomach. Still, I managed to drink half and suppress my feelings of pain. 'See, Mum. I've drank half – and I feel fine,' I lied – still trying to convince her.

3.30pm: drank the other half of apple juice. 'Look Mum – all gone and I haven't been sick!' I proudly announced, shaking the empty carton, still trying to gain her approval of my discharge. 'Better get dressed to go,' I said aloud to myself. Mum didn't say anything.

3.40pm: I buzzed for a nurse. 'Hi Nurse. I think I'm going to go home. I feel so much better. I haven't vomited since 5.35am, I'm no longer in pain – and I've managed to drink a carton of apple juice.' She looked at me and didn't answer, but read my medical notes. 'It would be better if you could wait to be seen by a doctor, tomorrow. They'll exam you and give the okay to leave,' she stated. Her words 'give the okay to leave' resonated. I thought 'they don't fucking own me' and decided that I was definitely going home. 'Ummm, I really don't need to stay another day. So, I'm going to discharge myself,' I replied, containing my anger. 'You may not want to stay another day, but you may need an examination,' she competed. 'Ummm, no, I think I'll be okay. I feel much better,' I contended. 'Well, you'll have to wait a while, for us to remove the cannula, and to allow us to write up a discharge sheet,' she concluded with disapproval.

4.25pm: discharged.

6.30pm: at home. I drank tomato soup which caused a burning sensation in my stomach, but no 'real pain', and I didn't vomit. I wondered, 'Do I really have 'Gastroenteritis' and 'What could I do to remedy myself'. So, I looked up the definition of 'Gastroenteritis'. Symptoms included 'vomiting and diarrhoea', and lasts up to three-five days. I think Toni was right – perhaps I did have 'Gastroenteritis?' Today is 'day three' since these symptoms started and they are subsiding. Some medic's do know what they're talking about.

I decided the best cure for 'Gastroenteritis' would be a 'Fast'. I'd read that Fasting can be a great remedy to heal and promote a healthy digestive system. So, I'm going to drink only water for the next twenty-four hours to give my stomach a rest from working and time to repair. Experiencing 'Gastroenteritis' made me realise that I've been narrow-minded regarding having a stoma and surgery. I've been relating any symptom to it. I 'forgot' I could have ailments unrelated to the stoma or surgery. And, I've been using the stoma and surgery as reasons for – any illness – any restrictions – any frustrations – and any source of misery.

* * *

Sat 25th Mar '00

8am: woke up feeling tired and with stomach cramps, but decided to go to the library and shopping for Doreen and Mark's Birthday presents. I 'had' to go – I couldn't allow this 'minor suffering' to prevail.

CHANGING 'BAD' BEHAVIOUR

* * *

Sun 26th Mar '00

8.35am: woke up feeling refreshed – I don't feel sore at all. Fasting has really helped.

7pm: Trevor called. As soon as I heard his voice – I became defensive and my heart began pounding. 'Hi Sam,' he greeted cheerfully and continued, 'Heard from MIND?' 'I don't want to talk about it,' I replied in a cold manner. 'Why?' he asked in a serious tone. 'I just don't want to,' I answered bluntly. There was a silence. 'Oh. Okay…. So how have you been?' he continued to quiz. I could feel my anger intensifying and I didn't want to shout at him. I struggled to remain calm, and said, 'Trevor, I really don't feel like talking.' I disconnected the call without hearing what he'd said – anger had consumed all my senses.

9.35pm: been thinking about having a drink since Trevor called. I've allowed him to piss me off. I don't want to think about my mental state, and that's what he's made me start doing – 'made me start thinking more'. And that's what the MIND assessment done – 'made me start thinking more'. Fuck – I need a break! I hastily went to the kitchen and poured some brandy with hot blackcurrant. I drank with a straw to increase the impact and quicken the effect. I wanted complete numbness – immediately. I needed to stop thinking and reduce my angry feelings.

10.15pm: sitting in my room contemplating – 'made me start thinking more'. Trevor and the assessment 'made me start thinking more?' I don't think so. 'I've' started thinking more – they haven't 'made me' do anything.

11pm: just thought, 'thinking more' isn't necessarily 'bad'. It's what we do with the thoughts, and what type of thoughts we have that matters.

11.45pm: retired still thinking. 'Thinking more' and feeling quite relaxed. 'Thinking' isn't necessarily 'bad!'

* * *

Mon 27th Mar '00

6.30am- woke up feeling tired and perturbed – I needed to ring MIND to confirm Counselling sessions. 'Counselling?' Not sure that I need 'Counselling' anymore…

9.30am: I should be ringing MIND to confirm that I still want 'Counselling'?

11.30am: rang MIND and confirmed my sessions – my 'need' for Counselling. Decided I need to talk about the thoughts I'm having, and sort out my dilemmas. I know talking will help – I just don't want to experience past events – the stoma – 'Friends' and family – 'Me (who I am)' – the challenge of needing to change diet and eating habits – these have caused so much distress. And, I don't want to get angry – and I don't want to feel sad – and I don't want to feel like dying.

* * *

Wed 29th Mar '00

6.30am: lying in bed wondering what the Counselling session will be like later – with 'dread'.

11.35am: pacing my room and experiencing panic (racing heart beat, pounding temples and dizziness, and shortness of breath).

12.30pm: still at home! I need to leave now to arrive on time. I don't want to go – I've got to go. 'Counselling?!'...

12.58pm: arrived at MIND. 'Hello. I'm here for Counselling with Helen,' I nervously informed the receptionist. 'Okay. Please take a seat over there. I'll let Helen know you're here,' the man replied in a friendly voice. Few moments later – a woman appeared. 'Hello. Samantha?' she asked in an assuming voice. I nodded and replied, 'Yes.' She continued, 'I'm Helen – one of the Counsellors. If you'd like to follow me – I'll show you where the sessions will take place.' I walked slowly behind her and my heart began racing and temples pounding as I thought 'I've made a mistake – I shouldn't have come'. The route was 'familiar' – the same one Gwen had taken to assess me, and my body filled with anxiety as we made our way to 'where the sessions will take place'. I hoped it wouldn't be the same room where the assessment was carried out. The room that was 'too quiet' – 'too still' – 'too calm'. The room where there was 'nothing to distract your thoughts'. The room that 'made you want to cry'. But, Helen stopped walking along the corridor and opened the door to the very same room. I was struck with panic, but I told myself 'this time you're not going to cry'.

'Take a seat Samantha,' Helen invited, pointing to one of the comfortable chairs. She sat, took a deep breath and smiled. 'Hi, again. I'm going to be your Counsellor for the next twelve weeks,' she explained whilst resting a folder on her lap. 'These sessions are confidential, but I'm obligated to break confidentiality if you express that you may harm yourself or someone else,' she informed as if reading from a script. I immediately felt deflated as her words resonated, 'obligated to break confidentiality if you express that you may harm yourself or someone else.' I desperately wanted to talk about my intense anger regarding Nathan – my rationalisation of murder, and my suicidal thoughts. She continued, 'These sessions are for you to talk about whatever you feel is necessary.' Sounded like a contradiction to me – and it didn't make sense. Her words repeated in my mind, 'for you to talk about whatever you feel is necessary.' It would be 'necessary' for me to talk about 'my intense anger regarding Nathan – my rationalisation of murder and suicidal thoughts'. But, that would be an expression that I 'may harm [my]self or someone else'. I sat feeling disheartened – and thinking, 'I knew Counselling wouldn't be useful'. If I tell her the truth – if I tell her about my 'intense anger regarding Nathan – my rationalisation of murder and my suicidal thoughts' – I'll probably end up in a psychiatric ward. I began feeling angry and disturbed – 'I knew Counselling wouldn't be useful'. Helen sat looking at me with inviting eyes 'for [me] to talk about whatever [I felt] is necessary', but I couldn't think of anything 'safe' to say. So, I sat staring blankly at the carpet, shifting in my seat, and sighing – for 'the whole session'.

* * *

Tue 4th Apr '00

4.30pm: met Hugh in University library (by chance). He was engrossed in reading and didn't see me, but I wanted to talk to him, and I was excited by his presence, so I approached him. 'Hi Hugh,' I greeted. 'Oh, hi Sam,' he replied cheerfully and continued, 'How are you? How's your health?' I was taken back at the heartfelt tone of his voice and questioned his sincerity. 'Physically – I'm fine, but I'm struggling mentally. The operation has given me so much to think about, and I'm finding the result of surgery difficult to come to terms with. You know, when you can rationalise suicide – things are bad,' I explained with a false chuckle. He frowned and said, 'Oh Sam, don't say that. I had a friend who did that a couple of months ago.' 'Anyway, I've started Counselling, for what it's worth. I had the first session last week. Not sure if they will be of any use, but I've started,' I sadly shared. 'Counselling is quite common now, and I think a good thing. Keep them up,' he encouraged. A lump developed in my throat. 'See you Hugh,' I said hastily, walking away before tears advanced to my eyes, as my struggle to maintain life dawned upon me.

7pm: at home. Haven't written in journal for over a week (been feeling lethargic and depressed), but meeting with Hugh spurred me to write today. It's amazing – energy is definitely transformed, passed on, and affected by interaction with people.

* * *

Wed 5th Apr '00

7am: woke up remembering a dream. Dreamt I was in a relationship. He was wonderful – 'we were wonderful' (Loving –Passionate – Sincere). I never visualise intimate relationships in my conscious state – they're always in my dreams – maybe they'll soon be reality.

9am: lying in bed thinking – 'Counselling' later. I never talked during the last session and not sure how useful these are going to be. Still, even though I didn't say anything it was 'nice' that 'I'd' been acknowledged and time allocated to 'me'.

1pm: Counselling session. I thought, 'to make these sessions useful – I should talk'. After sitting in silence for about five minutes, I mumbled, 'Helen, I can't recall conversations with people, or activities that I've carried out.' 'Oh,' she replied with eyes that invited me to expand. 'It's so embarrassing, and distressing,' I cautiously elaborated. 'What makes it embarrassing and distressing?' she asked calmly. 'My forgetfulness and I feel so stupid,' I retorted. 'So because you forget – you feel stupid,' she checked. 'Yes,' I replied. 'Why do you think you forget?' she asked. 'Because I've got a lot on my mind – and can't remember everything,' I explained in an assuming tone. 'Oh. What do you think could help you?' she questioned. 'I need to stop thinking and get rid of some of the thoughts,' I said desperately, and started crying. She handed me a box of tissues. 'The thoughts are too much and they cause distress,' I continued through sobs. There was a silence. We were just fifteen minutes into the session and I cried for sometime without saying anything. 'Sam we've just ten minutes of the session left. It might be useful to consider what you can do to help rid of your thoughts, that you say are causing distress,' she suggested. I looked at her and nodded. We continued sitting in silence – until the end of the session.

I left with a sense of relief – even though little was said and loads of thoughts spurred. Helen had helped me to work out the source of my distressing 'forgetfulness' – 'a lot on my mind'. And, it felt like this 'massive problem' had almost been solved. All I need to do is 'consider what [I] can do to help rid of [my] thoughts that are causing distress'. As I pondered on this – I realised that I already had two activities that were useful – Writing in my journal – releasing the thoughts from the mind, and realised one today – Counselling – talking about the 'problem' and considering possible 'solutions'.

* * *

Fri 7th Apr '00

7pm: met with Sharaz at our favourite Indian restaurant (she instigated this date). 'Oh, Sam, it's nice being out with you again. It been a long time since we did any socialising girl! I was getting worried that I was losing my friend. Right what you having to drink – your usual glass of white wine?' she rapped with a smile. 'Yeah. What you having – your usual glass of red?' I teased with excitement and feeling relaxed with the familiarity. It was lovely being in an environment that I had fond memories of before the dilemma of all the changes. 'So, how ya bin? – What's bin happening? – Tell me about university – the students – Life!' she said eagerly sipping from her large glass of red wine and sitting forward in her seat. 'Oh, before we start – Cheers to this reunion!' she said raising her glass and I raised mine for them to contact. 'Study's been interesting. I got two First Class grades for my last pieces of work'... She interrupted and shrieked, 'Two First Class grades! We're going to have to celebrate these on a separate occasion. Where did that intellect come from?! You were so dumb at school!' she joked and we both roared with laughter. 'I don't know, call it beginners luck,' I chuckled. 'And, I've met some really interesting people. 'Students'... we come in great variety. Most of us range from slightly stupid – to really stupid! Most people don't seem able to think for themselves – bit strange. And, well, as for Life, I'm still trying to get my head around having two bums!' I said in a jovial tone. 'What, you got two men on the go?! Sam, you have been busy!' she jested and continued in an encouraging tone, 'Sounds like loads of change and you know what they say 'Change is as good as the rest'.

9.45pm: at home reflecting on the evening. I enjoyed being out with Sharaz – we had a good laugh. And, I realised that different relationships fulfil different requirements. I've been expecting 'Counselling' from friends and I've been expecting them to fix my problems. Today I understand that all relationships have 'pluses' and 'minuses'. And, now I've experienced this – there's no need for frustration and anger.

10.30pm: feeling relieved and happy at this realisation 'different relationships fulfil different requirements'. To honour this breakthrough – I drank a few shots of brandy and hot blackcurrant.

* * *

Sun 9th Apr '00

6.35am: woke up thinking about my last intimate relationship (I enjoyed having a partner and sex) – I really want a partner! This desire is now manifesting in my conscious state – no longer hiding in the subconscious and creeping in via dreams! And, shit! I became aroused just thinking about this last relationship – in my conscious state!

* * *

Mon 10th Apr '00

7pm: attended 'Writers Live' at Centreprise an evening for new and seasoned writers to share their work. I had been invited to share my work at this event, but didn't feel confident to read to an 'audience' of writers, prospective agents, and publishers – my work was for fun. It was great meeting new people and catching-up with old students in an area that interests me. I told 'new' people what I'd started writing. 'It's based on my childhood experiences and the aim is to display the events from a child's perspective to demonstrate how adults discipline, and teachings can be so 'wrong',' I explained. 'Sounds interesting,' was the general response.

* * *

Wed 12th Apr '00

1pm: Counselling. 'Helen it's really weird that I want to maintain friend-ships, but then don't. I struggle being with friends, even though I enjoy their company,' I shared with a puzzled expression. 'You say 'struggle.' Does it feel like 'hard work' being with friends?' she clarified. 'Yeah,' I agreed. What makes it 'hard work'?' Helen asked calmly. I sat for a while thinking. 'Our conversations. I want to talk about issues causing me to experience sadness, anger and resentment – I want to sort out my problems, but they don't want to hear them. They don't want to hear my distress, or new ideas. So they pacify me with comments like, 'I know you've been through a lot', 'the operation was a shock', 'I guess it would make you look at life in a different way', 'Sam', you can handle anything – you'll be alright.' Or they change the subject. And, I want to scream 'let me talk about me having 'been through a lot' – 'let me tell you about 'the operation [being] a shock' – 'let me tell you that it has made me 'look at life in a different way,' I angrily explained. 'Do you enjoy the activities and dates that you have with friends?' Helen asked. 'Yeah,' it's nice going to a restaurant, being in a Wine Bar, and having a sauna with them, but I find it difficult to 'enjoy' unless I can talk about my problems – until my troubles are sorted out... Sometimes, I feel like cutting friends out of my life, but I need their company for enjoy-ment, and to help me strike a balance,' I explained confused by what I was sharing. 'Sounds like you're experiencing ambivalent feelings that can arise when change is taking place. You say you need the company of friends for enjoyment, and to help you strike a balance,' she said with enquiring eyes. 'Yeah,' I replied. 'Do you think striking a balance is important?' 'Yes, very important,' I keenly confirmed. 'Well, then maintaining your friendships are probably going to be important too,' she advised. 'Ummm, I think you're right,' I agreed with a heavy sigh. 'Maybe you can find a place to share and solve your problems like here, in a support group, or via a Telephone Helpline?' Helen suggested.

I left the session knowing that true friendships have great value, espe-cially in times of change and distress. They can offer the necessary bal-ance to combat 'distress' – even when they feel like a 'struggle'. And, I remembered what I realised when I went out with Sharaz that 'dif-ferent relationships fulfil different requirements'. And, I was reminded that there are other people, places and activities to share and help solve my problems. 'Helen' – 'MIND' – and writing in my journal are grand examples.

* * *

Thu 13th Apr '00

10.25pm: been thinking about Natan's visit in January 1999. I 'hate' having a shitty stoma – and he thought it was fucking 'funny'! I'm trying to live with a mutilated body – he's still got a 'perfect' body! I still experience intense anger (as if this visit was just yesterday) that makes my body shake from inside. I need to reduce this anger, because nearly a year and five months later, although I don't feel capable of murder anymore, I feel it would be justified if I seriously hurt him. I don't like the extremes of relaxation and tension. Yet, perhaps, these are just the rollercoaster of states – reflecting the mixture of thoughts and emotions. And, perhaps it's not 'the extremes' that matter, but what I do with the feelings.

* * *

Fri 14th Apr '00

9.30am: 'The Effects of Ill Health and Loss' was the title of the lecture today. It was great, but shocking and I was in tears by the end of it. The 'Bereavement process' was explained via Elisabeth Kubler-Ross's, *Five Stages of Grief*:

Denial – *"I feel fine."; "This can't be happening, not to me"*. Denial is usually only a temporary defence for the individual. This feeling is generally replaced with heightened awareness of situations…

Anger – *"Why me? It's not fair!"; "How can this happen to me?"; "Who is to blame?"* Once in the second stage, the individual recognises that denial cannot continue. Because of anger, the person is very difficult to care for due to misplaced feelings of rage and envy…

BARGAINING – *"Just let me live to see my children graduate."; "I'll do anything for a few more years."; "I will give my life savings if…"* The third stage involves the hope that the individual can somehow postpone or delay death. Usually, the negotiation for an extended life is made with a higher power in exchange for a reformed lifestyle…"

DEPRESSION – *"I'm so sad, why bother with anything?"* During the fourth stage, the dying person begins to understand the certainty of death. Because of this, the individual may become silent, refuse visitors and spend much of the time crying and grieving.

ACCEPTANCE — *"It's going to be okay."; "I can't fight it, I may as well prepare for it."* This final stage comes with peace and understanding of the death…

It was explained that although these stages were applied particularly to people suffering from terminal illness, they were also relevant to people experiencing 'personal loss', such as job, income, and freedom. This may also include significant life events such as the death of a loved one, divorce, drug addiction. The lecturer explained that these steps do not necessarily come in the order noted, but people may experience several stages in a 'roller coaster' effect – switching between two or more stages, returning to one or more several times before working through it.

I sat shocked to learn that I was experiencing 'personal loss' – bereavement. I'm grieving the loss of my colon – the loss of control over my bowel – and the loss of my body image. And I was shocked to learn that I'm stuck in the 'Anger' stage! Even though 'I hate the stoma' – I thought I'd accepted it. 'The fucking 'Anger stage' – a year and five months later!' I began crying. As soon as the teaching was over I rushed to speak with Kate (the lecturer) who was surrounded by students waiting to talk to her. I stood sobbing uncontrollably waiting to speak. When she became free, I blurted with huge tears rolling out of my eyes, 'Kate, I'm stuck in the 'Anger' stage – I'm stuck in the 'Anger' stage. I need to hurry up and get past this period. I need to accept my loss – the operation – and the stoma.' She replied calmly, 'Sam, you've been through a lot. It's a process and takes time.' There was a silence. I stood shaking my head and then sadly said, 'It's been a year and five months. How much more time do I need?' she placed her hand on my shoulder and said, 'As much time as it takes.' Her words resounded in my mind and in my heart, 'As much time as it takes.'

2pm: met with Lizzy for sauna. I felt miserable and greeted Lizzy by telling her, 'I don't feel like talking.' 'Okay. That's cool,' she replied in an understanding voice. She gave me my familiar back massage, whilst I lay thinking about 'nothing'.

5.30pm: arrived home feeling relaxed. However, about five minutes later and all of a sudden – from 'nowhere', I started crying – hysterically, and a voice in my mind was repeatedly screaming 'You're not coping'. I was glad no-one was home.

* * *

Sat 15th Apr '00

9pm: had a cry today – actually, I cried nearly all day. I don't know what made me start, or why I was crying. It was as though, 'I just felt like crying'. I was weeping whilst in the shower and Mum entered. She looked at me with 'sad eyes', but said nothing.

11.15pm: feeling slightly perturbed. 'Mum saw me crying, but said nothing?' Still, the prevailing feeling is relaxation. 'Crying seems to be therapeutic'.

* * *

Sun 16th Apr '00

5.55am: woke up thinking about Mum ignoring me yesterday, whilst I cried in the shower. I wanted her to ask me, 'What's wrong?' And, 'I wanted to tell her how I was feeling', but she never asked. I feel angry, but I'm remembering Brendon words, 'I don't know what to say or do to help'. I assume it's the same for Mum – she doesn't 'know what to say or do to help'.

7.30pm: Mum has just left my room. 'I could see you were hurting yesterday, but I didn't know what to say. When you're hurting – I'm hurting too,' she said in a croaky voice, and with tears in her eyes. 'I know Mum. There's nothing you can say – I have to go through it – it's a process. I'm just so fed up... I'm fed up of feeling sad, and lonely, and angry,' I blurted. She started crying – and so did I. She hugged me and said pitifully, 'Yes, it is a process, and processes take time. And, it's as long as it takes,' she advised and gave me a kiss. Her response reminded me of Kate's, 'as much time as it takes', she'd said. I sat on my bed crying with a sense of relief. I felt better after Mum explained her action – and content knowing that she cared.

* * *

Wed 19th Apr '00

1pm: Counselling. I wanted to talk about my 'desperation' for an intimate relationship and fear of never having sex again, because of the stoma, but I didn't know how to start. We sat in silence for about ten minutes. Then I nervously said, 'Helen. I've been thinking about intimate relationships, and I can't see me having another one now.' 'Oh, why's that?' she asked. 'Because of the stoma. No man's going to find me attractive now – now I'm shitting in a plastic bag out the side of my abdomen!' I abruptly replied rubbing my temples. There was a silence. 'You told me you are a member of a support group for people with stomas. Are there no members who are having relationships?' Helen enquired. 'Yes,' I retorted, wondering what that had to do with me. 'So people with stomas do have intimate relationships?' she confirmed. 'Yes, and some get married and have babies,' I informed with irritation. There was another silence. 'How were your relationships before having a stoma?' she questioned. 'Not successful,' I grimly informed (not wanting to talk about past relationships). There was a longer period of silence as my mind contemplated, 'Not successful'. I hadn't had 'successful' relationships before having the stoma (so success wasn't an issue), and it was evident that with a stoma – I could (others have formed relationships with a stoma). I left this session with 'another problem halved' – and with feelings of relief.

* * *

Thu 20th Apr '00

10.45pm: finding it difficult to write essay. I feel bored – and as though 'I'm not living'. And, 'everyone and everything are zooming past and around me' – the 'world and everyone ticking – but not me'. And, 'I feel invisible'.

* * *

Fri 21st Apr '00

5.35am: woke up with essay on my mind. I've given myself a deadline of Sun 23rd. I managed to work on it today, but didn't get much done. I can't concentrate – same feelings as yesterday.

* * *

Sat 22nd Apr '00

9.30am: still feeling the same as yesterday, but I've got to start working on the essay. I've got to write one-thousand five-hundred words by tomorrow!

12pm: I started writing at 10.30am. I've only produced one-hundred and fifty words – and they don't make sense!

1.30pm: another fifty words written that don't make sense! Perhaps I need a break, or perhaps I need to relax – to get the thought process going? A stimulant to get ideas flowing? Some wine will help to relax and stimulate. Drank three quarters of a bottle of wine.

3.30pm: started writing again and now I'm able to think, and the words make sense?…

* * *

Sun 23rd Apr '00

2am: still working on essay – only four-hundred words to write!

4.30am: one-thousand five-hundred words written! Retired with a few shots of brandy – I deserved it.

* * *

Then Life Took Control

Wed 26th Apr '00

8.45am: woke up feeling relaxed (I managed to complete essay)!

9.15am: practised Yoga and as I lay doing and thinking 'nothing' (relaxation period) a calmness prevailed over my entire body. 'This is what it is like when you allow 'Life' to Take Control', the Almighty Creator advised.

2.30pm: Counselling. 'Helen, I think someone is going to attack me when I'm outdoors. A rapist, someone experiencing mental health challenges, or I'll be mugged. And when I'm at home I think something bad is going to happen to me. Like, I'll trip down the stairs – slip in the bath – or choke to death on food,' I said and then quizzed silently to myself in shock – 'Did I really think these?' 'So, you feel in danger all the time?' she questioned. 'Yes. I suppose I do?' I replied. 'Why do you think that is?' she asked. There was a silence. 'Something to do with trust – I think. I don't trust people much. I used to, before the operation, but people proved not to be trustworthy,' I explained. 'And the accidents at home. Why do you think about having fatal accidents?' she continued. 'Maybe, because I now know how vulnerable I am. Never thought I'd be a victim of dis-ease to the point of fatality. And the scary thing was that I never knew – it was unexpected. Bit like an accident – you never know,' I explained. 'Ummm. Have you ever been attacked?' she asked in a calm tone. 'No. I've never been attacked,' I replied with irritation. 'Oh. Can you prevent accidents?' she continued. 'No. No-one can prevent accidents. That's why they're 'accidents',' I answered in an assuming manner. There was a silence as I thought about what I'd just said, 'I've never been attacked' and 'No-one can prevent accidents'.

* * *

259

Thu 27th Apr '00

9.25am: woke up feeling tired, but unable to go back to sleep. It's Joan's Birthday and I'm feeling anxious about visiting her later.

5.30pm: steadily, the nervousness has been increasing as the time to visit Joan gets closer. I considered cancelling, but remembered that I've enjoyed going to restaurants, being out in Wine Bars, and having saunas with my 'old friends'. And, 'Life' reminded me that friendships are valuable, and different ones fulfil different needs. And, it's time to rid of this self-indulgent stage – people need me – and I need people.

7.15pm: sipping brandy with hot blackcurrant to calm myself. I had tension in my abdomen that was so intense – it was causing cramping pains. The brandy eased the tension and pain.

11.55pm: back from Joan's. I enjoyed the visit. So glad I didn't cancel.

* * *

Sat 29th Apr '00

8.45pm: returned from Oxford Street from shopping with Dad, Doreen and Mark. Dad bought me a book titled *Yoga* that instructed how to practise. When I don't feel like socialising – I can practise at home. Now I've got no excuse not to apply daily. Enjoyed being out with family. 'Family' relationships – great opportunity to cultivate 'Love' and 'understanding'.

* * *

Sun 30th Apr '00

7.30am: read the book Dad bought me *Yoga* and then practised.

10am: I plan to cleanse my body today and tomorrow by eating only fruit and water. 'What we eat is very important for both body and mind. Toxic body – toxic mind'.

11.50pm: hadn't eaten all day. I felt hungry and faint, and so I ate an apple and banana, and drank a glass of water.

* * *

Mon 1st May '00

6.30am: awake with a 'grumbling' stomach – I felt sooo hungry. Drank a glass of water.

5pm: I've been in bed most of today to resist the temptation of eating.

8.30pm: ate an orange and an apple, and drank a glass of water. Back to bed...

* * *

Tue 2nd May '00

12.05am: I've only eaten four pieces of fruit and drank water – during the last twenty-four hours and fifteen minutes! I've given my body time to repair, and helped it to rid of toxins...

3am: finding it difficult to sleep. Perhaps, because I 'feel' hungry and I'm used to going to bed with a full stomach.

7.45am: woke up remembering profound visions or dreams? Don't know what they were, but they spurred thoughts. And, I don't know if I was in a conscious or unconscious state. But remember the vision or dream being about the capitalist system (how it's indirectly killing people) – how racism flourishes (used as a fundament for capitalism) – the misery and anger of the masses (as we are exploited and how we're existing – rather than living) – and feeling that this system is very cruel. I had an overwhelming feeling of sadness and heartbreaking grief – for the whole of humanity – and I felt totally hopeless.

2pm: lecture at University. 'Sam, it's good to see you. How are you?' Hugh asked with a broad smile and looking pleased to see me. 'A lot better than when I last saw you – I'm still here,' I replied smiling (referring to my disclosure of feeling suicidal the last time we met). 'Good. I told you to be optimistic,' he reminded. 'Yes, you did,' I agreed. 'Are you eating?' he asked in a serious tone. 'Yes. Since Sunday I've been eating just fruit and drinking loads of water. And, I'm going to do this for the rest of this week,' I anxiously replied. 'Why?' he asked with a frown. 'Because I'm detoxing,' I retorted. 'Um, careful you don't fade away!' he chuckled. As I walked towards the door at the end of the lecture, he shouted, 'Eat Sam! 'Plantains and yam'. I laughed and replied, 'I am eating – and I'm just cleansing for a week,' I chuckled and he laughed. I proceeded feeling pleased – it was nice knowing someone had a genuine interest in my Wellbeing.

6.30pm: attended RAC meeting at University. I've been going for the past seven weeks, enjoying chatting with fellow students and learning about the diverse cultures in our world. During the past five weeks I've become 'friendly' with a student named Orlando. 'Hi Sam. How's things?' Orlando asked cheerfully as he sat beside me. 'Oh, I'm fine. Bit stressed out with study, but that's a prerequisite for us students,' I chuckled. 'Shall we go for a coffee afterwards – to de-stress?' he invited. 'Oh, I've got...' He interrupted, 'I know – revision to do. Well so have I, but it's useful to take a break – chill out. Anyway, I'm not taking no for an answer!' he chuckled and stroked my chin. I didn't say anything, but a flush of awkwardness took place in my body.

11.15pm: returned from having coffee with Orlando! We talked for nearly two hours! 'Returning to University has opened my eyes. I've met people like-minded and some not so minded at all!' Orlando chuckled. 'Yeah, apparently people meet 'Lifetime Friends' at University,' I commented. 'I think you might be a Lifetime Friend, Sam. We've got so much in common and I really like you,' he said with glitter in his eyes. 'Orlando, there's no time for romance at University – only study!' I jested trying to bring humour to our serious atmosphere. 'Well, what about the study of romance,' he said in a deep tone and blew me a kiss. A hot flush came over me and I smiled at him. Orlando walked with me to the bus stop. He linked his arm with mine – and strangely – it didn't feel uncomfortable...

* * *

Wed 3rd May '00

3am: awake thinking about Orlando. 'I think you might be a Lifetime Friend, Sam. We've got so much in common and I really like you,' he'd said. And, 'he linked his arm with mine – and strangely – it didn't feel uncomfortable'.

7.30am: woke up thinking about Orlando.

2.30pm: Counselling. 'I'm getting fed-up with these moods that I'm having. I'm so happy one moment and so sad the next – and for no apparent reason – just thoughts,' I explained with desperation. 'And they're so extreme. One moment I can be singing and giving thanks to the Almighty Creator – and the next I can be thinking about having a stoma and crying hysterically. Psychiatry would diagnose me as having 'Bipolar'. I've had all the classic symptoms such as a 'racing mind' – 'seem full of energy' – 'not sleeping much' – feel 'extreme sadness' – 'feelings of guilt' – 'feel down about myself and life in general' – 'neglect myself' – and feel suicidal,' I ranted. 'I'm not sure about diagnoses and psychiatry. What might be more important is what you think? You say these moods happen 'for no apparent reason – just thoughts,' Helen stated. 'Yeah, just thoughts,' I repeated and continued, 'Apparently, Bipolar occurs when work, studies, family or emotional pressures are at their greatest. I've got stress in all these areas. And, I've never had such extreme moods or thoughts before surgery.' 'What do you think you could do about the pressures you have?' Helen quizzed. 'Talk about them and make changes to release some of the stress... Even, if I've got what is considered 'Bipolar' – it's created by having too much pressure. Once stress is released – so too will the extreme moods,' I answered. 'You say you're fed-up of having these moods. Why's that?' Helen calmly asked. 'Well, I'm not reliable – I don't know how I'm going to feel from one moment to the next,' I explained. 'And when you're not reliable and don't know how you're going to feel – what happens?' she asked. 'Well, nothing happens – I just don't know,' I replied. I left thinking 'Once stress is released – so too will the extreme moods' – and 'Nothing happens – I just don't know'.

* * *

Thu 4th May '00

10.30am: practised Yoga using the book Dad bought me. Feeling equally relaxed and energised – I will definitely practise every morning for at least an hour.

4.30pm: returned from shopping. Whilst out there was an older woman who was begging. 'Have you got any spare change?' she asked us (the public) as we waited for buses. I shook my head (the same as the other bystanders), and stood listening to her repeat the question and receiving the same response. I wondered what her story was. How did she fall into such a circumstance? – Why did she need to beg? I watched her walking around wearily and saw hunger in her eyes – and sorrow. I stood regretting that I hadn't given her any change and began to feel very guilty. 'Why aren't you able to give?' 'You have two bottles of wine in your bag – luxuries! 'You do have 'spare change'. And, 'have you not experienced the need of help from others – for your survival?' 'Life' asked. I panicked – dug in my pocket and took out some 'spare change'. I walked towards her and said, 'Here,' and handed her some money. The hunger and sorrow in her eyes seemed to disappear instantly. 'Thank you Mam. Very kind of you,' she said with a glorious smile and bowing.

As I travelled home I thought about my near missed opportunity to listen to 'Life'. To honour 'Life's' quest to fulfil its Humanitarian role. And, I heard the woman's response, 'Thank you Mam. Very kind of you.' And thought, 'Life' is kind'.

10.15pm: honouring 'Life' is very fulfilling. 'Very kind of you,' she'd said. I felt 'very kind'. Opened a bottle of wine and finished it.

* * *

Fri 5th May '00

7am: woke up feeling refreshed and practised Yoga.

6.30pm: returned from University. I had a productive and enjoyable day. Kate said my report was fine – I had a lovely lunch and talk with fellow students – and a relaxing time in the sauna – chatting with a couple of women. It was great socialising?!

10.30pm: to bed feeling very relaxed and tired.

* * *

Sat 6th May '00

8.30am: woke up feeling refreshed and plan to go shopping.

9.35am: out shopping. I bought Sharaz a pair of earrings to display my appreciation of our friendship. I decided to deliver them on my way home (even though part of me didn't want to). As I stepped off the bus – my heart was pounding and I felt dizzy. I walked slowly towards Sharaz's to allow time to calm down, but as I approached her house, my heart pounded faster and my dizziness increased – throwing me off balance. I was scared? I was scared to met with Sharaz? Or maybe, I was scared, because I was going to give her a gift to display my appreciation of our friendship and didn't want to get emotional? As I approached her door my whole body was shaking and my arm felt stiff – I had to force it to reach for the bell. As I stood waiting for a response – time seemed to be ticking swiftly. When the door swung open Sharaz stood with an equally surprised and welcoming expression. 'Hi, Sha. How are you? I'm not stopping?' I rapped (ending the visit before it had merely started). 'Oh, hi Girl – it's good to see you,' she said hugging me. I struggled to hug her and felt like I'd snap. I hastily handed her the bag containing the earrings. 'What's this?' she asked looking puzzled. 'Open them and see,' I instructed. 'Oh, they're beautiful!' she said with awe. 'What are they for? It's not my Birthday or Christmas,' she quizzed. 'It's to say 'Thank You' for being a friend,' I replied holding back tears. 'Oh, you didn't have to buy me anything,' she reassured and hugged me again. 'Well, I'm off,' I said hastily, trying hide my tearful response. 'Oh, that was a quick visit,' she commented with a hint of disappointment. 'What are your plans for the rest of the day?' she interrogated. 'I haven't got any,' I replied with fear – assuming she was going to suggest a 'plan' for us – and she did. 'Do you want to go shopping later? About 1.30pm? We can have lunch and shop till we drop!' she invited with excitement. There was a silence. I liked the idea of the two of us out, having lunch – it sounded like fun – and I'd be 'socialising'. I wanted to socialise – but I didn't! 'You don't have to,' she said sounding disappointed. 'No, I'd love to. Where shall we meet?' I asked. 'At the 'Town Hall' bus stop?' she suggested with a grand smile.

6pm: returned from shopping and had so much fun. We tried on clothes, tested perfumes, and had a nice chat as we ate lunch.

10.30pm: feeling refreshed (after napping) and ready to go to Debra's 50th Birthday Party. Yet again, part of me wants to stay at home, but a larger part of me is excited about 'socialising'. Poured myself the usual amount of brandy and blackcurrant (to get in party mood) and felt very tipsy?! I think this is due to my body being efficient (been detoxing). Thus, the affect of alcohol is more potent.

11.30pm: arrived at party…

* * *

Sun 7th May '00

4am: at home – really enjoyed myself at the party! 'Will you honour me this dance?' A man asked in a pleasant tone, offering me his hand. I panicked – 'he might feel the bag', but then I remembered Trevor saying that he couldn't feel it. And even this man could feel the bag – I think he'd assume it was my stomach – I reassured myself. 'Yes,' I replied and we danced a few times.

11am: lying smiling. I enjoyed being out with Sharaz and partying was fun. I'm turning into a bit of a social animal – and 'Life' likes it!

* * *

Mon 8th May '00

7.30am: realised a great contradiction – I'm rushing to relax. 'Rushing to relax!' Might be better to slow down and pace myself. Then, if I don't get time to relax – it won't matter, since I wouldn't have incited the tension.

8.30am: practiced Yoga and Deep Breathing (taking in breath via nose and breathing down into abdominal area. Then breathing out twice as slow through mouth with pursed lips.) for fifteen minutes. Deep Breathing is useful to reduce tensed muscles, calm the mind and re-duce fatigue. Whilst practising Deep Breathing, I had three dizzy spells. Apparently, this can happen when the body is not used to receiving greater amounts of oxygen. And, these dizzy spells often subside with practice – they're nothing to worry about.

3pm: read information on 'Thrush', because I just can't seem to get rid of it. The symptoms suggested are headaches, depression, irritability, dizziness, severe forgetfulness (I experience all these symptoms). Pos-sible remedies include replacing fruit with raw vegetables, not eating Quorn, and not drinking tea, coffee or alcohol. Also, taking Evening Primrose, Lactobacillus acidophilus, natural yoghurt, extra virgin olive oil (antifungal).

7.30pm: thinking about the symptoms of Thrush and the remedies (especially abstinence of alcohol). I'm wondering how significant it is regarding promoting Thrush, because I 'can't stop drinking alcohol at the moment' – it helps me 'tick' – it helps me 'live'.

8.30pm: thinking about the remedies of Thrush – 'can't stop drinking alcohol at the moment' – I'll put the other remedies into practise.

10.30pm: Thrush is not such a serious ailment. I'm sure cutting out all the other offending foods and drinks will reduce symptoms?

10.45pm: had a shot of brandy with hot blackcurrant and again felt very tipsy. And, I realise that I've only been drinking on average three times a week?!

Expelled pinky and bloody mucus (distress – eustress!).

* * *

Tue 9th May '00

2.20am: feeling exhausted and guilty – I shouldn't have drank. I need to rid myself of Thrush – the symptoms aren't 'good'.

7.45am: woke up thinking about Orlando with a smile, and then panic! I was looking forward to seeing him later at the RAC meeting!

6.30pm: RAC meeting. Near the end of the meeting Orlando passed me a folded piece of paper. It read: Haven't had coffee in a week! Please help me honour my addiction! XX. I laughed and wrote: Okay, but not a long one! We went to the Student Bar and chatted for over two hours!

9.40pm: as we waited for the bus to arrive I commented, 'Gosh, the temperature's dropped – I'm freezing.' Orlando motioned towards me and hugged me. 'I'll keep you warm,' he said and he cuddled me for ten minutes until the bus came... And I wished it had taken longer to arrive.

* * *

Wed 10th May '00

2.30pm: Counselling. 'Helen, I used to drink alcohol daily, and now I drink about three times a week – I just can't stop drinking,' I blurted. 'Oh. Why can't you stop drinking, and is it a problem?' Helen asked with concern. 'I can't stop drinking, because it helps keep the thoughts away and it's a problem, because I'm drinking and I don't want to. But, I can't stop, because the thoughts won't stop,' I explained. 'Sometimes I wonder if I'm addicted to alcohol, but that would make me an 'Alcoholic' – I'm not an 'Alcoholic' – I just need to have a drink to relax my mind – more of 'habit' than an 'addiction,' I continued. 'Oh. You say you think your drinking is a problem, because you're drinking and you don't want to... And, you consider it a habit – rather than addiction. What could you do to break this habit?' Helen asked. 'I think once I manage my thoughts – I'll also control my alcohol intake. So, 'all' I really need to do is sort out my thoughts,' I concluded. 'Ummm. It seems like you're beginning to 'sort out your thoughts', because you say you're now drinking about three times a week instead of daily,' Helen reflected.

I left feeling motivated. Helen had reflected, 'that it seemed like I was beginning to sort out my thoughts, as I was now drinking three times a week as opposed to daily. Still, it felt distressing that my alcohol intake should be on my agenda via Counselling. Counselling was the place for 'problems'. So, now it was official – my drinking was a 'problem'.

10.45pm: 'My drinking was a problem?' Poured myself a glass of wine. 'My drinking was a problem?!' No! It was a 'thought problem' – not a 'drinking problem'.

10.55pm: had another glass of wine and felt very tipsy. 'Tipsy' on just 'two' glasses of wine – as opposed to a bottle.

* * *

Thu 11th May '00

11.55pm: stayed in bed most of today – feeling a bit 'overwhelmed' with the changes that are taking place. The 'reduced drinking' – 'liking Orlando' – 'enjoying friends and family'. Drank two glasses of wine.

* * *

Fri 12th May '00

8.50am: awake and not feeling refreshed. I'm supposed to be meeting Tycho at 12pm, but I'm considering cancelling, because I feel sickly due to drinking two glasses of wine (usually I need to drink at least a bottle to have this outcome)?! I can't cancel – I can't allow 'drinking alcohol' to affect my plans. If I do, then drinking would be a 'problem' and I would be an 'Alcoholic?'

12pm: Met with Tycho. 'Hi Tycho. This looks interesting,' I said gazing at the buffet displaying a range of cooked and raw foods including rice grains, vegetables, and fruit dishes. 'I hope you enjoy,' he smiled and continued, 'Apparently, a Vegan approach to eating can help maintain good health. The avoidance of meat and high-fat animal products, is as-sociated with lower blood cholesterol levels, lower blood pressure, less obesity and consequently less heart disease, stroke, diabetes, cancer, etc!' he informed with a chuckle.

4pm: at home and feeling positive about life. I enjoyed meeting Tycho. Chatting with him made me realise how simple Life can be and it was refreshing learning this. 'We complicate Life,' is what he said. And, I enjoyed lunch too! It was healthy and tasty – never realised there could be such combination!

* * *

Sun 14th May '00

6.50am: practise Yoga for an hour.

7pm: Feelings of loneliness consuming me. Strange, I feel content honouring 'Life', yet it's a lonesome experience.

10pm: drank a 'smaller' than usual shot of brandy with hot blackcurrant and felt very relaxed. Retired.

* * *

Mon 15th May '00

6.30am: woke up feeling fine – Relaxed – and at Peace.

Practised Yoga and affirmed, 'I am Relaxed – and at Peace. I know what I need – and I know what I don't need'.

* * *

Tue 16th May '00

6.45am: woke up feeling Peaceful.

6.30pm: RAC meeting. Orlando didn't arrive until 6.45pm and for fifteen minutes I kept wondering 'Where is he?' When he arrived I whispered, 'Where you been?' 'Nowhere, just late,' he replied looking at me with a cheeky smile. When the meeting was over (without discussion) we went to the Student Bar with linked arms. 'Why were you late?' I enquired. 'Oh. Was you missing me?!' he teased. 'No. Just wondered if you were alright,' I replied in an unconvincing tone. He broke our linked arms – held my face with both hands and kissed me on the lips. 'I missed you for fifteen minutes too,' he said calmly, gazing in my eyes – and a wave of 'happy panic' stuck.

10.30pm: arrived home feeling happy – 'Life' likes Orlando.

* * *

Wed 17th May '00

6.30am: thinking about the many contradictions. Everything seems 'right' and 'wrong' at the fucking same time! I must accept former friends – I must get rid of them. I must practise healthier options to relax – I must drink to relax. I must keep busy – I must calm down and rest?!

8.15am: 'Everything seems 'right' and 'wrong' at the fucking same time'. I don't want to go for Counselling session today. Talking about these contradictions will cause dis-stress and I visualise me crying – I hate crying. I feel like I've lost control when I cry. But 'I won't cope without Counselling sessions' – and I feel like I'll 'lose it' if I go? Another fucking contradiction!

2.42pm: arrived late for Counselling and with great anxiety. I decided that it would be better if I didn't speak about my dilemmas. So I sat feeling very uncomfortable with my head down, and listening to the loud ticking of the clock. It read '2.45pm' and I wondered if I could sit and not say anything for thirty-five minutes – when the session would be over. I sat for a long while. I looked at the clock – '2.55pm' – only ten minutes had passed? I couldn't sit for another twenty-five minutes and not say anything. I looked at Helen and she was looking at me with inviting eyes. I forced a smile. I wanted to talk about my contradictions – and I didn't – another fucking contradiction! I broke the silence. 'Helen, it's been a tough week.' 'Oh, why's that?' she asked in her usual calm manner and sitting upright. 'I'm in constant conflict in most areas of my life,' I explained. 'Are you finding it difficult to make decisions?' she questioned. 'Yes, I am,' I replied. Her words resonated, 'Are you finding it difficult to make decisions?' It sounded so simple. 'Do you want to talk about these difficult decisions?' she continued. There was a silence. I didn't know if I wanted to talk about my 'difficult decisions' – but then I did! 'I don't know what to do. Must I accept friends or not? – Must I adopt healthier options or not? – Must I keep busy or not? – Must I study hard to gain 'good' grades – or not? – Must I like the stoma – or not? I'm constantly confused and out of control,' I blurted through sobs. 'Sam, you're working in extremes – black and white. It might be useful to strike a balance – like the need you spoke about regarding your distress and friendships. Remember you decided that friends could bring enjoyment and there was an acceptance that they had a role to play in your life? You question whether you 'must adopt healthier options or not?' It doesn't need to be absolute. You could opt for eating healthier more of the time. And, perhaps you need to keep busy and also have relaxation periods – another 'balance?' And, regarding 'liking the stoma', perhaps you might consider accepting it? And your acceptance might be that you don't 'like' the stoma?' Helen offered. I didn't reply, but sat crying for the remaining ten minutes – I hate crying.

4.30pm: at home reflecting on Counselling session with a sense of relief. I 'forgot' we could a strike a balance – and that we can experience mixed emotions and views in the same area. It doesn't have to be 'either' – 'or' – and it can be useful to do a bit of both.

* * *

Sun 21st May '00

8.30pm: thinking about the need to revise. Drank half a glass of wine and felt relaxed.

9.45pm: expelled pinky mucus and blood (forth time today – distress).

10.45pm: drank half a glass of wine and felt relaxed. Retired.

* * *

Mon 22nd May '00

6.30am: woke up with revision on my mind.

7.45am: I'm reading, but nothing's going in.

8.30am: still reading and nothing's going in! Still, I needn't get distressed. The Almighty Creator is taking care of everything – I'm not in control, and I'll get what I deserve.

9.30am: taking a break. Been reading for over an hour and nothing's going in.

11am: resumed study, but again – nothing's going in! Perhaps the break wasn't long enough – I'll relax for another forty-five minutes.

11.45am: started reading notes – and nothing is still going in!

12.30pm: tried reading again, but only seeing the words. Perhaps some protein food will help – 'brain' food? Ate loads of houmous, boiled potatoes, and broccoli, drizzled with olive oil.

2pm: tried to revise, but still nothing's going in – shit! Perhaps a nap will help.

5pm: woke up feeling tense – it's 5pm and I feel like I haven't revised – nothing has been retained! I needed to relax. Drank half a glass of wine. Felt relaxed and thought of a 'creative' idea to assist revision – I drew and coloured key words from my notes. I enjoyed making them, they looked attractive and what I read was going in!

10.45pm: stuck the notes on my wall, feeling content with what I'd revised and created.

* * *

Tue 23rd May '00

6.45am: woke up feeling refreshed and looked at notes that I'd stuck on the wall. I'd remembered everything!

6pm: arrived early to the last RAC meeting for this semester. I didn't want it to be the last meeting – it would mean not seeing Orlando for nearly three and a half months! 'Hi Sam,' Orlando said as he came and sat in the seat that I'd 'saved for him.' 'Hi,' I replied excitedly (happy to see him). 'This is for you,' he said and gave me a small envelope. 'What's this?' I asked. 'A donkey!' he said laughing and instructed, 'Open it.' There was a card inside with a beautiful yellow flower on the front. Inside he'd wrote: 'Beautiful Sam. We're going to be 'Lifetime Friends!' I Love You – be in touch'. And he'd written his telephone number. I looked at him and he was looking at me with glary eyes. I didn't say anything – I didn't know what to say, but smiled. 'Just because this is the last meeting – it doesn't have to be ours,' he calmly stated with a smile. 'Okay. I know,' I nervously replied. He walked me to the bus stop – we hugged 'Goodbye.' 'See you soon,' he said. 'Yeah. I'll give you a call,' I replied. And I meant it.

9.30pm: at home. I took out the card Orlando had given me and re-read what he'd wrote. 'Beautiful Sam. We're going to be 'Lifetime Friends!' I Love You – be in touch'. I recalled him calmly stating, 'Just because it's the last meeting – doesn't have to be ours'. He was right – I had his number.

10pm: thinking about Orlando. 'I really like him – and he likes me'...

11pm: 'I really like him – and he likes me'.

11.50pm: 'I really like him – and he likes me'. I feel anxious about 'us' – but there is no longer any panic. I'm experiencing eustress, but 'Life' is managing it – I didn't need a drink.

* * *

Wed 24th May '00

8.30am: up revising – and nothing seems to be fucking going in! My mind is consumed with thoughts of Orlando!

10.30am: 12.30pm: revising. 'Orlando – Orlando – Orlando!

1–2pm: revising. Still thoughts of 'Orlando' distract me!

2.30pm: Counselling. 'Helen I'm finding it difficult to know whether I'm making friends or not,' I explained. 'What's the difficulty?' she asked. 'I think it's because I don't trust people and I haven't made new friends for years. I've met 'new people', but my friends have remained the same. But now I've changed and I'm not sure what I need from friendships. The people I meet seem to have a lot of problems. I do all the 'caring', 'understanding', and 'listening', I explained. 'Well, perhaps you could imagine you're in a room with two doors. Think about who you're letting in and who you're shutting out,' Helen offered. There was a silence as I 'imagined'. 'Well, I'm letting in people who are 'needy' – those who are suffering or experiencing pain – in one door. And in the other, I'm often shutting out people who are 'fulfilled. People who are 'caring', 'understanding' and 'listen', I reflected in shock and retorted, 'This is crazy.' 'Do you remember expressing a need for people to be understanding and caring? And a need for a partner?' she asked. 'Yes,' I replied frowning. 'Well, it might be useful to think about how you'll identify caring and understanding people and a prospective partner,' she suggested.

I left the session realising that I have 'let in' a few people (Kevin, Anne, Karen and Orlando) who are caring and understanding. 'I am making new friends' and there is a 'prospective partner'. I hadn't identified these new relationships – I'd lost touch with recognising 'Care' and 'Understanding'.

4–5pm: arrived home and immediately started revising. Nothing!

6–8pm: revising – again Orlando accommodates my mind.

9.30–10pm: revising and still nothing appeared to be going in. Decided to stop resisting and allowed happy thoughts of Orlando to prevail...

* * *

Thu 25th May '00

1am: still awake and so was Sidiki. I crept into her room and whispered, 'Hi Sid. What you doing up.' 'Revising', but I'm about to go to bed,' she yawned. 'Snap! Nothing seems to be going in for me. Can you test me on a few questions before bed?' I asked. 'Yeah sure,' she replied. I gave her the questions. 'Give a clear distinction between HIV and AIDS,' she asked. There was a silence – I didn't know! 'Ummm. I love Orlando – Orlando 'likes me!' I laughed. 'Not the right answer,' she replied with a chuckle and continued, 'How about this one, 'Give two examples of the impact of HIV in pregnant women'.' Again I couldn't answer and chuckled, 'Experience anxiety' and feeling very Loved!' 'Again – you're wrong!' She replied laughing. 'Okay. Last one. HIV and AIDS studies have shown an increase in transference to unborn babies in a particular population. Explain why this might be.' I roared with laughter. 'What's so funny?' she asked. 'Again – I don't know, but I think relationships could possibly help to prevent dis-ease!' I joked. 'Oh – my – goodness! You've been studying for nearly a year and all you can come up with are responses to 'Love' and a 'Relationship'. You've been studying the wrong subject! Better switch your learning to the 'Study Of Orlando' – you'll get First Class grades!' She shrieked with laughter and I joined her...

1.35am: set my clock to alarm at 6am. I'll rise early to revise – I've got to pass these exams.

6am: the alarm sounded, but I was already awake with revision on my mind. Made a cup of Mint Tea and began reading notes. Still seeing just words.

7.30pm: time for a break – been revising all day (wonder how much I'll remember). I'll worry about revising tomorrow – the exam isn't until 10.30am. I'll get up at 6am and do two hours reading. Thinking about 'failing' and need a 'brain break' – I need to relax. Drank a shot of brandy with hot blackcurrant.

8.45pm: rang Orlando (two days after meeting)! 'Are you around tomorrow? I've got an exam. Perhaps we can meet afterwards?' I invited. 'Yeah,' he said with excitement. 'The exam finishes at 11.30am. Shall we meet for lunch at 12pm, in the dining room?' I suggested. 'Sounds perfect – see you then. All the best for the exam,' he concluded. I disconnected the call and thought 'I really like Orlando'.

9.15pm: 'I really like Orlando'.

10.30pm: exams tomorrow – and 'I really like Orlando'. Drank another small shot of brandy with hot blackcurrant. Feeling very drunk and 'relaxed' – fell asleep instantly.

* * *

Fri 26th May '00

6am: woken by piercing alarm clock and with a pounding headache. I drank too much – even though it was less than the usual amount?! Went back to bed in a panic. I couldn't revise – because of my headache, but 'I should be!'

11.30am: exam finished and I was in shock – twofold. I answered most of the questions and Orlando was waiting outside for me! 'Hey! What a nice surprise. I thought we were meeting in the dining room at 12pm?' I said, giving him a hug. 'Would have missed you for thirty minutes!' He said with a grand smile and asked, 'How did it go?' 'Amazingly good!' I said with excitement. Our meal was over too quickly. 'Let's sit out on the green,' Orlando suggested. 'Good idea,' I agreed. 'I laid my jacket on the grass and sat. 'Always feel like napping after eating,' Orlando yawned and placed his head in my lap, staring up at the sky. 'Oh,' I exclaimed feeling slightly nervous.

6.30pm: at Student Bar. 'Gosh. Can't believe this is the last day of University. We've got no commitments for over three months. I'll go insane if I don't find something to do,' I sighed. 'I'm off to travel – South America,' Paul said with excitement. 'Well, I'm going to work for a charity that supports Asylum Seekers during the break. And, I'm sooo looking forward to it,' Sharon shrieked. 'Go insane,' Orlando repeated mimicking me and continued, 'There's so much to do – you can't go insane!'

10.30pm: at home. 'What will I do with myself for over three months?' 'Life' will find me something to do?

* * *

Sun 28th May '00

12pm: Family Gathering at home. 'Hi Aunty... Hi Uncle... Hey Cousin...' They seemed to pile in by the hundreds. All dressed in smart, colour co-ordinated, designer wear. 'Well that's just the way things are – it's a dog-eat-dog world. You've got to take care of number one…' 'A nice car with a decent salary and to be able to go on holiday that's 'Life…' 'Second year at University – really proud of you'…. Were the general remarks made and I seemed to retort to every comment. 'Really and when we're busy taking care of number one – how does the rest of the world keep ticking?' 'Do nice cars, decent salaries and holidays bring contentment?' 'Academic success teaches us nothing about 'Life'. By 3pm I was exhausted and wanted to be away from the 'family'. However, 'Life' whispered, 'It's not them – it's you. You've changed accept them and accept you'. Immediately, I felt energised and agreeable. I could see their point. Now the general idea of 'Well, that's just the way things are – it's a dog-eat–dog world. You've got to take care of number one…' was acceptable. It was 'the way things were' and it was a 'dog-eat-dog world' and we needed to 'take care of number one'. I realised that I appreciated all that was being said – it was just that I didn't think the ideas were conducive to 'Life'. And it wasn't the family's 'problem' what I thought – it was mine.

10.30pm: today was 'strange'. I didn't drink any alcohol and felt very relaxed?! I thought it was going to be a very tensed atmosphere and I'd 'have' to drink. I guess me not drinking was a manifestation of 'listening to Life'.

* * *

Sat 3rd Jun '00

6.45am: haven't written in my journal for a week. I've been busy with daily activities (washing, cooking, cleaning) and speaking with friends and family. I must keep busy – 'I've got no commitments for over three months'. 'I need to keep busy' or 'I'm going to go insane'.

* * *

Tue 6th Jun '00

5.30am: since Saturday I've been thinking, 'I've got no commitments for over three months'. 'I need to keep busy' or 'I'm going to go insane'.

5.30pm: would have been at RAC Society meeting, and felt a bit unnerved about this 'free time'. My brain felt hazy. I opened the windows – considering the air will 'clear my head'. Hoping it was a lack of oxygen type of haziness, and not a muddled thinking type of haziness, but opening the windows didn't help.

7.30pm: practised Deep Breathing for fifteen minutes – haziness cleared.

* * *

Wed 7th Jun '00

2.30pm: Counselling. 'You can chose your friends, but you can't chose your family,' I remarked with a heavy sigh. There was a silence and Helen looked at me with inviting eyes to elaborate, so I did. 'I'm finding it difficult relating to my family. There was a Family Gathering a couple of Sundays ago and initially I retorted to every comment that was made, and felt mentally exhausted after three hours,' I shared. 'Why do you believe this happened?' Helen asked calmly. 'I suppose it's because my values have changed,' I replied. 'Do you find your new values difficult to handle?' Helen quizzed. 'Yes. I think that's the 'problem' – not the family – they've always been as they are. And, I realised this on Sunday. Still, it seems difficult,' I admitted hopelessly and continued. 'I want them to accept my new values – I want them to accept the new me'. 'Well, acceptance of your values by the family may be useful. However, what might be more important is your acceptance, of your values. You've believed and aspired to a particular set of morals, perhaps most of your life. So, getting used to, and accepting your values will take time,' Helen assured in a comforting tone.

7.05pm: Orlando called. 'Hi Sam. How have you been?' 'Okay-ish. I've got no commitments for over three months. I need to keep busy, or I'm going to lose it,' I replied in a low tone. 'Well, how about keeping busy with me? It's been nearly two weeks since I saw you – I'm having withdrawal symptoms!' he teased. 'Ummm, okay. When did you want to meet?' I asked struggling to contain my rising excitement. 'Tomorrow – 12pm, at Dalston Junction,' he informed. 'Dalston Junction?' I repeated and continued, 'What are we going to do there?' 'Nothing – just meet. We're going to travel onto somewhere else,' he informed. 'Where?' I asked. 'It's a surprise,' he teased. 'Oh. I don't like surprises,' I whined. 'You'll love this one,' he said confidently.

9.05pm: I've been thinking about the surprise outing tomorrow. 'It's a surprise' – 'You'll love this one' he'd said. This was exciting and scary! Experiencing eustress and practised Deep Breathing for an hour. I retired with a smile and feeling relaxed.

* * *

Thu 8th June '00

12pm: met with Orlando. 'Hi Beautiful. You look nice,' he complimented as we hugged and kissed. He was carrying a large plastic bag. 'What have you got in there?' I asked. 'Some board. I'm going to help a friend with some Do-It-Yourself later,' he informed and continued, 'Bus 277 will take us to our Secret Destination!' When we arrived at Victoria Park he said, 'Right this is us!' 'Vicky Park!' I shrieked and continued, 'How did you know this was one of my favourite places!' 'You told me a few weeks ago,' he reminded. We strolled for a while. 'Is it okay to sit here?' he asked, stopping under a tree along the canal. 'Yep,' I replied. He dug in his large plastic bag and took out two boards sized A3, paper and paints! 'I can't paint!' I exclaimed in shock. 'Yes you can. Get out your mind and enjoy,' he instructed, passing me a pencil. This was stirring – I hadn't painted since attending primary school. He began sketching. 'What are you going to draw?' I asked. 'Something Beautiful,' he said. 'Oh, I don't know what to draw,' I moaned. 'Look around and sketch what attracts you. A tree – the canal – a bird – a boat – whatever!' he suggested. We done little talking as we drew and painted and it felt strange – yet relaxing to be with someone and not talk. We got engrossed in our creations. After what seemed like a short while – I glanced at my watch. 'It's 3.35pm!' I exclaimed in shock. 'Ummm. We got out of our heads – and lost in time,' Orlando chuckled. 'What have you drawn?' I asked. 'Something Beautiful,' he said and turned his unfinished painting towards me. I couldn't believe it. He'd sketched and began painting a portrait of me! And it was 'Beautiful'. 'Orlando! It's beautiful,' I complimented. 'You're beautiful!' he laughed and asked, 'What did you draw?' 'Guess. Not as good as yours,' I said showing him what I'd done. 'A tree and a hare. That's nice, Sam,' he praised. 'It's not a hare! It's a squirrel! I told you it wasn't as good as yours,' I whined. 'I was only joking! Anyway, art isn't about 'goodness', but 'expression'. Did you enjoy doing it?' he asked. 'Yes – I – did!' I replied looking at my creation and feeling proud. 'Good,' he concluded and kissed me. We left the park and ate roasted vegetables and salad in a cafe. 'Orlando. I can't remember enjoying myself so much in a long-time. Your company was 'good' – the activity 'amazing' – and the atmosphere 'nurturing'. Thank you,' I said in a serious tone. He didn't say anything, but lent forward and kissed me.

7pm: arrived home feeling overwhelmingly happy. 'Orlando' – 'Painting' – 'Park'...

9.30pm: 'Orlando' – 'Painting' – 'Park'. I needed to relax. Drank half a glass of wine...

11.15pm: retired feeling perturbed – 'drinking doesn't offer relaxation anymore?'

* * *

Sat 10th Jun '00

6am: it's beginning to feel strange drinking – like an 'out-of-date' routine. The association I've made with 'Thinking' and 'Drinking' now feels jarred. I'm going to resist next time.

7.30pm: the phone rang and I cheerfully answered, 'Hello.' 'Hiya,

Sam. It's Peter. How ya doing?' he asked in a low tone. 'Fine Peter. How about you – you don't sound happy,' I commented. 'Naw. I've been thinking about 'Life' and wondering how we became so cruel. I sometimes hate this existence,' he sighed. 'Ummm. What makes us so cruel?' I asked with interest. 'Well, that we should purchase cut flowers from parts of the world where people are fighting for land to grow food and go hungry. That we should be so keenly 'fashionable' – whilst others are losing their limbs to provide fashion for us. That natural foods without pesticides and dangerous additives are not affordable to all,' he sorrowfully rapped. 'Oh, Peter, I see your point about us being cruel… It might be useful to think of your part in this 'existence' and what you can do about the cruelty. What I do is where possible, not fuel what I consider cruel. So, I don't buy cut flowers, and when I need clothes – I purchase from recycling and charity shops, and I don't buy more food than I need. And, I'm always sharing my views and practises with anyone who can hear!' I chuckled. 'Sam you've changed. You're calmer and seem really content,' Peter reflected. 'Do you think so?' I quizzed and continued, 'It's interesting you should say that, because although I'm still experiencing stress – I do feel more relaxed and at peace. I've been practising Yoga, eating healthier and changing my way of thinking. These have really been helping,' I concluded and we disconnected the call. I sat feeling content. Peter had helped me realise that although I'm experiencing stress – I've learnt to relax and accept my states of tension. I guess it's because I've been listening and allowing 'Life' to Take Control'.

11.20pm: thought about 'drinking some wine' – and then thought about 'being content'. Retired without wine and in Peace.

* * *

Tue 13th Jun '00

1.30pm: delivered talk the *Patients' Perspective* at City University to nurses pursuing specialist course in stoma care.

4.30pm: arrived home. The students on the course always make me feel so important. Apparently, what I'm sharing helps them understand how they can assist in the care and Wellbeing of others. Life's quest?

8pm: called Trevor. My heart raced as I nervously waited for him to respond. 'Hello,' he answered in an abrupt tone and I immediately wanted to end the call. My mouth went dry and my jaw almost locked. 'Hi Trevor, it's Sam,' I struggled to reply. 'Cor, I haven't spoken to you for ages! It's good to hear from you. You've brought a smile to my face,' he said now sounding cheerful. We spoke for about fifteen minutes and much to my relief he didn't ask about my Counselling sessions. At the end of the call he repeated, 'It's good to hear from you. You've brought a smile to my face.' I hadn't contacted him since we last spoke – when I considered his 'caring' – interrogating, and his interest in my Wellbeing, for his own selfish reasons. But, today I focused on his intention – 'he was trying to help' and so I called. And, I was glad I did – nice to '[bring] a smile to [someone's] face'.

* * *

Wed 14th June '00

6.30am: wondering how I'm going to tell Helen that I need more Counselling sessions. Today is the eleventh of twelve sessions planned.

2.30pm: Counselling. I entered the room worrying, 'How was going to tell Helen that I needed more sessions?' How I was going to say 'I didn't think I'd manage without them'. As I sat thinking my heart began racing. I needed to tell her immediately or I wouldn't tell her at all. 'Helen, I need more Counselling sessions,' I blurted and reluctantly admitted, 'I won't cope without them.' She looked at me with questioning eyes, 'Why do you think you won't manage without them Samantha?' A pang of anxiety advanced in my chest as I thought about how desperate I was – that I needed someone and something (apart from myself) to survive. A lump advanced in my throat indicating that I wanted to cry and I tried to suppress it by swallowing. 'I've got no-one to talk to about my problems and I'm so confused all the time. You and these sessions help me solve my problems, and sort my head out. I would have lost it by now without these sessions,' I struggled (competing with the lump in my throat). "Lost it'. What do you mean?' Helen asked. 'Gone insane,' blurted. 'Oh, I see,' she said calmly. 'I'll have to speak to my supervisor regarding the possibility of extra sessions,' she advised. There was a silence. My mind angrily quizzed, 'Speak to [her] supervisor?' 'What would the supervisor base their decision on – they didn't know me! They hadn't seen my distress. Couldn't Helen 'see' I needed more sessions? There was nothing to 'speak' about! And, suppose the supervisor decided I didn't need anymore? We sat for the rest of the session in silence. I thought, 'if the supervisor decided that I didn't need more sessions I would have to manage alone – so I might as well start now.

3.20pm: as I walked home I had ambivalent feelings. 'How would I cope? – I would manage'. My thoughts were disrupted by my phone ringing – it was Orlando. 'Hi, Orlando,' I greeted forcing a cheerful tone. 'Hey, Hi Beautiful. Let's meet up. It's been nearly a week since I saw you and I'm...' I interrupted, 'Having withdrawal symptoms.' 'Yep!' he chuckled. 'When did you want to meet?' I asked. 'Today – 5.30pm in Clissold Park,' he instructed in a cheerful tone. 'Today?!' I shrieked. 'Yes today!... You're right – you can't say no. You're wrong – you can say yes! See you at 5.30pm.' The call was disconnected and I was smiling?! My mood had changed within five minutes! Orlando had brought 'a smile to my face' – like I'd brought to Trevor's. And I was reminded that friendships have different roles. And I felt so much better.

5.30pm: met with Orlando. 'Hi Beautiful,' he greeted with a grand smile and we kissed. 'Hi Orlando,' I replied with an equally pleased expression. 'It feels like it's been a long-time since I saw you,' I admitted. 'Yes, many fifteen minutes have passed!' he joked. We strolled holding hands. 'Beautiful, I'm appreciating you more each day,' he informed in a serious tone. There was a silence and my heart felt like it wanted to stop working. He continued, 'I just wanted you to know that.' 'Look Orlando there's something I must tell you. I'm not as 'Beautiful' as you think,' I snapped. 'What do you mean?' he asked stopping our stroll and making eye contact. 'I've had surgery and I've got a stoma,' I said breaking eye contact. 'A what!' he barked. I explained what a stoma was. 'Sounds awful and disgusting. But, what's having a stoma got to do with your beauty?' he asked with a puzzled expression. 'Well, as you just said, 'It sounds awful and disgusting',' I stated angrily. 'Yeah. The surgery and the stoma does. But I can't see the relation to your beauty. You're 'Beautiful' – the stoma isn't – that's separate isn't?' he asked in a commanding tone. 'How can they be separate – when the stoma is part of me?' I retorted, letting go of his hand. 'Let go of focusing on surgery and the stoma. You were beautiful when you were born – you are beautiful now – and you'll be beautiful when you die. The essence of you is beauty and that's a fact,' he sternly affirmed – kissed me and firmly held my hand. We walked in silence. And, something inside me shifted. It was as though 'Life' was saying 'I've been telling you this ever since you had surgery.'

* * *

Thu 15th Jun '00

7.10am: thinking about what's on my list of 'Things To Do'. Call doctor's for Sidiki – wait for furniture delivery – food shopping – cook dinner. 'I need to keep busy' or 'I'm going to go insane'.

8.30am: practised Yoga.

9.45am: called doctor.

11am: furniture arrived.

1.30–3pm: out shopping.

4.30pm: cooking dinner….

Busy – busy – busy!

* * *

6.30pm: called Tano (former neighbour and friend). 'Hi Tano. How have you been?' I asked cheerfully. 'Hey! Samantha is that you?' he asked with surprise. 'Yes, it's me. Been sometime, hey?' I answered. 'Yes. What are you up to?' he asked with interest. I'm on a break from University, and trying to keep busy. The break is for nearly three and a half months!' I exclaimed. 'So, what will you do to keep busy?' he asked. 'Not sure. I haven't got any plans,' I informed. 'No plans?! When you have nearly three and a half months to spare?!' he barked and continued, 'You could go to my place – and stay with my family. Go and visit Ghana – see something new,' he encouraged. I said, 'I'd think about it'…

10pm: 'Ghana?' Travelling to the African continent would be a great experience…

11.05pm: 'Ghana!' But I'm worried about leaving Uncle Solomon (a man with a 'mental health problem' according to the medics). I've been supporting him whilst Grandmas been away, and I'm not sure that he'll manage to fend off the neighbours and medics – alone…

11.40pm: 'Ghana'. It would be good to get way, but I must support Uncle Solomon.

11.55pm: abdomen feeling uncomfortable and stoma is finding it difficult to expel. Expelled blood and mucus – 'distress'…

* * *

Fri 16th Jun '00

12.20am: severe cramping pains – vomited four times – and the stoma is only expelling liquid. And – fuck! According to the advice of the 'health professionals' (based on these symptoms) – I should be calling for an ambulance – I should be on my way to A&E. But I don't want to go to hospital. 'I'll be my own doctor and wait a while – symptoms might cease'.

1.45am: sweating, experiencing dizziness and cramps (the pain is so severe – I'm finding it difficult to breathe – I thought I was going to faint. I worried 'is this a blockage or something more serious?' Practised Better Breathing to release tension (tension can cause pain) and I massaged the area around the stoma. Fell asleep.

5am: woke up in bearable pain. Practised Better Breathing and more massaging.

9.35am: woke up feeling much better. The stoma is very swollen and sore, but it's working! Well done, Dr. Shakes!

6.30pm: been dosing in and out of sleep for most of today – pain really zaps our energy.

11.55pm: woke up and it's 11.55pm?! Doesn't feel like I've been sleeping for that long, but I woke up at – '11.55pm!' Feels weird, family are winding down from the day and I'm just starting mine. I remember when this nocturnal habit felt normal.

* * *

Sat 17th Jun '00

8.20am: feeling refreshed and with no pain! Can't afford to waste 'feeling well' – I must do something…

9am: called Lizzy. 'Morning Lizzy. Fancy a day in Hampstead Heath?' I asked. 'Yeah,' she enthusiastically replied.

11am: arrived at the Heath. We spread our blanket, ate houmous and salad, napped, chatted and wrote in our journals.

11.50pm: arrived home feeling content. A day out with an inspiring friend and being nurtured by nature (the scenic grass and trees) – socialising was 'good'.

* * *

Sun 18th Jun '00

8.20am: lying – looking at the ceiling and contemplating, 'Our thoughts really do influence our reality'. Yesterday, whilst in Hampstead Heath a few 'negative' thoughts popped into my mind as I thought, 'the atmosphere is too peaceful' – 'the scenery surreal' – and 'people too harmonious'. I sat wondering, 'Why is it that, 'I haven't heard anything disturbing – like someone swear or raised voices?' – Why does everywhere look so beautiful?' 'Where's the dogs excrement?' – 'Why are people being so loving to each other (smiling, greeting children, chatting about their dogs, and not playing music from radios loud)?' Moments later – someone swore – a dog came within three meters of where we were sitting and urinated – and the volume on a radio was turned up! I understand this to be termed as 'willing and experiencing'. A spiritual encounter with the universe – anything we 'will' we experience.

1.30pm: this event of 'willing and experiencing' spurred me to re-read a book titled *You Are What You Think* by Tycho. The word 'Think' is what excited me – 'Think' is what I did yesterday that *willed* the experience. I read the first chapter that began:

> *Our thoughts can work for us, to enhance our lives, or, if our mind is filled with fear, negativity and dread, it can make our lives much more difficult than it need be…. Our whole reality depends on the way we think… The mind is responsible not only for our happiness and success in life but also for our health and fitness.*

Yes indeed! Now this theory and my experience rung 'True'. I have no doubt of the power and influence of our minds.

5.30pm: Tano's words are resonating 'Go and visit Ghana – see something new'. I think 'I need a break', but 'I must support Uncle Solomon?'

10pm: Tano's words have been resonating most of today. 'I need a break' – but 'I must support Uncle Solomon?'

10.30pm: decided that I'm going to Ghana! 'I need a break and I need to see something new'. And, 'Someone will take care of Uncle Solomon?' Thought about drinking some brandy. 'Someone will take care of Uncle Solomon' – I affirmed – satisfying my worrying thoughts. Retired – trusting that 'Life' would 'take care of Uncle Solomon' – and the thought of drinking some brandy disappeared.

* * *

Mon 19th Jun '00

7.30am: woke up with lots of energy and feeling happy.

3.30pm: called Steve. 'I'm going to Ghana,' I screamed with excitement. 'Oh, Sam, can I travel with you? I've wanted to visit Ghana for a long time, but needed a Travel Companion,' he informed. 'Of course you can!' I replied. 'Right, I'm going to contact my friend Rass in Ghana and tell him I'm going to be visiting – so make space!' he yelled.

It will be a challenge accompanying Steve. He experiences Multiple Sclerosis (MS) and uses a wheelchair. Still, Life will cope – and 'I must help others'.

10pm: returned from an evening at Centreprise were authors and poets were sharing their work. 'How's the book coming along? Val (former tutor) asked excitedly. 'It's taken residence under the bed!' I chuckled. 'Sam, it will do well – Sieze The Day,' she said looking disappointed.

10.40pm: at home. 'Sam, it will do well – Seize The Day', Val had said and I'm remembering comments from other people on the course. 'Can't wait to find out what happens next' – 'You must finish this'. And, if it's as good as they say – I couldn't cope with the possible 'success'.

* * *

Tue 20th Jun '00

6.35am: thinking about the book I've started and the fear of 'success'? I need to *Feel The Fear and Do It Anyway* (Susan Jeffers). And, actually – 'I want to finish it?' I scrambled out of bed and swiped my arm frantically underneath it to retrieve the manuscript. I grasped it and read part of the first chapter:

Chapter One

Mum rarely looked happy. One day I sat on her lap trying to make her smile, by pulling her cheeks. When her teeth showed threw the opening of her mouth, they were all the same size, and I asked, 'Mum why you got funny teeth?' Her eyes widened, she grasped me tightly and placed me abruptly on the floor. 'Stop ya cheek. Ya rude, hey,' she answered. Mum often said that I was 'full a cheek' or called me 'rude' when I asked questions she didn't like, or couldn't answer.

I enjoyed reading this? It was worth pursuing?!

* * *

Wed 21st Jun '00

8.30am: thinking about Counselling – 'hope the supervisor agrees that I need more sessions'.

2.30pm: Counselling. 'Samantha. My manager has approved another six sessions for you,' Helen informed with a smile. 'Oh, that's really good news,' I replied and excitedly changed the subject. 'Helen, I'm attracted to a fellow student called Orlando. It's really weird, because he feels like a friend.' She sat upright and smiled with inviting eyes. 'Why do you say it's weird?' she asked. 'Because most of my past partners haven't been 'Friends' – we been 'Lovers' that socialise. With Orlando it's different. He appears to be a friend that I'm attracted to!' I explained. 'Sounds exciting, Samantha,' Helen suggested.

5.30pm: needed to pursue 'book'. I wrote Chapter nine – creativity flowed easily and I'm pleased with what I've written.

7.45pm: the phone rang and I dashed to answer it. 'Hello,' I greeted. 'Hi Sam. It's Rachel. How are you?' she asked in a low tone. 'I'm fine. Just trying to keep busy now studies are finished,' I chuckled. How about you? How's things?' I asked. 'Not good. I've been diagnosed as having 'fibroids', and they've suggested surgery,' she explained. 'Oh,' I replied. 'I wondered what you thought, as you're studying Health Studies and you've had surgery,' she said. 'Why do you think you've got fibroids?' I asked. 'Not sure, just one of those things,' she said in an unconvincing tone. ' Do you think you can get rid of them?' I asked. 'Only by surgery. They tell me they're very large and will only get bigger,' she reiterated what she'd been told. 'My understanding is that every disease of our bodies can be cured by adopting lifestyle changes such as foods, exercise and our thoughts,' I informed. 'Really? So what you're saying is that I don't need surgery?' she asked in a surprised tone. 'Well, if you reach a crisis point and the Fibroids become life threatening – surgery has its place. But you have a grand opportunity to rid of these naturally, because you're not in crisis. So yes, that's exactly what I'm saying – you don't need surgery,' I confidently informed and continued, 'Hang on, let me look up what Louise Hay suggests. I grabbed the book and read, 'Probable cause for fibroid tumors is Nursing a hurt from a partner. A blow to the female ego'. 'Gosh! That's so true for me. I've never forgiven Jack for leaving me and making me feel useless,' she said sounding shocked. 'Ummm. There you have it! The power of our thoughts and the affect on our bodies,' I confirmed and shared, 'Last Saturday I experienced the influence of our thoughts and the power of our minds whilst in Hampstead Heath. And, the experience alleviated any doubts in my intelligence that our minds influence the state of our bodies, and circumstances. I've found affirmations help. Apparently they're useful to change thoughts, attitudes, and beliefs. If we can alter 'negative' connotations to 'positive' ones then we can improve health, become more relaxed, and be more successful in all areas of life – I think. Hay suggests the affirmation 'I release the pattern in me that attracted this experience. I create only good in my life', could counteract the thought process that spurs fibroids,' I shared. 'Thanks Sam,' Rachel concluded in awe.

* * *

Thu 22nd Jun '00

8am: woke up feeling low of energy and with the desire to go swimming.

9am: went for a swim. I swam mostly on my back imagining a blue sky and the sun beaming down on me. I swam eighteen lengths (don't know where the energy came from)!

2.30pm: Swimming released the tension from my body, and my visualisation offered great relaxation for mind. Felt exhausted and relaxed – fell asleep.

7pm: called Orlando. 'Hey! Nice to hear from you. It's been a long-time,' he answered with excitement. 'Oh Orlando. It's been just over a week,' I chuckled. 'Yeah, well I'm used to seeing you every week and missing you for fifteen minutes!' he teased. 'I'm going to Ghana for a month,' I informed with excitement. There was a silence. 'Oh. That sounds good. I'm going to miss you. When are you going?' he asked in a low tone. 'Not sure. Sometime in August,' I replied. 'We must meet twice a week before you leave. And speak everyday to fulfil this absence,' he jested and we both laughed.

* * *

Fri 23rd Jun '00

9.25am: rang travel agent to book a flight to Ghana, but didn't. I was told I was unable to travel without having a vaccine for 'Yellow Fever'! I immediately rang my doctor's surgery and was advised that the 'Yellow Fever' vaccine wasn't available via the National Health Service, and I'd need to go to a clinic where it was. It was also suggested that I would need to 'protect' myself from the possibility of getting malaria, polio, diphtheria and typhoid! This 'protection' would be in form of medication! Loads of drugs in the name of 'protection' based on 'fear' – 'What ifs'. I don't think those toxins can be any 'good' for the body – wonder if I really need them.

* * *

Sat 24th Jun '00

9.35am: read an interesting article. An author named Rupert Thompson shared his experience of writing. He expressed how an unhappy childhood had 'fired his imagination' and that he didn't know how you could be a writer without discipline (he works eight hours a day; seven days a week; ten weeks at a time)! He's now the bestselling author! I need to adopt this discipline.

I intend to work on Chapter nine of the book. I've been motivated by Val, fellow writers, and what I read (first part of Chapter one).

7.30pm: haven't managed to work on chapter nine. 'Eight hours a day; seven days a week; ten weeks at a time'. If I want to complete this book, I need to be committed and I need to gain some discipline.

* * *

Sun 25th Jun '00

7.45am: looked around my room – it was cluttered and dusty. It needed cleaning and clearing – nothing had been shifted for months. There were draft copies of the book, and scrappy University notes covering most of the floor. The atmosphere felt stagnant.

10am: I cleaned everything – the windows – the window ceil – the photo of myself – the candle-holder – the computer screen – the keyboard – the scanner – the radiator – the skirting-boards. I placed the papers out on the landing to be recycled and I hovered the carpet. The room looked so bright and the atmosphere felt refreshing. And, I felt 'lighter' and 'better'.

Doreen and Mark helped me place the papers in bags for recycling. As they gathered the sheets they stopped and read parts of the manuscript. They were laughing and in awe? These were reactions to my writing? – To my work? – To my story?! These were young readers – eleven years old and they were enjoying it?! Children and adults were enjoying this read?! My siblings reactions – Val's encouragement – fellow writers enthusiasm – and my enjoyment of first chapter spurred new motivation. I will strive to find the discipline to write – 'eight hours a day; seven days a week; ten weeks at a time'.

1.30pm: met Karen for lunch. 'Hi Sam. How are you?' she greeted. 'I'm going to Ghana in August!' I informed with excitement. 'Gosh! That sounds great,' she screamed and then adopted a low tone. 'Sam, you know I was given Metformin medication for Diabetes a month ago, well things haven't got any better. I was in hospital last week for three days. I had a Diabetic coma.' 'Oh…. Karen I'm sorry to hear that,' I responded calmly. 'Have you done anything in the last month to help control your sugar levels? Remember myself and the doctors advised that exercise, relaxation and reducing sugar intake would manage Diabetes. Have you been able to change or adopt any of these?' I asked. 'No,' she replied pitifully and continued, 'I'm still in shock with the diagnoses and feel 'disabled' – I just can't do anything. Me – Karen – Diabetic. Doesn't make sense,' she blurted and started crying. There was a silence. 'Karen, I'm encouraging you again to do some exercise, practice a form of relaxation and cut out sugar. It will make a difference,' I reiterated in a soft tone and gave her a hug. 'I know – I know. And I hate taking tablets. I started taking them and the side effects are awful. I had upset gut, nausea, diarrhoea and loss of appetite,' she angrily informed. 'Look, you're taking medication now, but you don't have to,' I sternly advised. 'And, 'a loss of appetite',' I repeated and continued with a chuckle, 'Now, that's serious for you,' and we both laughed.

10.45pm: feeling relaxed. Practising Deep Breathing whilst in my mind I'm affirming that 'I love and approve of myself. I create my own joy. I choose to be a winner in life'. I'm using suggestions from Hay's book. These were the recommended affirmations for people experiencing 'Colitis'. The probable cause was over exacting parents. Feeling of oppression and defeat. Need for affection. Retired.

* * *

Mon 26th Jun '00

7.40am: feeling Relaxed and Content – and I realise that I haven't drank any alcohol for over two weeks!

12.30pm: ate potatoes, raw carrots and two cloves of raw garlic. My eating habits and foods are changing and I'm getter healthier (more energy, glowing skin).

3pm: called Steve and told him I'd collect visa application form tomorrow at 8.30am.

9.25pm: haven't worked on the book for nearly two weeks and decided that 'a break – is a break' – I'm not going to do anything that involves mind or brain work. I think it would be useful to give both mind and brain a break.

* * *

Wed 28th Jun '00

8.30am: arrived at Steve's. 'Sorry, Sam. I could only manage to fill out half the form. MS was full of activity yesterday – 'It Took Control',' he informed with an unconvincing chuckle. 'That's the thing with what's known as a 'long-term health condition' – their on-going – a bit like 'Life'. And, so this 'on-going' must be honoured everyday with necessary exercise, food, relaxation and change in thoughts,' I advised. 'Yeah,' he agreed. 'What did you do on Monday?' 'I washed clothes – painted small cupboard – prepared raw vegetables – and done recommended physiotherapy exercises,' he informed. 'Gosh! I feel tired just hearing what you done!' I laughed. 'Yeah, well, I was exhausted by 8.30pm. I lay on the settee and couldn't get up, until nearly 12am,' he informed. 'Why did you do so much, Steve?' I quizzed. 'Because, I felt so well. I never know when MS will want to 'voice it's opinion' – so when I'm feeling good – I do what needs doing!' he chuckled. 'I understand, Steve. That's what people with 'long-term health conditions' do. We feel well – and abuse the wellness by over-doing activities. But, doing more than we can manage is stupid, because we're then forced to rest to recover. And, recovery can take more time than we spent on the activities we carried out!' I stated with a chuckle.

2.30pm: Counselling. 'I'm uncomfortable about not being able to express my anger. I fear one day – I'm going to explode. I can feel it,' I explained with desperation. 'What will happen when you explode?' Helen asked calmly. 'I don't know, but I don't want to be out of control,' I retorted. 'Oh,' she uttered. There was a silence. 'Anytime, I'm out of control – everything goes wrong,' I continued. 'Can you remember a time when you were out of control and things went wrong?' she asked with interest. 'Yes, when I was little,' I sadly said. There was a silence. I continued, 'I'm writing a book.' 'What are you writing about?' she asked. 'About my experience of childhood from the age of four years. I want to convey from a child's perspective how adults' discipline can be so 'wrong,' I informed confidently. 'Sounds interesting. What was your childhood like?' she asked, straightening her posture. My heart thumped a painful beat and I felt dizzy. I didn't want to talk about my dreaded childhood. There was a silence and I tried to hide my agitation. 'Miserable,' I said faking a chuckle and continued, 'I don't think my parents done well.' 'Are you angry with your parents?' she asked. 'Yes, I suppose I am…. And… And I've just realised I've expressed this via the writing I've done,' I said with a frown on my face. 'Sounds like writing about your childhood is a way of expressing your anger?' Helen quizzed. 'Maybe. But why, now? Why do I feel so angry towards my parents, now?... Actually, I think I know why. Because, when I was ill and had surgery – when I was in need, they didn't look after me. Especially Mum,' I croaked swallowing, trying to force the lump in my throat away and not cry. 'Oh,' Helen uttered. 'And, it's because of them that I've had this surgery. They never allowed me to express my anger – so it all went to my tummy and bowel,' I rapped with my head bent towards the floor. I left feeling distressed. The session uncovered that I'm very angry with 'the parents'. I'm glad I'm meeting with Karen at 6pm. If I didn't have this date, I'd continue thinking about my 'dreaded childhood' and my feelings of anger would increase.

6pm: met with Karen at a restaurant. 'Hi, Sam. How are you?' she greeted with a smile. 'Hi Karen. I'm fine,' I lied burying the memories of childhood and anger. 'How have you been – Blood Sugar levels?' I continued. 'High and low – and I don't want to talk about it,' she sternly informed. There was a silence. 'Okay,' I livelily replied and changed the subject. 'Karen, you know I've become friendly with Orlando.' 'Yeah, he seems really nice,' she replied with excitement and a broad smile. 'I'd really like a partner, but with this retched stoma – it sometimes feels impossible,' I said in a serious tone. 'Look Sam, if men don't like you because of your stoma, then they're not worth liking. You want someone with substance – someone who's gonna like you for you – not because of what you wear, what you look like, or what job you have. I reckon having a stoma is an added value, because when you find a fellow who wants to be with you – and your stoma, you'll have probably found an everlasting relationship,' she reassured.

9.05pm: returned from meeting with Karen. We spent two hours eating and chatting (we'd only met last Sunday!) – definitely, a 'New Friend'.

10.15pm: lying remembering Karen's reassuring words, 'I reckon having a stoma is an added value, because when you find a fellow who wants to be with you – and your stoma, you'll have probably found an everlasting relationship.' Wonder if this 'everlasting relationship' might be with Orlando.

* * *

Thu 29th Jun '00

9.30am: woke up with 'Love' on my mind and realisation 'Love' is the motivation of 'Life' – and 'Love' is the only 'weapon' required by 'Life?'

* * *

Fri 30th Jun '00

9.10am: feeling 'out of sorts' and crying. I feel tense – I feel relaxed – I feel happy – I feel sad – I feel grateful – I feel resentful – I feel vulnerable – I feel powerful – and I don't know why I'm crying. I'm laughing and huge tears are rolling out of my eyes! And, after crying and laughing – I felt better. This is insane?!

11am: Orlando called. 'Hi Sam. I'm inviting you for dinner today,' he said with excitement. 'That's nice. Where?' I asked. "Orlando's Place', Highbury, at 6.30pm,' he told me using an Italian accent in a deep voice. There was a silence as I thought, 'His place?!' He continued, 'The chef will cook an authentic Italian dish. The table, food and chef will be waiting for you – don't let them down,' he chuckled and disconnected the call. I sat for a while in panic – 'His place!'

6.40pm: arrived at number 'ten'. A Victorian house with a beautiful front garden. I walked slowly up the cobbled path and depressed the bell on the front door. Within moments the door was lively swung open. 'Hi Beautiful! You're late! I missed you ten minutes!' Orlando said posing a grand smile and gave me a kiss. As I entered his home – there was a lovely aroma of garlic and onions. I slowly walked along the hallway were the walls were decorated with paintings that he'd created. 'Orlando! These are amazing. You studying 'Fine Art' seems natural to you,' I complimented. 'Well, I first learnt to paint in my mind. The degree course is just formality,' he chuckled. I followed him into the living area that was sparsely filled with a two-seater settee, small table, forty-two inch flat screen TV and the portrait he'd painted of me last week! 'You've put me on display!' I exclaimed. 'I paint and display significant people I met,' he stated. 'Oh,' I uttered feeling overwhelmed. We entered the dining room that was complete with a dining table suitable for six, which was set for two. It housed a bottle of wine, two glasses and a bottle of water. 'Right you be seated. I'll bring our Starters,' he informed and headed to the kitchen. 'I'll pour us some wine,' I shouted (keen to feed my nerves). 'Okay,' he replied from the kitchen. He returned with two bowls of soup and sat opposite me. 'Ummm, smells good,' I complimented. 'Thank you,' he replied and continued, 'You have a calm and caring nature that I'm attracted to. It makes me instantly want to care and love you. Will you let me?' A hot flush came over me – he wanted to 'care and love me?' Sounded strange. I didn't know what to say, but 'Life' yelled, 'Yes – Yes. I've needed taking 'care of' and 'love' for years. 'Yes,' I replied allowing 'Life' to lead. 'He took my hand and we kissed. He raised his glass and I raised mine. 'To caring and loving you,' he stated with a chuckle. 'Likewise,' I abstractly replied and we took a slip from our glasses. I looked at the bowl of soup, 'Looks lovely. What is it?' I asked. 'It's 'Rustic Italian bean and spinach soup – without bacon. I don't eat meat. So it's not completely authentic. Still, hope it's okay,' he informed. 'I'm cutting out meat too – so the omission of bacon is perfect,' I replied and sipped a mouthful. 'Oh my gosh – this is lovely! You're as good at cooking – as you are painting! Or is this out of a can?!' I teased. 'I'll show you all the fresh ingredients later,' he chuckled. We completed our soups. 'Ready for Main?' he asked. 'Yep! I replied with excitement. He fetched two plates. 'And what's this?' I asked inquisitively. 'Aubergine Caponata. Loaded with aubergines, and salty olives,' he informed. 'Ummm. I love aubergines and olives,' I shrieked and took a mouthful. Oh, Orlando! This is divine!' I remarked. We ate in silence for a while. 'The people we chose to be with, are the most significant part of life. Relationships are everything. I chose my company very carefully,' he stated with a smile. 'Yes. I'm beginning to realise the importance of relationships,' I agreed and continued, 'I like being with you Orlando. No-one has ever tried to know me like you or shown that they really care.' 'I know,' he said with confidence and abruptly change the atmosphere by ordering, 'Lets dance!' He turned up the Salsa music that was playing and grasped one of my hands and placed the other around my waist pulling me close to him. He began dancing and I tried to follow. 'You've got two left feet!' he laughed. 'Well, I've never danced Salsa before,' I retorted with a chuckle. 'Well, at least pretend,' he jested as he spun me around. We danced for about twenty minutes and ended up in shrieks of laughter. I enjoyed 'learning to dance Salsa' and he enjoyed 'watching me try'. 'I'm going to have another glass of wine,' I stated. 'A glass?' he asked sounding surprised and continued, 'We're not going to finish it. Red wine in moderation is great for cholesterol and breaking down foods. But, in excess the liver doesn't like it. Half is enough,' he advised sternly. 'Yeah, I know,' I agreed (yet feeling anxious that my nerves might need more than half a glass to feel satisfied). At 11.45pm I abruptly broke our conversation. 'Orlando, I think it's time I was leaving. It's getting late.' 'Oh, I'm enjoying your company. Aren't you enjoying yourself?' he enquired. 'Yes, it's just that...' He interrupted, 'Well then, why not stay, and leave tomorrow? You're enjoying yourself, and we haven't had our dessert yet,' he encouraged and informed. Again, I allowed 'Life' to take lead. 'Okay,' 'Life' replied. We continued talking and dancing...

* * *

Sat 1st Jul '00

3.35am: 'Let's go to bed. I'm shattered,' Orlando instructed. I didn't reply, but followed him as he took my hand, and lead us upstairs to 'bed'. We kissed, cuddled and stripped our clothes off. 'The bag might burst,' I blurted in a panic. 'We'll deal with 'might'. I want us to make love,' he comforted. He entered me and simultaneously, tears rolled out of my eyes (I was glad it was dark). The tears were a manifestation of overwhelming disbelief and joy. I was having sex – it was possible (even though I had a stoma)! Now I needed to 'relax' and 'enjoy making love'. And 'Life' told me all I needed to do was 'trust'. Trust that Orlando loved me enough to share his love – and I loved 'Life' enough to share mine.

9.30am: 'Morning Beautiful. Are you okay?' Orlando asked and rolled over to hug me. 'Yeah, I'm fine,' I lied feeling slightly, perturbed and still in shock – I'd had sex and enjoyed it – and 'I had a stoma'.

11.30am: arrived home. 'Oh! Enjoyed yourself with Orlando,' Mum asked with excitement. 'Yeah. Had a good chat and dance. Really enjoyed the evening,' I said with a broad smile. 'And, night, and morning!' Mum teased and we laughed.

I went upstairs to bed – I was in need of more sleep. I lay smiling and thinking, 'I'd had sex and enjoyed it – and I had a stoma!' And, I wasn't dreaming – Orlando was 'real'!

7.30pm: Getting ready for Rowels Surprise Party…

* * *

Sun 2nd Jul '00

3.30am: arrived home from the party with mixed feelings. It was nice meeting with 'old friends' and I'm thinking about Teresa who I met. Her brother died last week. She informed us by a note that she'd posted, and I didn't have the capacity to call her. When I met with Teresa – feelings of guilt consumed every cell in my body. 'Teresa I'm so sorry for not being in contact,' I 'apologised' with fleeting eye contact. 'That's Life. We're all doing the best that we can do,' she sadly replied in a convincing tone that increased my guilty feelings.

3.45am: Teresa's words are resonating, 'That's Life. We're all doing the best that we can do'. I wondered, 'When I 'didn't have the capacity to call her' – was it 'Life' doing the best 'I' could do?'

4.05am: retired feeling perturbed….

8.20am: woke up with Teresa on my mind and wrote a poem to show my sympathy for the loss of her brother. I titled it *The Loss if Today*.

> Today I…
> Lost my Brother –
> Someone so Dear to me,
> The pain I feel so sharp and deep –
> Can someone rescue me.
> Today I…

Lost respect for time,
As numbness overwhelmed –
The shock that my Brother stopped –
Yet, the ticking still prevailed.
Today I…
Wanted to scream and shout –
'Life is so unfair'
My sibling has left without warning,
And I was not prepared.
Today I…
Remember my Brother –
My feelings are so mixed.
But in all the pain and misery –
I know I will be fixed.

* * *

Mon 3rd Jul '00

6.30am: worrying about the vaccinations I'm going to have today. I don't want any of the recommended immunisations. I visualise adverse reactions from all of them. Yet, the adage 'Prevention is better than cure' prevails – not in my spirit (instinct), but in my 'logic' mind.

10.50am: arrived at the clinic feeling very tense. I sat thinking about the possible side-effects of the vaccinations – the toxins. And, I sat thinking of 'problems' I could tell the doctor that might exclude me from these so-called 'protections'. 'Samantha Shakes,' the doctor called into the waiting area. I reluctantly made my way to the room where he was. 'I've got an intolerance to eggs – do you think this might affect how Yellow Fever works in my body?' I blurted as soon as I entered the room. 'Do you have an allergic reaction?' he asked calmly. 'Yes,' I hurriedly replied. 'What happens?' he asked in the same calm manner. 'Well, nothing, but an allergy test showed a sensitive reaction,' I replied feeling stupid. 'Well if there are no visible signs or symptoms, you'll be fine,' he advised with a smile. Then he – opened a sterile packet that contained the Yellow Fever 'poison'. Then he – grasped a needle and attached it to the container. Then he – readied to pierce me – to intoxicate me. Then I – rapidly blurted, 'I've got an ileostomy' (hoping the omission of my colon might offer a reason not to administer this vaccine), but to my dismay, he advised, 'That's okay, having an ileostomy won't affect the way Yellow Fever works'. He asked me to roll my sleeve up and pierced my skin – injecting me with the 'poison' – damaging my muscles and inserting dis-ease into my whole body. 'Prevention is better than cure' – I lied to my spirit in an attempt to justify what had just happened. I sat worrying, 'How my body would react to this act, and felt guilty. Guilty that I'd allowed the Yellow Fever 'poison' into every cell in my body – in particular into my brain. I sat holding my arm. 'You can roll your sleeve down now,' he advised. And within moments of rolling my sleeve down – he was asking me to open my mouth to receive more dis-ease. He squirted 'Polio' into my mouth. I sat with my mouth open. 'Close your mouth and swallow,' he requested in a stern tone. I struggled not to heave, not because of the taste, but because my spirit and body was yelling, 'We don't want this!' I left the surgery looking for possible adverse effects. Even though the information leaflet stated that any effects wouldn't manifest until at least three days after administration.

* * *

Tue 4th Jul '00

6pm: Karen called. 'Sam... I'm calling from hospital. I had another Diabetic coma,' she moaned. 'Oh Karen. What are we going to do with you?' I asked in a sympathetic tone and continued, 'How are you feeling now?' 'Terrible. I'm sure it's the medication causing these comas. These doctors don't know what they're doing,' she said angrily. 'I thought you weren't taking the medication?' I quizzed. 'Well I take it when I feel rough,' she informed. So you're not taking them as prescribed – it will make a difference. Yet, as you've experienced and know, side-affects and secondary conditions will appear,' I stated. 'Have you told them you're not taking the medication?' 'No,' she answered sounding hopeless. 'Well you can't blame the doctors or the medication for these crises. The doctors work with what we present them with and the medication suppresses the crisis. I used to lie to the medics about my symptoms and taking medication. It's Fear and Denial and it's not useful. When you get out – we're going to start exercising together. You decide what you want to do – I'll follow,' I sternly stated. 'Okay,' she agreed in a sad tone.

8.30pm: I'm wondering what my exam results will be – they're published tomorrow.

* * *

Wed 5th Jul '00

2.30pm: Counselling. 'In some areas of my life things seem to be going well and in others it's a nightmare. After leaving the session last week. I felt the need to speak with Mum and Dad to release some of my anger and resentment, and to let them know how I was feeling. So I did. I told Dad, 'I felt not listened to, or able to express my anger as child and adolescent. And, that I was completely misunderstood and unfairly treated. He explained that he didn't know any other way to release his frustration apart from shouting, occasionally throwing something at the wall, or having a drink to suppress his emotions. That's the way he'd seen his Father manage. He said he never thought his angry outbursts were having an affect on me, as they weren't directed at me. We both ended up crying. Mum explained that she'd never been allowed to voice her opinion as a child, and was never shown any affection. And, so, keeping quiet and hiding emotions became natural to her. Gosh, 'if only' their parents had raised them 'right'. 'If only' their parents had given them the chance to express their anger and voice their opinion – I might not be in this situation. See how, *We are made up of the stories of others...* I concluded with a sigh. 'Ummm. I see,' Helen empathised and continued, 'What you've just explained is sometimes known as 'Learnt Behaviour.' We can use the experiences we've had with our parents to show us 'how not to do it'. For example, some people don't adopt the same behaviour like your Father did. What they do is the opposite and don't drink alcohol at all,' Helen explained. I left the session feeling relieved – realising that I didn't have to continue my 'Learnt Behaviour'. I could start revealing my thoughts – and stop using alcohol to suppress my emotions. It was up to me what I did with the experiences and history I'd had with my parents.

4.40pm: at University – in shock. I received borderline First Class grades for all three pieces of work! I stood staring at the board in amazement – 'Borderline First Class grades?' I checked the results lined up with my student number – they did?! I thanked the Almighty Creator.

6.30pm: arrived home. 'Yeah! I got 'borderline First Class grades in all three pieces of work,' I yelled as I entered. 'Well done Sam,' Mum cheered and hugged me. 'What's going on?' Sidiki shouted, as she joined us in the kitchen. 'I got borderline First Class grades!' I shrieked. 'Whoop! Whoop! We need to Celebrate,' she cheered and continued, 'I'm going to get a bottle of Champagne.'

* * *

Thu 6th Jul '00

8.50am: woken by pain down my sides, in my ribs and back. 'I need to relax?'

10.30am: pains are getting worse? And they don't feel like pain due to tension. They're shooting aches and I'm getting cramping muscular pain. 'Pain down my sides, in my ribs and back.'

11.45am: now I've got a 'fever'. 'Pain down my sides, in my ribs and back?' 'Yellow Fever!' These were 'Yellow Fever' symptoms! And, the leaflet stated that symptoms may present themselves after three days – today is 'day three'.

2pm: lying in bed. Shivering – sweating and with cramping pain in all my muscles. And, my head is pounding. Apparently, one of the side-effects are 'mild' symptoms of Yellow Fever'. 'Mild!' – I dread to think what 'severe' is.

7.30pm: lying in bed with my knees drawn up to my chest and clutching my sides – in agony...

* * *

Fri 7th Jul '00

1.10am: still awake in agony and feeling exhausted.

7am: woke up in agony.

7pm: been dozing in and out of sleep all day – still in pain.

Switched on my phone and there was a message from Orlando. I returned the called. 'Hi, Orlando,' I said in a croaky voice. 'What's wrong Beautiful?' he asked in an alarming tone. 'I'm in pain and I've got a fever – symptoms of 'Yellow Fever' from the vaccine,' I explained. 'Oh Beautiful, come over – I'll nurse you. Get in a taxi,' he instructed. 'But, I'll be miserable company,' I moaned. 'What else would we be when were feeling ill or in pain? There's a place for misery in the world,' he comforted and concluded, 'Call a taxi.'

8.30pm: arrived at Orlando's. 'Hi Beautiful. 'Right. I'll set you a bath with Chamomile oil, so you can relax and help speed up recovery' he said as soon as I arrived. I got in the bath where I relaxed for forty minutes, and Orlando washed and massaged my back. 'Right, on the agenda is Bed Rest,' he shouted from the bedroom. When I entered the room an aroma of lavender was present, and on each of the bedside cabinets, candles were burning. I climbed into bed. My pain and tension had been eased by soaking in the bath, and the lavender was inducing relaxation. Orlando entered the room with cups of Mint Tea and climbed into bed. We drank our tea. 'Night, Beautiful, 'he said kissing me and wrapped his body around mine. I felt Content – Relaxed and Loved and the pain and fever seemed to disappear. I fell into a deep sleep almost instantly.

* * *

Sat 8th Jul '00

8.45am: Orlando was up. 'Hey, Beautiful. How ya feeling?' he asked bending over and kissing my forehead. 'Rough, but better than I did yesterday,' I replied. 'Tea?' he asked. 'Yes please. A Dandelion to promote circulation and help rid of these awful symptoms,' I requested.

Spent most of today in Orlando's bed, whilst he done household chores, painted, and nursed me. 'Beautiful. What do you plan to do once you've graduated?' he asked. 'Ummm, perhaps share our experience of 'Health Matters', and enhance lives. Be part of a team that influences the National Health Service to provide care that's useful for our Wellbeing. I guess I want to be a 'Health Advocator', or whatever the title might be,' I informed with a chuckle. 'Oh, so that's why you studied Health Studies. You'll be good at advocating Health Matters. You've got experience and knowledge that people will benefit from. And if it's what you want to do – then you should do it,' he advised. 'Mum and Dad always encouraged me to follow my heart, and not to get stuck in a rut. 'If your heart changes – change with it', was Dad's motto.' 'That's why I'm studying for a second degree – first degree was in Information Technology (IT),' he explained. 'And what will you do once you've completed you're Fine Art degree?' I asked. 'Similar to what I'm doing now. Continue working in IT, but freelance, and less hours. I want to paint more. I like painting – that's why I'm studying 'Fine Art'. To cultivate my creative nature and enjoy others too,' he explained. 'The financial benefits of IT are useful – it's how I acquired this comfortable three bedroom house, complete with study, and dining room. However, it's now time I honoured my creative nature,' he concluded.

* * *

Sun 9th Jul '00

4pm: at home.

10.55pm: retiring still suffering from symptoms of Yellow Fever.

* * *

Mon 10th Jul '00

7.30am: woke up thinking, 'You would benefit from having a swim and sauna. They'd help rid of 'Yellow Fever'.

9am: swim and sauna.

12.35 – at home. In bearable pain.

10pm: retiring feeling a lot better – I think 'Yellow Fever' is almost out.

* * *

Wed 12th Jul '00

9.30am: read an article about the damaging effects of shift work (in particular night work). It suggested that it can cause fatigue, stress, irritability, difficulties in family and social contacts, and errors and accidents. There is an increased risk of gastrointestinal, cardiovascular diseases, and women shift workers can experience adverse effects on their hormonal and reproductive functions, and are more likely to suffer from anxiety and depression! All of the above was true to my experience, when I was up at night – and slept by day! Interesting – highlighted the necessity of sleeping at night.

2.30pm: Counselling. 'Hi Helen. 'It's weird, but I feel uncomfortable when I enjoy myself! I think I've got used to being a misery!' I chuckled. 'It's probably change. Changes can feel uncomfortable for us. However, as we adjust to the changes – the uncomfortable feelings disappear,' Helen reassured. I left feeling content – and with 'uncomfortable feelings of happiness!

* * *

Thu 13th Jul '00

8.50am: woke up feeling refreshed and energised.

3pm: swimming with Orlando. We raced – and competed 'Who could stay under the water the longest'. 'Orlando – I love being with you,' I told him on one occasion popping out the water, and kissed him.

7pm: at Orlando's. As I lay on the settee I reflected on my relationship with him. I never realised I could have so much enjoyment and so much in common with an intimate partner. I never realised relationships could be so much fun and healthy?! I walked over to Orlando who was reading and kissed him. 'What did I do to deserve that,' he quizzed with a smile. 'Nothing, just Love,' I shared.

* * *

Fri 14th Jul '00

12pm: lunch with Sidiki. 'Hi Sis. What you having,' I asked cheerfully. 'Something healthy that's all that's on offer – vegetables – pulses – vegan – vegan!' she teased. 'Sid. I don't think I've ever said 'Thank You' for being so understanding, listening to me, and putting up with my mood swings, as I struggled to manage the dreaded stoma. You made me laugh when I needed to – and cry when I had to. It meant so much. Not sure how I would have coped without you,' I said with tears in my eyes. 'Aargh. It was nothing – ain't that what sisters are for? Now let me tuck into this rabbit food,' she laughed.

7.50pm: to the cinema with Mum, Dad, Doreen and Mark. We watched 'Big Mamma's House'. We had a good laugh – and it felt good.

11.30pm: back at home. I thought, 'Its Friday – could have a drink'. But 'Life' felt Content – Relaxed – Loved'. And, I realised that I'd only drank alcohol twice (wine at Orlando's and Champagne celebrating grades) in nearly five weeks! 'I've only drank alcohol twice in nearly five weeks!' When did that happen?!

* * *

Sun 16th Jul '00

9.05am: woke up feeling very calm and relaxed. I felt so peaceful – I couldn't feel my heartbeat and wondered if I was alive! I could see my room – and all the objects in it – and I could move my limbs. But, I still wondered if I was alive. I pressed my hand hard on my chest to feel my heartbeat. I felt a faint rhythm – panic over – I was alive! Strange – feeling totally relaxed spurred panic! 'Changes can feel uncomfortable for us. However, as we adjust to the changes – the uncomfortable feelings disappear,' Helen had said. I guess this is one of the changes – feeling peaceful.

* * *

Mon 17th Jul '00

8.30pm: returned from Yoga class at University. I practise at home, yet I enjoy classes – socialising with fellow students.

* * *

Tue 18th Jul '00

2pm: lying in the garden looking up at the sky. I felt free as I absorbed its infinite 'Freedom'. I observed the wind – blowing around me – on me – where it liked without restriction – and I absorbed it's 'Freedom' also. I watched birds flying – dipping and diving – without restraint – and absorbed their 'Freedom' too. And, as I lay – absorbing these 'Freedoms' – I felt part of the World – instead of a stranger in it. And, I felt Content – 'Relaxed – 'Loved. Family – Friends – Orlando'.

* * *

Wed 19th Jul '00

9.30am: booked flights to Ghana!

2.30pm: Counselling. When you allow 'Life To Take Control' some really amazing things happen. 'Observation' and 'Experience' are now leading, and I'm remembering and using them,' I sighed. 'What do you mean?' Helen quizzed. 'Well, now I watch the outcome of my behaviour, consider what I've experienced and follow my instinct,' I explained, and continued, 'And, what usually follows is exactly what I've needed.' Helen advised that I'd reached the 'Awareness Stage'.

* * *

Thu 20th Jul '00

7pm: at Orlando's. 'Maverick's invited us to his place tomorrow. He's celebrating his Birthday,' Orlando informed. 'Oh, it will be nice to meet him – at last! He's one of your 'favourites',' I said. 'Yep! One of few friends,' he agreed.

* * *

Fri 21st Jul '00

8.30pm: arrived at Maverick's home. 'Hey! So this is the Angel! The one that can do no wrong! Nice to meet you Sam,' Maverick yelled upon opening the door and gave me a hug. 'You're so... You're so...' Orlando struggled to speak through his embarrassment and they hugged too. Orlando left us alone to fetch some wine. 'You know, he's only ever had two girlfriends in his life – one at Primary School and one at College. He's so choosy who he socialises with. It's an honour to have the presence and friendship of Orlando. And I sense it's the same for you – you're particular with who you relate with. You have an Angelic aura about you,' he complimented and continued, 'I think you deserve each other. And will have babies and live forever,' he laughed. 'Steady on. We've only been 'friends' since May,' I chuckled. 'Time and Space doesn't define Love,' he concluded...

* * *

Sat 22nd Jul '00

4.35am: arrived at Orlando's. 'What a lovely night. Maverick seems really nice,' I yawned as we got into bed. 'Yeah, he's alright. Guess that's why we've been friends since Primary School. Night Beautiful,' Orlando replied and kissed me. 'Night Orlando,' I answered.

11.30am: 'Morning Beautiful. We need leave by 12.30pm to get to Mum's and Dad's by 2pm. Mum will complain if we're late, and say the dinners been ruined – when really it's her cooking!' Orlando yawned with a chuckle. 'Well, you'd better get up then!' I teased and started tickling him.

2.15pm: arrived at Orlando's parents home in Hertfordshire. 'Oh, my goodness! Welcome Sam. Orlando told me you were Beautiful and you are!' His Mum shrieked upon opening the door and hugged me. 'Hi. Nice to meet you,' I nervously replied as I entered the six bed roomed house, complete with swimming pool. 'Hey Kid!' Orlando's Dad bellowed from the lounge, 'Come in and show me your Girlfriend!' 'Show?!' And, 'Girlfriend!' I felt very nervous as I followed Orlando into the lounge. 'Hi Dad.' Orlando introduced us, 'This is Sam. Sam, this is my Dad'. 'Wow! Look at you – my son Orlando's Girlfriend! Pleased to meet you,' he said standing up and shook my hand. 'You are 'Special'

– well you had to be. He's only had two Girlfriends – in his Life. One at Primary School – the other at College,' he informed. 'Sam, can you come and give me a hand,' Orlando's Mum shouted from the kitchen. I went to join her. 'So, I want to know. How did you meet and how's it all going?' she asked with excitement. 'We met at University and it's going very well,' I informed and continued, 'It's strange me having a partner,' I concluded. 'Well you really do have something in common with my Dear son. He too must be finding it 'strange' to have a partner. He hasn't had a Girl…' I interrupted her, 'I know, since Primary School and College. Maverick and your husband have told me,' I chuckled. 'Yes. We were getting worried about his reclusive personality. But he constantly told us, 'I'll get a Girlfriend – when I get a Girlfriend. And here you are,' she happily informed. 'I have never experienced a relationship like this before. Being with Orlando is so easy. He's encouraging and inspiring. I love his simplistic attitude with Life. I think that's been my downfall in the past. I've always complicated 'Living'. Orlando has showed me that 'Life' is 'simple', 'easy' and 'loving', I said in awe. 'That's lovely Sam. Orlando's enjoying you too – he thinks you're an Angel,' she chuckled. We carried the platters out and entered the dining room. It contained a very long table that could accommodate about twenty diners, and Orlando and his Dad were seated. Wine had been poured. 'Welcome Sam. This is a historic moment – my son Orlando has brought home a Girlfriend! A Beautiful one that we can see! And, he's told us that you're a loving one too. 'Alright, Dad – Alright. No need to go-on,' Orlando said sounding embarrassed. 'Alright, just let me finish, Son,' Orlando's Dad protested and concluded, 'So, the very best to the two of you.' He raised his glass and we all raised ours. 'You have a nice home,' I complimented, trying to distract my nervousness. 'Thank you,' Orlando's Mum replied and continued, 'We reaped the benefits of our labour,' she said sounding content. 'What was your labour?' I asked with interest. 'We opened a restaurant. He was good at cooking – I was good at organising. It seemed natural to open a restaurant and we loved it,' she said with a smile. 'She loved it! All she had to do was shift paperwork and make phone calls – I was the one doing the real work!' Orlando's Dad laughed and we joined him.

9.30pm: as we travelled home on the train. Orlando took out his familiar note pad and began writing. He then showed me what he'd written. It read:

Falling in Love with you – that's no 'Lie'.

Something kinda 'Beautiful' that I can't deny.

Are you in Love with me? Look me in the eye.

Doesn't matter what you say – the Spirit doesn't lie!

I smiled and looked him 'in the eye,' 'You're so silly Romantic!' I said and kissed him.

11.50pm: arrived at Orlando's and enjoyed sharing Love.

* * *

Sun 23rd Jul '00

8.30am: at home practising Yoga. During Relaxation Period I reflected on the Counselling sessions I've had. They've helped me review my perception and behaviour. I'm accepting the past and practising to live with 'today's knowledge' – not 'yesteryears abuse'. It's very relieving – and it's what 'Life' wants.

* * *

Mon 24th Jul '00

11am: Kevin called. 'Hi Sam. We're having a Bar-B-Q. on Saturday. Would be great if you and Orlando could make it,' Kevin cheerfully invited.

2pm: lying in garden. 'Hi Sam. Would you like to play Tennis? This Thursday, at 5.30pm?' Nina (neighbour) asked tip-toeing over our fence. 'Yeah!' I shrieked with excitement and continued, 'I've been meaning to talk to you about this since I got me 'Sports Protector', but forgot'. I've wanted to play Tennis for some time, but was scared that the stoma might be damaged if it got blasted by the ball. However, via an advert in an IA journal I saw a 'Sports Protector' and ordered one. When it arrived I thought, 'What the heck is this?!' It looked hideous (large plastic cap with a gap – and a detachable belt). Still it would allow me to play Tennis 'without fear' and 'safely'.

* * *

Tue 25th Jul '00

8.30am: thinking about the first of four Reflexology sessions that I'm having today, and I'm really looking forward to it. Apparently, Reflexology is good for stress, anxiety, tension, stimulating circulation, and insomnia – so, I thought I'd try it.

6pm: returned from Reflexology session. I'm lying on my futon with a headache, feeling weak, and nauseated. I understand this to be the 'Healing Crisis' which is when the body tries to eliminate toxins at a faster rate than they can be properly disposed of. And, apparently, the more toxic one's bodily systems are, the more severe the detoxification, or healing crisis. Drank water and retired.

10.05pm: woke up feeling lively. Every cell in my body felt energised and without symptoms I went to bed with!

10.30pm: retired – still feeling full of energy – yet, relaxed.

* * *

Wed 26th Jul '00

2.30pm: Counselling. 'Sam, this is our second from last session. We need to talk about saying 'Goodbye' and what you will put in place of these sessions,' Helen advised. There was a silence. I wasn't sure what I'd 'put in place'. 'Helen I'm not sure what I'd 'put in place', but Orlando might hear a bit more!' I chuckled and continued, 'I think I'll use my reflections in my journal and continue carrying out the useful actions and changes. Perhaps talking and knowledge has been exhausted,' I offered.

* * *

Thu 27th Jul '00

6.40am: woke up feeling full of energy. I think I'm still reaping benefits from Reflexology.

3pm: thinking about playing Tennis later with Nina.

7pm: returned from playing Tennis. I really enjoyed the match. Completely focused on hitting the ball and winning! Great Distraction – great Exercise and great Socialising. We decided to play every week.

9.30pm: called Orlando. 'Hi, Orlando. Can we meet in Camden tomorrow, about 10.30am, I need a pair of jeans?' I lied. 'Yeah, I could do with a new pair myself,' he replied. 'Okay. I'll see you tomorrow. Kisses to you,' I replied with excitement. 'Night, Beautiful,' he whispered. I didn't 'need a pair of jeans' – I'd purchased tickets for a Canal Boat Trip. I don't like surprises – but he does.

* * *

Fri 28th Jul '00

10.30am: 'Hey, Hi Beautiful,' Orlando said with a smile and we kissed. 'Right, let's make our way straight to the Lock,' I instructed. 'But, we're missing shops we could try for our jeans,' he contested. There was a silence and I handed him the tickets. 'No shopping for jeans today! We're going on a Boat Trip!' I shrieked. His face displayed shock. 'You said you needed a pair of jeans! You... You... Romantic Liar!' he chuckled with a pleased expression. I kissed him – feeling warm inside – I'd spurred his happiness.

11.15am: on-board 'London Water Bus' to London Zoo. The atmosphere was relaxing and peaceful. There's a calmness of water – that forces you to relax. When we arrived at the zoo there were giraffes overlooking us. They had a gracefulness that was nurturing. Animals are nurturing – they have a connection with nature that escapes foolish logic.

7.30pm: arrived at Orlando's. 'Thanks for arranging our outing. I've created a million paintings from the scenes along the canal… And cultivated 'Love' from being with you,' Orlando whispered in my ear, hugging me in the porch.

10.30pm: we readied for bed. 'Tea?' Orlando asked. 'Yes, please,' I accepted. We sat drinking in bed. 'I'm looking forward to the Bar-B-Q tomorrow. It'll be nice meeting Kevin and Anne,' Orlando said, whilst yawning, 'Night Beautiful,' he concluded and kissed me.

* * *

Sat 29th Jul '00

7.30am: woke up and Orlando was still sleeping. I crept out of bed and made a cup of tea. I prepared Muesli with yoghurt and fruits for our breakfast. When I heard him stirring – I took our breakfast into the bedroom. 'Oh thanks, Beautiful. Just what me tummy ordered!' he chuckled.

2pm: arrived at the Bar-B-Q. 'Sam we need a secretary for IA Greater London West branch. Can you help us fulfil this role?' Rod asked. 'Yeah. It'll be my pleasure! You – IA was invaluable when I first had Stoma Surgery. And it because of volunteers like you that we get help. I'd love to be able to support others,' I agreed with excitement. 'Oh, Thanks, Sam. We meet once a month. The next meeting is on Monday 21st August,' he informed. 'Right, I'll place that date in my diary,' I said, feeling privileged that I'd been asked to undertake such a position.

9.20pm: returned from Bar-B-Q at Orlando's. 'So you're going to be a secretary,' he sighed. 'Yep!' I confirmed, excitedly. 'Be mindful that you don't take on too much, Sam,' he advised.

* * *

Sun 30th Jul '00

9.30am: 'Let's have a lazy day,' I suggested. We spent most of the day in bed kissing, cuddling and sharing our love.

* * *

Mon 31st Jul '00

8.30am: lying in bed feeling excited about going swimming later with Trevor, his son, his nephew, Doreen and Mark.

11am: Swimming. We played 'Piggy in the Middle' and 'Had' in the pool. We ate lunch at the Poolside Cafe. I had a nice talk with Trevor

303

and an enjoyable swim. And, I observed that 'Little People' (children) are not half as 'insane' as adults! Really enjoyed this outing.

9.30pm: feeling tired and relaxed! And this 'natural tiredness' and 'natural feeling of relaxation' feels great. Expelled brown discharge (telling me that my body is at 'ease'. And, I know this is due to Reflexology – Tennis – Swimming – Saunas and Yoga!

10.30pm: retired.

* * *

Wed 2nd Aug '00

2.30pm: Counselling. 'Right, Sam. As you know this is our final session. Would you like to talk about what you've accomplished and what you will do?' 'I've heard you make some great reflections that you think have really helped. In particular, appreciating others intentions, knowing your limitations, and forgiving,' Helen reflected. 'Ummm. I've been thinking about this ending, and there has been some moments of panic. I've found these Counselling sessions very useful – they've helped solve a lot of problems,' I sighed. 'Yes, you've done well, Sam... I know we've spoken about this session as an 'ending', do you see it as anything else?' Helen probed. 'Yes, I do. As I thought about this 'Ending' I realised that there was also a new 'Beginning' that feels very exciting. I've uncovered my problems, found solutions, and it's now time to allow 'Life to Live'. Counselling is now redundant, along with most of my problems,' I explained with a sense of overwhelming liberation. 'I think you'll be fine,' Helen said with a grand smile and she got up and hugged me. I had tears in my eyes. I don't like 'Endings', but I like new 'Beginnings'.

6pm: out jogging with Karen. 'This is our forth week jogging twice a week,' Karen panted. 'Yes, I know. You're doing well,' I replied. 'How do you feel?' I continued. 'Much better. Blood Sugar Levels in control. I don't feel as moody and I've got so much energy! I never realised exercise could do all this!' she exclaimed with excitement. 'Oh, yes – it – can,' I replied. 'I'm playing Tennis with my neighbour tomorrow. Why don't you join us?' I invited. 'Tennis! Never played before!' she exclaimed. 'Well now's your chance!' I encouraged. 'Okay, I will,' she replied.

* * *

Thu 3rd Aug '00

5.30pm: Tennis with Nina. Karen joined us. 'That was excellent – good fun! And, I read that the conditioning affects of Tennis helps the Immune System function – so more resistance to dis-ease! A win win activity! Having and fun and promoting Wellbeing! Can I play again next week?' Karen shrieked, jumping around. 'What, losing matches is fun?! Yeah, you can play next week – it'll be 'fun' having two people to beat!' Nina jested. 'It will be nice winning for a change!' I joked. 'Yeah, well I won't be a novice forever,' Karen remarked with a chuckle, and we all laughed.

* * *

Fri 4th Aug '00

12pm: accompanied Uncle Solomon to purchase grocery shopping.

7.30pm: arrived home.

* * *

Sun 6th Aug '00

Been at Orlando's since Saturday.

* * *

Wed 9th Aug '00

Received a letter from Toni asking if I could do another lecture! This time for two hours! Gosh I really do have a place in this World!

2.30pm: would have been having Counselling if the sessions hadn't ended. I've got ambivalent feelings. The prevailing feeling is relief and I feel strange, but not uncomfortable.

* * *

Thu 10th Aug '00

5.30pm: Tennis. 'Hi, Sam and Karen. I can't afford to play Tennis any-more. So next week will be the last one for me,' Nina informed.

8.30pm: arrived at Orlando's. 'Hey, Beautiful, I'm in here making up the bed. Maverick's staying tomorrow night. This is his favourite room. It's where he always sleeps,' Orlando informed. 'Oh, does he stay of-ten?' I asked. 'Whenever he like's. He hasn't stayed for a while. Telling me it's because he doesn't want to get in the way of us! I told him that's 'impossible', but he thinks it's important that we establish some space in here – for us. Shawn and Peter stay whenever they like too. That's why I purchased a three bed roomed house. So that friends and family can stay over. Sometimes people need a break from their environment and I love being able to offer these spaces,' he explained. 'That's so nice, Orlando,' I replied. 'Well, what else would a single person purchase a three bed roomed house for? Unless they were into dusting and tidy rooms?!' He chuckled.

10.30pm: 'I'm looking forward to our Bike Ride tomorrow,' Orlando yawned. 'Me too,' I replied, gave him a hug and snuggled up to him to retire.

* * *

Fri 11th Aug '00

10am: met Karen and Maverick at train station to travel to Enfield for Bike Ride into Cheshunt.

7.30pm: we arrived back at local train station. 'I've only ever used my bike to do daily chores like shopping, going to the library, and to the park. Never thought about going on a 'Bike Ride' – using it for leisure purposes. I enjoyed it – Thanks for arranging this Maverick,' I said. 'Yeah, Thanks, Maverick. I only used my Bike for commuting to work – now it has another use – Enjoyment! And, it was nice getting out of London – the Fresh Air and Scenery – very energising,' Karen commented before departing. Myself, Orlando, and Maverick cycled home (to Orlando's).

* * *

Sat 12th Aug '00

10am: left Orlando's early to allow him and Maverick time alone.

11.30am: arrived home and decided to go to the park.

12.30pm: in the Park. I'm lying on a blanket and feel wonderful. The sun is beating on my back – the breeze is cooling and refreshing. The branches are being swayed by the breeze, and the rustle of the leaves are reminding me that I'm outside and close to nature. I feel very relaxed and as I lay – it's almost as if the earth is pulling me into peacefulness.

* * *

Mon 14th Aug '00

7pm: visited Sally (patient in hospital who'd requested a visit). 'Hi,' I greeted cheerfully. 'Oh, hi, you must be Sam, the Visitor. Doesn't look like you've had this awful operation,' she replied. There was a silence. 'No, it doesn't. So you've been told you need surgery?' I confirmed. 'Yeah. And, I'd like to see the stoma – and know how you've managed – and if can you do the same as before – and what about relationships and sex,' she rapped. I showed her the stoma – explained how I'd managed – and told her about my relationship with Orlando. 'Why do you think you have UC?' I asked. 'I have no idea,' she replied with a puzzled expression. 'I think you can get rid of UC,' I advised. 'I don't think so! That's why it's come to this. There is no other way,' she retorted. 'Okay,' I calmly responded.

I left feeling disheartened. It was obvious that this 'patient' had a fixed idea – she'd decided that she 'had to have' the operation. I felt sad – she was going to have radical surgery when she didn't have to! Why wouldn't she listen to me? Then 'Life' spoke to me, 'It doesn't matter that she hasn't listened to you. What's important is that you offered an alternative approach – it's up to her what she does with this – you have no control over her actions.' My discouraged feelings – lifted.

* * *

Tue 15th Aug '00

4pm: Reflexology (last one of four). These sessions have been really beneficial. They have uncovered underlying dis-ease (Thyroid – Repetitive Strain – Circulation) and I've adopted remedies and practices to help. For my thyroids – I'm eating Asparagus and Spinach – and taking Kelp. For my Repetitive Strain – I'm taking more breaks when using the computer, and use a Wrist Rest. And, I'm doing twenty minutes a day of aerobic exercise to improve my circulation. And, my energy has increased.

* * *

Thu 17th Aug '00

5.30pm: Tennis. 'Aargh, Nina, shame this is our last match,' I whined. 'You and Karen will continue to play – won't you?' Nina suggested. 'Yeah, still, I'm going to miss our matches and catching-up,' I replied. 'Yeah, it's only been two matches and meetings, but I'm going to miss you too!' Karen added and gave Nina a hug.

10.30pm: at Orlando's. 'Night Beautiful,' Orlando said and kissed me 'Goodnight.' 'Night Orlando,' I replied giving him a hug. I felt his heartbeat – it was rapid. I recognised this as anxiety. 'What's the matter, Orlando?' I asked. 'Nothing, just feeling a bit nervous about meeting your family tomorrow,' he sighed. 'Ohhh, I understand why. They all have two heads, breathe fire, and they don't like nice people like you!' I joked. He began tickling me and we ended up in roars of laughter.

* * *

Fri 18th Aug '00

6.30pm: myself and Orlando arrived at Bond Avenue. Everyone was in the lounge watching the TV. 'Hi. This is Orlando. Orlando this is my Mum, brother Mark, and sisters Doreen, and Sidiki,' I introduced. 'Oh. I've heard a lot about you' – 'Hi' – 'Hello' – Hi Orlando,' they said in turn. 'Hi,' he responded nervously. We chatted (about nothing in particular) and watched TV.

9pm: arrived at Orlando's. Prepared a picnic for our trip to Brighton tomorrow.

* * *

Sat 19th Aug '00

11am: arrived at Brighton. We laid, allowing the sea breeze to soothe our minds, and the waves and chirping Seagulls to be music to our ears. We raced along the sea edge getting our feet wet and played 'Had'. As we sat on the pebbled beach, a Seagull swooped down and took a slice of our bread! Orlando sprung up and began chasing it. 'Hey give us back our bread thief!' he chuckled twisting and turning his run to follow the Seagull in flight. 'Ohhh, he wasn't stealing, just joining our picnic,' I shrieked with laughter. And, as he chased the 'thief', another one came and took one more slice! 'Hey Orlando get him too!' I roared with laughter and he began chasing the second thief.

12.50pm: arrived at Orlando's. We stayed at Brighton until dark – under the moon. 'Gosh... What... An... Amazing... Day,' I said, pausing to kiss him at each word, as we hugged in the porch. 'Yes... It... Was,' he agreed with the same jester and a smile.

* * *

Sun 20th Aug '00

8.40am: Breakfast with Orlando.

2.30pm: leaving Orlando's. 'Right, Orlando. See you in a months' time,' I said trying to contain my sadness. 'Yep, 'in a months time',' he repeated. We kissed... and kissed.... and kissed. 'Take care of yourself, Beautiful,' he ordered. 'You too,' I replied, and hastily left. Tears had filled my eyes and I didn't want him to see them. Silly me. I felt sad – I wasn't going to see My Sweetheart for over a month.

As I walked to the Bus Stop and the distance between myself and Orlando widened – the tears became plentiful and streamed out of my eyes. I wasn't going to see My Sweetheart for over a month – and I was already missing him.

* * *

Mon 21st Aug '00

6pm: first IA meeting. 'Thank you for agreeing to be Secretary, Sam. We really appreciate it,' Rod commented after introducing me to the members of the Committee. 'It's my pleasure,' I replied. And, it really was.

10pm: at home packing for trip to Ghana – leave tomorrow!

* * *

A Sense Of Freedom

4am: getting ready to travel to London Heathrow Airport. Our flight leaves at 7.40am.

TRAVEL JOURNAL

7pm: Ghanaian time – we arrived! I've given thanks to the Almighty Creator for our safe journey and for the chance of being here. The air smells fresh – the temperature cool and welcoming. 'Akwaaba Lady Samantha – Welcome Lady Samantha,' a man bellowed from a barrier marked 'Arrivals'. 'Uncle Kobena?' I quizzed. 'Yes,' he replied with a glorious smile. 'Oh, there's Rass,' Steve blurted pointing to a man standing behind the same barrier. I pushed Steve in his wheelchair towards him. We introduced each other and then departed for our homes in Ghana.

8.30pm: myself and Uncle Kobena arrived 'home' and a man opened the gates to the entrance of the eight bed roomed house and we drove through.

10.30pm: lying wondering if I should tell members of the household that I have a stoma. My luggage bags have been carried in, doors opened, and tea waiting when I arrived. There was a sign on the door of the room that I'm staying in, that read: 'Welcome Samantha' in gold writing. The room contained a double bed with matching curtains and bed sheets. I've been treated like 'Royalty'. But, I don't want any 'special treatment' – I want to fit in with minimum fuss... And, the hospitality feels overwhelming.

* * *

Wed 23rd Aug '00

3pm: Nanyanika knocked on my door. 'Dinner's ready for you,' she informed. I followed her to the dining room. There was a table laid for one person and fit for a Queen! There was Yam in a china decorative bowl with lid – stewed meat in a similar bowl – an empty plate with shining cutlery – a bowl of water (to wash hands) – and a packet of napkins. All were sheltered under a netted cover! Sisi was seated away from the table and ate from a ready served plate on a tray. 'Nanyanika, it isn't necessary for you to do all this. I'd prefer my next dinner served like that, please,' I requested, pointing to Sisi's plate. This act quashed my deliberation – I wouldn't tell anyone that I had a stoma. 'I don't want 'special treatment' – I want to fit in – with minimum fuss'.

* * *

Thu 24th Aug '00

6.30am: the household is awake! We're having breakfast – at 6.30am! 'You people don't understand the value of the Extended Family,' Uncle Kobena chatted. Instead of utilising your own members you'd rather hire strangers to do your chores. You have useful members, but instead of paying them and supporting them in their careers – you encourage them to work for others and struggle – crazy! You people watch more TV than talk – you buy more clothes in a Fashion Season that can last a lifetime! Buy machines that are unnecessary and make us human beings redundant. Instead of talking and working with each other – you gawp at TV, clothes and items in shops! I've never been to London – and I have no intention to. When I travel I want to be enlightened – not introduced to lies of contentment,' he proclaimed. 'Ummm,' I sighed in agreement.

4.30pm: myself, Nkrumah, Nanyanika and Sisi were eating. 'Let's go to Labardi Beach tomorrow,' Sisi suggested. 'Oh, yes! I love the beach,' I said with excitement. 'Okay, let's all be ready to leave at 10.30am,' he said.

* * *

Fri 25th Aug '00

11.30am: at Labardi Beach. The beach had white sand, sea rolling with silver waves, and palm trees. There were people with horses offering rides. There were carvers making and selling wooden artifacts – there were people selling cooked food – and there were footballers. And, the Sun beamed on us all. We lay on the sand – ate fried fish – dipped in and out of the sea – and played 'Had'...

3.30pm: we left the beach. I really enjoyed today.

* * *

Sat 26th Aug '00

7.10am: practising Yoga.

7.30pm: speaking with Nanyanika and Nkrumah. 'Samantha, what's it like living in London?' Nanyanika asked. 'Well, the pace is so fast that sometimes it's difficult to contact family and friends, which can make it a challenge to care for each other. If you're into 'Education and Training' there are loads of courses available – and London is twenty-four hours – it doesn't sleep, there's always something to do!' I shared. 'It sounds like a place to visit – not live! How can the pace be so fast that it's difficult to contact and care for each other – that doesn't make sense!' Nanyanika chuckled with bemusement.

* * *

Sun 27th Aug '00

5.30am: I could hear footsteps, chatting, and cutlery clinking?! Sounded like everyone in the house was awake – and they were! There was a knock at my door. 'Morning, Samantha,' Nanyanika greeted as she opened the door and continued, 'Are you ready for breakfast. We eat early on Sunday, because we have to travel to church,' she explained. 'Oh, I'll eat a bit later. I'm not going to church,' I yawned. She looked horrified and said, 'I think you should come. In this household everyone goes to Church – unless they're sick. It's an opportunity to say 'Thank You to God for all the Blessings we've received throughout the week, and to pray for others who are sick and in need. Don't you want to do that?' she asked in a serious tone. 'Yes, but I do that daily – when I Meditate and practice Yoga,' I replied. 'That's solitude – we congregate to offer support – and it helps to maintain togetherness,' she concluded. 'Ummm,' I uttered thinking, 'I'm not a 'Christian!' But what Nanyanika said, sounded like the 'Truth' – it sounded like 'Life'... I went to Church.

9.30pm: packing for three day trip to Kumasi, tomorrow. Myself, Steve and Nkrumah are travelling.

10.15pm: retired.

* * *

Mon 28th Aug '00

8am: at coach station. 'Hey Steve – you're walking!' I shrieked. 'Yeah, well, hobbling with my stick,' he chuckled. 'Yeah! Yeah! You're walking! What's happened in the last six days – some sort of miracle?!' I jested. 'It's the Rest – the Fresh Food – the Sun – and the Love,' he reported with a chuckle.

1pm: arrived in Kumasi. We relaxed, chatted, and ate in the hotel for the rest of the day.

* * *

Tue 29th Aug '00

8.30am: getting ready to visit Kumasi Market (Africa's second largest market). As we approached I was astonished by the display and at-mosphere. There were souvenir items such as hats, scarves, and bags depicting the Ghanaian flag and colours. There were Wooden Carv-ings ranging from furniture stools, benches and chairs, to ornamental sculptures. And, there was a variety and quantity of foods in heaps – Tomatoes, Egg Plants, Wild Mushrooms, Spinach, Bananas, Yams, and Rice (Orlando would have loved this place)! Sellers seemed to be everywhere – sitting along the street, behind stalls, and on walls. Peo-ple were chatting – negotiating, eating, feeding babies, singing, plating hair, cooking, shopping. 'Life' was happening in many roles – and I felt like part of, each and every one of them – the atmosphere was warm, inviting, and exciting.

* * *

Wed 30th Aug '00

11.15pm: arrived back 'home' to Accra from Kumasi.

I can't believe what I did on the coach journey back. The bag was filling up with gas and was in desperate need of emptying. However, when we stopped at a rest area there were only communal urinals available! I got back on the coach, hoping that the bag would last the remaining two hour journey to Accra. But, about forty-five minutes into the trip, the bag was about to explode! I'd passed more gas and the bag was pull-ing away from my abdomen. It would either ease off or burst, before the end of the journey – shit would be everywhere! I began to panic, but then calmly told myself to 'think of a solution'. I sat trying to think of an idea. Then one came! It was quite dark in the coach and we were travelling through suburban areas, where the stench of cattle dung was filtering through the vents. I could release the gas from the bag on the coach! The stench of my gas was no match for the cattle's dung. I looked at the passenger sitting next to me – he was dozing, so wouldn't notice me undoing my jeans. I slumped back in my seat, undone my jeans and pulled the tail end of the bag out and upwards. I released the clip, and pressed gently down on the bag, until all the gas eased out! 'Crisis' and 'Panic' over!

* * *

Mon 4th Sept '00

10.30am: Oko and I visited Elmina Castle. The Tour Guide explained that people were captured and restrained in this building to be made Slaves for the Transatlantic Slave Trade. People were placed in areas with no light and little oxygen where temperatures are scorching. He explained that in these areas people were dying from disease, excreting, vomiting, and eating. Blood was present (women menstruating). 'Any resistance to this captivity was met with starvation, beatings, sexual abuse, and death,' he concluded. I'd read about 'Slavery' and heard accounts via History Events, but actually being in one of the significant places was more emotive than I'd imagined. Tears filled my eyes – and Oko rubbed my shoulder to offer comfort. As we travelled home, I thought about what people had been put through for the sake of money. Tears filled my eyes again, as I wondered, 'How did material wealth became more valuable than Life?'

7pm: arrived home.

8.30pm: the familiar knocks on my door began and we flocked for our evening chat. 'Samantha, you look unhappy,' Oko said with concern. 'Yeah, I feel sad about the way human beings treat each other for the sake of money,' I replied in a depressing tone. 'Oh, Samantha, let history be the past. Think of how you would rewrite it, and live it,' Oko said. 'Yeah, we see evidence of the horrible history every day. What we say is 'That was the past – this is the present,' Nanyanika stated.

11pm: lying recalling Oko's words, 'Oh, Samantha, let history be the past. Think of how you would rewrite it, and live it.' Reminded me of some of the exercises in Holder's book. And, what profound advice.

* * *

Fri 8th Sept '00

4.30pm: returned from Labardi Beach. We've been going almost every day! 'Aren't you people afraid of turning in Tilapia Fish!' Uncle Kobena roared with laughter when he saw us entering the house with wet towels (yet again).

8pm: been capturing experiences by taking photos and mental memories, so haven't been writing much. Still, I wanted to note that I've been busy. Visited Legon University, WEB Dubois Centre, Aburi Botanical Gardens, Mokola Market, and to Dansoman to visit Steve.

* * *

Sat 9th Sept '00

'Happy Birthday Nkrumah. This is for you,' I smiled and handed him a wrapped parcel. 'Oh, Samantha, why?' he asked looking embarrassed. He opened the parcel that contained a text book titled *The Electrician at Work*. 'Oh, thank you. You're helping me make a decision,' he smiled. 'Yes, I am. You said you weren't sure if you should pursue a career as an Electrician, or working for The Military. I think an occupation as an Electrician is preferable to joining the Military,' I affirmed with a smile.

In the book I'd written:

> *Nkrumah*
> *I'm praying for your success. Keep your focus on electrical work. It is far better to love than support defence and killing.*
> *Love Sam*

* * *

Sun 10th Sept '00

6.30am: woke up thinking about Aunty Celia – it's been two years since she 'passed away'. I lay crying – missing her and feeling very sad. I then recalled the joyful times we'd shared, and feelings of happiness prevailed.

7.30pm: went to the 'Canadian Spot Bar'. I had a brandy with fruit juice. And, for a fleeting moment – I thought 'I might begin drinking daily'… The brandy reduced my sadness about missing Aunty Celia, but then it also reduced my happiness of reminiscing on the time we'd had together… And, the thought of drinking daily disappeared – I didn't want to drown my happiness.

* * *

Mon 11th Sept '00

7.30pm: 'We've been flocking to your room every evening for the past two weeks, Samantha. Is it okay?' Oko asked with a smile. 'Of course! I've been enjoying our chats,' I replied. There was a knock on the door. 'Lady Samantha! You have taken away our small need of a TV – you're our new amusement! Good that you don't consume any energy – you would cost us a fortune!' Uncle Kobena roared with laughter. 'You're all great entertainment too – glad I don't have to pay – I'd be in debt!' I jested and we all laughed.

* * *

Sat 16th Sept '00

11.30am: to Labardi Beach – last day in Ghana.

7.30pm: at the Canadian Spot Bar with Nkrumah. 'Can't believe I've been in Ghana for nearly four weeks. I feel sad leaving your home where I've experienced Comfort – Joy – Love – and Peace,' I reflected. 'We have enjoyed you too, Samantha. And, I've learnt a lot from you – mostly, that not all people from England are miserable!' he teased.

* * *

Sun 17th Sept '00

10.30am: leaving my 'home' in Accra to return to London. 'Hey, Samantha! We're going to miss you,' Nanyanika said sadly as she hugged me. 'Where will we flock in the evenings? Your room – our nest will be no more without you!' Oko teased. 'I'm going to miss our trips to Labardi,' Sisi chuckled. I got into Uncle Kobena's car. 'Return!' Nkrumah shouted as Uncle Kobena slowly drove along the driveway. Tears filled my eyes and Uncle Kobena noticed them. 'It's not a Death – Lady Samantha – you can come back!' He roared with laughter. 'I know – I'm so silly,' I said and forced a chuckle.

12.30pm: we arrived at the airport. 'Bye, Lady Samantha. We're only six hours away – and you are always welcome,' Uncle Kobena said as we hugged 'Goodbye.' 'Thank you for everything, Uncle Kobena. I really enjoyed my stay – I've acquired a new family,' I said struggling not to cry.

* * *

5.55pm: arrived at London Heathrow Airport and Orlando was waiting for us! 'Hey! Hi Beautiful,' he yelled from the barricaded side. 'Sweetheart! What a lovely surprise,' I shrieked wanting to quicken my pace, but restraining myself, as I guided Steve who was walking unsteadily with his stick. It seemed like it took a long-time to get to Orlando and as soon as I did – I hugged him tightly. 'Gosh – I've missed you,' I confessed. 'Don't you ever do that again,' he said kissing me firmly. 'Do what,' I quizzed. 'Go away for so long without me,' he chuckled with a smile.

7.35pm: arrived home. 'Samantha! We missed you. How was it – how was Ghana,' Mum rapped, hugging me as I entered. 'Mum it's an amazing place and the culture of people – generally, 'Loving and Caring'. They look after their own children, eat breakfast and converse before starting the day,' I shared.

* * *

Mon 18th Sept '00

6pm: IA meeting.

10.30pm: at Orlando's. 'It's nice having you back,' Orlando said as we cuddled in bed. 'It's nice to be back,' I replied and snuggled up closer to him.

* * *

Fri 22nd Sept '00

6.30pm: arrived at Orlando's. 'What's all this?' I asked looking at the range of vegetables, and pulses on the kitchen sideboard. 'I'm preparing salads and a vegetable curry for Sidiki's 18th Birthday party tomorrow,' he said. 'Oh, Sweetheart – she's going to be so pleased,' I said giving him a kiss.

10.30pm: 'Night Sweetheart. I'll call a taxi at 9am tomorrow, so we can get these salads to Bond Avenue early, and help Sidiki prepare for her party. 'Okay. Night, Beautiful,' Orlando agreed giving me a kiss.

* * *

Sat 23rd Sept '00

10.30am: arrived home. 'What you got there?' Sidiki asked with a smile when she saw us carrying the plastic containers with curry and salad into the kitchen. 'Foods for a Special Young Lady and her guests. Happy Birthday,' Orlando replied and gave her a kiss. 'Potato Salad – Coleslaw – Green Salad – and Curried Chickpeas – Ummm. Thank You!' Sidiki shrieked and gave Orlando a hug and kiss.

10pm: 'Happy Birthday to You!' We (and about forty-five guests sung). Mum began passing plastic cups around and Dad opened two bottles of Champagne and served the guests. Several Party Poppers were exploded and we all cheered. Orlando played Stevie Wonder's song 'Happy Birthday' and we starting singing and dancing around Sidiki, who was waving one arm and sipping Champagne with the other...

* * *

Sun 24th Sept '00

4.30am: the guests had left. 'Wow! There was a party going on,' Orlando exclaimed as we cleaned and tidied up. There were plastic cups on the floor – on the table – and on the kitchen sideboards. Paper plates half filled with food were littered on the stairs, in the lounge, and kitchen. There were streams of Party Poppers everywhere and CDs were out of their cases. Ripped wrapping paper and Sidiki's gifts were strewn on the lounge floor. 'Thanks for all your help,' Sidiki slurred and staggered to us (intoxicated with alcohol) giving me and Orlando a hug.

5.45am: myself and Orlando travelled to his home.

* * *

Mon 25th Sept '00

3pm: Enrolled at University and met RAC Society Chairman to discuss and prepare for first meeting.

* * *

Tue 26th Sept '00

1.45pm: at University. After the lecture the lecturer announced that we should elect a Student Representative. The role includes liaising between staff and students reporting issues to academic staff and reporting back responses to Students, and requires being a Board of Study member.

* * *

Thu 28th Sept '00

5pm: Elections for Student Representatives – I was elected!

* * *

Fri 29th Sept '00

9.30am: rang University Sports Centre for information about playing Tennis and then called Karen. 'Hi, Karen. Just to let you know. We can book Tennis courts at University four weeks in advance,' I informed her. 'Okay. Let's do that,' she said with excitement.

3pm: at Orlando's. 'You're doing so much. Patient talks at universities – member of Lank's Hospital – visiting people in hospital and at home – RAC Society Secretary – Student Representative – IA secretary – and this weekend training to become a telephone counsellor for IA,' Orlando reflected. 'Gosh, sounds like a lot. Got to keep busy'! I declared.

* * *

Sat 30th Sept '00

10am: arrive at Hotel to pursue two days training for IA Counselling course.

* * *

Sun 1st Oct '00

4pm: concluded first part of IA Counselling course.

7.30pm: arrived at Orlando's. 'I missed you – weekends aren't weekends without you,' Orlando greeted giving me a kiss and continued, 'How was it Beautiful?' 'Interesting. Loads of reflection, as we focused on how beneficial we'll be for others. And, a great opportunity to evaluate where we're at, regarding having a stoma,' I explained.

* * *

Tue 3rd Oct '00

12.30pm: Met Karen for lunch. 'Sam I never realised that foods had such an effect on our Wellbeing,' Karen said as she tucked into her green salad. 'Let thy food be thy medicine and thy medicine be thy food – I think is what Hippocrates said,' I chuckled in a deep tone. 'I've been eating healthier and my energy has increased so much,' she shrieked. 'Yes, I can hear!' I jested.

* * *

Wed 4th Oct '00

6.30pm: myself and Karen played Tennis. 'Look forward to thrashing you again next week!' I joked. I felt full of energy after the match and my mind had no thoughts of 'Things To Be Done!'

* * *

Fri 6th Oct '00

7.15am: at Orlando's. 'Morning Beautiful. Ready for our Gardening Adventure?' Orlando asked. 'Yep! I'm all Green Fingered and raring to dig! What are we going to do?' I asked. 'Sow Broad Beans, Spinach, and Lettuce seeds,' he informed.

9.30am: in garden. 'Orlando, where did you learn to farm?' I asked. 'In our garden – Dad taught me. He used to grow vegetables and herbs at the back of our garden. Use them for ingredients in the restaurant, and sell any surplus to customers. It was extra profit, great nutritional value, and made great Public Relations. Dad would highlight the ingredients from our garden on the menu. 'Local' and 'Home Grown Produce' and customers would pay more, especially as they came from 'Raphael Mancini's' garden – the owner and chef whose food they adored,' he explained. 'Gosh, your Dads a smart man,' I exclaimed. 'Naw he ain't. He just followed suit – his Dad did the same!' Orlando laughed.

* * *

Sat 7th Oct '00

9.30am: 'Right. Do you need help preparing dinner for our guests?' I offered. 'Naw. It's pretty straightforward. I'm going to do a Green Salad – followed by Chana Masala – and Fruit Cocktail for dessert. Does that sound okay?' he asked. 'Sounds perfect, Sweetheart. Karen loves Green Salad, Chickpeas, and Fruit,' I reassured.

7pm: Maverick and Karen arrive. 'Orlando this is delicious! What dressing have you used?' Karen complimented as she chomped on her salad. 'Secret,' Orlando replied. 'More like 'out of a jar',' Maverick teased. We chatted, played few Card Games, and Chess...

* * *

Sun 8th Oct '00

2.30am: 'Right, I'm off,' Karen announced and continued, 'I've had a lovely evening. Orlando – you're an excellent Chef,' she complimented, and gave Orlando a kiss. 'Hey! Back off – he's mine,' I teased and continued, 'I'll call you a cab.' Karen and I waited in the porch. 'Sam. Orlando is such a nice person – you deserve each other,' Karen commented with a smile. 'Ummm, I feel very fortunate that we met. I never knew such a relationship could exist – it feels 'perfect',' I said in awe. The taxi arrived and we said 'Goodbye'. 'Where's Maverick?' I asked when I returned to the lounge. 'Gone to bed – and I'm off too,' Orlando replied. 'Me too!' I added. 'Night Sweetheart. And Thanks for making us such a wonderful meal,' I complimented as we got into bed.

5.30pm: 'Sweetheart, I'm going to have a nap,' I told Orlando. 'But it's only 5.30pm!' he said sounding alarmed. 'So!' I retorted with a chuckle and continued, 'Sleep whenever and wherever you can to continually refresh yourself when you're tired,' Aunty Kitty told me. And, I'm going to adopt this practice,' I chuckled. 'What you mean if you're at a Bus Stop – you're going to have a snooze!' he teased. 'Very funny Orlando,' I said and made myself comfortable on the settee with the cushions. Aunty Kitty's advice reminded me of the Buddhist proverb: 'Eat when you're hungry. Drink when you're thirsty. Sleep when you're tired'.

* * *

Thu 12th Oct '00

2.30pm: the seminar of Sociology of Race and Racism stirred up anger. Most Students expressed that legislation protects black people?! I thought these ideas are ludicrous! 'Legislation and Policies don't protect people!' I stood up and retorted, 'Legislations or Policies don't change our attitudes.' 'How many people have been murdered via racist attacks and continue to be with 'Legislation and Policies' in place?' I challenged. There was no response. This was the first time that I'd spoken out with so many 'opposing' my ideas and I didn't feel scared, or worried about their thoughts. I didn't like feeling angry, or being in opposition, but my liberation was needed, and my antagonism was calmed.

* * *

Fri 13th Oct '00

9.30am: rang Lank's Hospital to cancel Out-Patients appointment. I'm free from 'illness' and able to 'maintain daily activities' etc. (I think this is what's known as 'Self Management').

* * *

Sat 14th Oct '00

11am: at Orlando's. 'I had an 'outburst' on Thursday at University,' I informed him with a sense of pride. 'Did you? What happened?' Orlando asked with interest. Well, Students were suggesting that Legislation and Policies 'protect' black people, and I thought 'What nonsense,' and shouted, 'How many people have been murdered via racist attacks and continue to be even with 'Legislation and Policies' in place? Legislation or Policies don't change our attitudes'. Even though most of the students opposed this idea – I didn't feel scared or worried about their thoughts. It was as though the words – the idea wasn't mine – they belong to someone else and they were the 'Truth',' I explained. 'Well, as far as I know, this happens when we trust what we are thinking and doing. We speak without restriction or fear. Well done to you!' he complimented. 'Oh. I wondered if I was being 'Narrow-minded' or 'Ignorant',' I quizzed. 'I don't think so, Beautiful. Sometimes we 'just know' and it's 'self-evident'. Students often get so absorbed in text – they don't observe – they don't experience what 'Life' is presenting us with – the all too simple 'evidence'. All we've got to do is 'look – use our eyes!' He laughed and I joined him.

* * *

Sun 15th Oct '00

8.30am: woke up thinking about the idea of Meditation. 'Sweetheart. I'm going to try Meditation, tomorrow at the Buddhist Centre. Apparently, it reduces emotional distress as it increases serotonin production which influences mood and behaviour,' I asserted. 'Beautiful, I didn't know you were feeling distressed. What's the matter?' he asked with concern. 'Nothing really, just that I sometimes feel overwhelmed by the information given at University. So many injustices and so much suffering in the world. And, now I'm beginning to understand the way the political system works – the enormity of the injustices and inhumane way of living... Well, sometimes it's a bit too much to realise,' I sighed. 'Yeah, I understand – it can be overwhelming. Good idea to try Meditation. It might help you cultivate relaxation and peace with yourself. Then such realisations needn't overwhelm. You'll do your part and leave the rest in the hands of the universe!' he chuckled. 'Coming with me?' I asked. 'Naw. I tried Meditation a few years ago. Ummm – Daaa – Ummm!' he droned with a chuckle and continued, 'Not for me. My Meditation is painting.'

* * *

Mon 16th Oct '00

1pm: Meditating at the Buddhist Centre.

2pm: 'Are there any questions from the beginners regarding this Meditation session? The Dharma Chari (person leading the Meditation) asked. 'Yes. I thought Meditation was supposed to reduce emotional distress, but mine' has increased,' I nervously chuckled. 'This can happen. It's because we have unconscious thoughts in our minds – in our subconscious. So, when we quieten our thoughts we are surprised to realise that more are there, and our thoughts appear hectic. But as we realise the insignificance of many thoughts – that are usually based in the past or future – our mental busyness decreases, and we become calm,' he advised.

6pm: IA meeting.

* * *

Sat 21st Oct '00

7.30am: at Orlando's.

10.30am: in Battersea Park with Orlando. As we walked pass a children's play area my thoughts were directed to my childhood. 'It's weird, but everything that I'm seeing and thinking now – feels familiar.' 'What do you mean?' Orlando asked with a puzzled expression. 'Well, all that I think and see now – I already realised when I was six years old.' 'Like what?' he questioned. 'Like, the actions of adults, they seemed to defend a world that wasn't right, and they still do. It didn't make sense people were going hungry and we were able to throw food in the bin. 'Eat your dinner – people are starving in the world', Mum would say when I couldn't eat all my dinner. It didn't make sense that just because people were adults – that they should have the authority to advise on 'everything' and override children's views. 'Do as I say – not as I do', adults would sternly advise when their actions didn't follow their advice. It didn't make sense that they thought a lot of the 'wrongs' could be made 'right' through 'education'. 'You need to get a 'good education' and then you'll get a 'good' job and be happy', they (everyone) stated. And, all this still doesn't make sense to me,' I explained. 'You think you were a Prodigy Child!' he halfheartedly mocked. 'No you do!' I laughed – letting go of his hand and running off. 'Catch me if you can and I'll do dinner later,' I teased and he chased me. As we left the park I declared, 'I feel 'Childlike' when I'm with you. Like when I was a child and nothing was 'worrying' – I 'just' responded to the environment and circumstances. When events happened – I just did whatever was necessary – with little planning and little panic'. 'It's not 'Childlike' – its 'Life' evolving,' Orlando advised and continued, 'Welcome back to 'Reality.'

* * *

Tue 24th Oct '00

1.30 – 3.30pm: at City University to speak about the *Patients' Perspective* and I introduced for the first time the on-going challenges of having

321

radical surgery and its adverse affects (tiredness, leakage, sore skin). By the end of the talk the atmosphere felt tense – I asked the familiar question, 'Are there any questions?' 'You've focused on the negative aspects of the surgery,' one student commented. 'Experience is what-ever we make it. I've highlighted some of the problems and challenges, for you to be aware that they exist, and to be thinking about possible solutions or ways to alleviate them. As nurses you might like to assist improving patients' Wellbeing and care,' I calmly offered. I left the talk wondering where this response came from. Not from 'me', and it felt like the 'Truth' – similar to the 'outburst' at University – in opposition – but no fear.

5.30pm: RAC Society meeting.

* * *

Thu 26th Oct '00

8.30am: leaving for University. Today is the 'Deadline' to register the RAC Society – we need six people to sign up by 5pm!

3pm: got our necessary six people to sign up!

* * *

Wed 1st Nov '00

4pm: Tennis with Karen. 'Sam we've been playing Tennis for seven weeks, jogging twice a week and I've been eating healthier. I feel like I've got a new body and I'm not taking any medication! And, I'm a different person – not as moody! Never realised how much our lifestyle and habits influence our health. Thanks for encouraging me, Sam,' she said sincerely. 'Well, I'm glad your health is improving, because your game isn't – I'm still winning all our matches!' I joked and she laughed.

7.30pm: visited Grandma – she's seventy-four today. 'Hello – Hello,' Grandma greeted looking and sounding very pleased to see me and Orlando. I immediately began to sing 'Happy Birthday' and Orlando joined me. I gave Grandma her gift. 'Oh, 'it's a nice dress',' she said holding it up against her body. 'It look lek sim-ting fa a queen,' she chuckled. 'You look like a queen to me,' Orlando complimented and hugged Grandma. She nervously giggled and said, 'You-a-nice man. You should marry him, Samantha.' 'Yes, you should!' Orlando laughed. 'Me naw mek joke,' Grandma stated. 'Let's play some music,' I invited, changing the subject. I played Grandma's favourite tune – Arrow's song 'Hot – Hot – Hot', and the three of us sung and danced.

* * *

Sat 4th Nov '00

9.30am: at Orlando's. We're getting ready to attend Stoma Care Open Day.

8.30pm: at Orlando's. 'Gosh, what an interesting day. I understand more about the challenges of having a stoma. Preventing leaks, concerns about access to public toilets, remedying sore skin, and keeping the whole affair – the bag as discreet as possible! Beautiful – you're even more 'Beautiful' today. What I want to know is 'how – do – you – do – it?' Orlando complimented and stressed. 'Do what?' I asked. 'How do you keep smiling, help others, study and remain well,' he exclaimed. 'Oh, Orlando, it's simple. I listen and learn from others who have a stoma – take supplements – and accept my limitations! The greatest thing is that the physical doesn't have to hinder 'Living'. 'Life' finds solutions to all problems – 'Life' finds a way to 'Live' – no matter what it's presented with,' I chuckled.

* * *

Thu 9th Nov '00

4.30pm: attended Board of Study meeting – to fulfil Student Representative role.

* * *

Fri 10th Nov '00

3.30pm: at Orlando's. 'It's been two years since I had the operation,' I sighed sadly as I washed up the dishes. Orlando walked over to me, turned me around, and hugged me. 'Everything happens for a reason – you know that,' he comforted. I started crying and sobbed, 'I know. Just feels a bit sad today, as I remember the event.' He made eye contact. 'You – are – amazing, and all emotions need honouring,' he assured. We hugged for a spell, and some of my sadness was relieved. 'Better finish these dishes. They won't wash themselves!' I chuckled as I wiped away the tears. 'Yeah – you better,' he laughed.

* * *

Sat 11th Nov '00

8.30am: at Orlando's in Study writing article for IA.

* * *

Thu 16th Nov '00

7pm: met with Karen at restaurant. 'My mind's been racing. I just can't seem to relax – always thinking about something, and I'm finding it difficult to sleep,' Karen informed. 'I started Meditating about a month ago, and it's helped my racing mind. Why don't you try it? We could go for a Lunchtime Meditation at Buddhist Centre, tomorrow,' I invited. 'Not sure... 'Meditation' and 'Buddhist' sounds a bit 'Hippy-ish',' she teased. 'Yeah – power to the people and to a relaxed mind,' I joked and continued, 'Try it – it might work for you.'

* * *

Fri 17th Nov '00

2pm: finished Meditating at Buddhist Centre. 'Gosh Sam, I feel so relaxed. It was difficult at first – thoughts seemed to run riot! But then, as I focused on my breathing the thoughts seemed to disappear,' Karen calmly explained.

5pm: at Orlando's.

* * *

Sun 19th Nov '00

8.30am: 'Morning, Sweetheart. I'm meeting Sharaz later for lunch,' I yawned. 'Yeah, I remember,' he replied.

1pm: met Sharaz for lunch. 'Sam I've been diagnosed with having Arthritis! Can you believe it? That's why I've been in so much pain,' she whined. 'Oh. I understand that dehydration and a lack of oils influence Arthritis. Perhaps, you can start drinking more water and drizzle salads with oils – like Olive, Sunflower and Flax?... And, drinking alcohol and fried foods apparently don't help – they dehydrate,' I advised. 'Ummm. Not sure,' she moaned.

* * *

Thu 23rd Nov '00

5pm: met with Karen. 'I've been Meditating and I feel calmer, my mind is clearer, and I can make decisions – without doubt!... We can do so much for ourselves. It's amazing the benefits of adopting a healthier lifestyle. Why do so many of us remain unwell? We needn't,' Karen suggested. 'Yeah, I know,' I agreed.

* * *

Fri 24th Nov '00

8.30pm: at Orlando's.

* * *

Sun 26th Nov '00

12.30pm: myself and Orlando arrive at station to meet Sidiki, Doreen and Mark to travel to Dad's (it's his Birthday today).

2.30pm: 'Happy Birthday Dad,' we all yelled as he opened the door and we piled in. 'Oh, Tank you, Tank you, and stop mek so much noise,' he smiled and grumbled at the same time. Orlando greeted Dad, 'Happy Birthday, Mr. Shakes,' and handed him a bottle of champagne. 'Oh, Tanks,' Dad replied with a glorious smile, as he ushered us in. 'Da dina ready,' he informed. 'So, Mr. Shakes. Another year – how was your last one?' Orlando chatted as we ate. 'Well, nut a ting change. Me jus ploddin un – trying fee mek ends meet,' he moaned. 'Oh,' Orlando uttered. 'You dun well. You 'ave a gud job and a house – ent – it?' Dad continued. 'Yeah, I suppose I do,' Orlando replied. 'An ya Mum and Dad dun well. You falla dem footsteps – hope dese lot na falla mine. Dey will be doomed!' Dad continued with a half hearted chuckle. 'Mr. Shakes, 'doing well' isn't just about houses and jobs – you have four wonderful children who you care for – being a Dad is 'doing well' and important,' Orlando stated.

* * *

Fri 1st Dec '00

7pm: at restaurant with Sharaz. 'The pain from this Arthritis is getting worse. I've been put on more medication that isn't working. They don't know what they're doing,' she exclaimed. 'Have you been drinking more water and oils?' I asked. 'No Sam. It can't be that simple – it's a condition. If it was as simple as 'a lack of water and oils' – none of us would have Arthritis! And, before you ask – I'm still drinking alcohol – I've got to have some enjoyment,' she retorted. I didn't say anything – I'd said enough, but felt sad that Sharaz didn't seem able to see 'the alternative'. Then I remembered what 'Life' told me, when I visited Sally in hospital. That 'what was important was that I'd offered an alternative approach… And, that I had no control over her actions'.

10.30pm: at Orlando's. 'I find it mind boggling how we respond. Some of us are able to take responsibility – whist others aren't,' I mumbled. 'What you on about?' Orlando quizzed. 'I'm thinking about Karen's and Sharaz's differing response to their 'long-term health condition'. 'Prime examples of 'internal' and 'external' Locus of Control,' I smiled. 'Locus of Control? What's that?' Orlando asked. 'Locus of Control' refers to how people believe they can control events that affect them. People with 'internal' Locus of Control believe that events result from their own behaviour. People with 'external' Locus of Control believe that others, or fate, determine their reality,' I explained and continued, 'I feel sad and angry when people won't take responsibility. They won't change their lifestyle or habits – know medication isn't working – suffer – and blame the medics! What have we become!' I laughed. 'External Locus!' He laughed. Then adopted a serious tone, 'Beautiful, see another perspective. Some of us are more comfortable being 'unwell'

– being 'well' would mean greater insight to a harsh reality. We're all seeking pleasure, and some of us fleeing from memories of unbearable pain,' he reminded.

* * *

Fri 10th Dec '00

7.30pm: at Orlando's.

* * *

Sat 11th Dec '00

9.30am: in the garden. 'Orlando! The Spinach and Lettuce seeds have started growing!' I shrieked. 'Yep! They don't take long,' he informed. 'I'm going draw 'the development,' I said. 'The development?' What do you mean?' he quizzed. 'I'm going to sketch every four weeks – showing the stages of growth,' I explained and left to retrieve some paper, and a pencil from the Study.

11.40pm: finished sketching.

* * *

Sun 16th Dec '00

Spent the weekend at Orlando's – again!

* * *

Thu 21st Dec '00

8.30am: at Orlando's. 'Morning Beautiful. What time is the appointment you've got with the hospital, later?' Orlando asked in a blasé tone. '3.25pm. Why?' I replied. 'Well I need to know what time to get ready,' he answered. 'Oh, Sweetheart, you don't need to come – it's very boring. I'm only going because I haven't seen Mr. Bows for a long-time – really just to catch-up,' I informed feeling a bit nervous. 'Yeah, well I'm going with you to be bored as well,' he adamantly stated.

3.25pm: 'Hi, Samantha,' Mr. Bows greeted. 'And, who's this?' he questioned, looking at Orlando. 'Oh, this is my friend, Orlando. Orlando, this is Mr. Bows,' I replied. 'Hi, Mr. Bows. I'm not just her friend – I'm going to be her fiancé soon,' he said with a chuckle. 'Are you?' I laughed. 'Oh, lovely,' Mr. Bows said with excitement and asked, 'Right – what's been happening?' 'Well, nothing and everything! I've not had a flare-up for months – even at the most stressful times. I've been eating healthily – with encouragement from Orlando – Thanks Orlando. And exercising, relaxing, and enjoying!' I reported. 'Sounds great. Is she telling the truth – Orlando? She used to lie to us – hoping to keep away, you know!' Mr. Bows laughed. 'Sam, you look really well. Keep doing what you're doing,' he advised and continued, 'See you in six months time.'

As we left the hospital, Orlando commented, 'I'm glad I came. I wondered if you needed more support from the medics, but you seem out of place in 'Out-Patients'.' 'Yeah, well it's been sometime since I felt like a 'Patient',' I replied.

* * *

Fri 22nd Dec '00

10.25am: out shopping with Orlando for Christmas presents. It was hectic and we couldn't decide what to buy. 'Sam, do you think my Mum will like this scarf?' Orlando asked. 'I don't know. I thought you said she liked perfume,' I abruptly replied. 'I wish you'd make a decision,' he retorted. 'Well, you should know if she'd like it – she's your Mum!' I snapped. There was a silence and I realised that this was our first argument! We travelled home to Orlando's – in silence. When we arrived, Orlando stood in the porch and chuckled, 'Let's not do that again.' 'What?' I questioned in a stern tone. 'Christmas shopping,' he explained. 'Okay. Not until next year!' I joked and we kissed. 'It was horrible arguing with you and for the sake of buying Christmas presents! We're not Christians and neither are the people we've bought presents for,' he chuckled. 'I know! Crazy how we 'follow procedure'!' I laughed.

* * *

Sun 24th Dec '00

8.30am: Christmas Eve (been at Orlando's since last Thursday!).

12.30pm: arrived at Orlando's parents. 'Sam this is for you,' Orlando's Mum said smiling, handing me a small wrapped box. 'Oh, Thank you,' I said and gave her a kiss. 'Hope my name's on it – it's from me as well!' Orlando's Dad blurted. 'Hush, Raphael. When did you become so into Christmas?!' Orlando's Mum quizzed with a chuckle. 'When you took my credit card!' he playfully retorted.

3pm: dining. 'So you've been married for forty-five years – how?' I asked in awe. 'I go deaf when she talks,' Orlando's Dad joked, roaring with laughter. 'And, I don't take what he says too seriously,' Orlando's Mum chuckled and continued in a serious tone. 'Give' and 'Take'... 'Yeah too 'Right – I 'Give' – she 'Takes',' Orlando's Dad interrupted with a chuckle. Orlando's Mum continued, 'It's a Friendship – a Partnership – and we never give up on each other,' she concluded.

9.30pm: arrived at Orlando's. Right, I'm going to call a taxi,' I said, gathering the presents I'd bought for the family. 'Here's your gift,'

Orlando said handing me a parcel. 'And here's yours. Hope you like them,' I said. I'd bought him a few plain Mandalas (cosmic diagrams that reminds us of our relation to the infinite – the world that extends both beyond and within our bodies and minds).

* * *

Mon 25th Dec '00

11am: Christmas Day. Myself, Mum, Sidiki, Doreen and Mark gathered in the lounge and I distributed the presents from under the tree. 'Oh, that's lovely!' Sidiki remarked when I opened the gift Orlando had given me. It was the scarf he'd asked if his Mum would have liked whilst we were out shopping (and I now felt guilty snapping at him)! It was striking – made with cream silk and hand embroidered with yellow and orange birds in flight. I then opened the gift Orlando's Mum had given – I was dumbfounded. It wasn't the gift in itself that had me speechless, but the effort that had been made. It was a pair of Handmade Silver Earrings. They were Butterflies and their wings contained the gemstones Moonstone and Amber. There was a note inside the box that read:

Created for Sam.

Butterflies for your sense of Freedom

Moonstone for your glowing appearance in White

Amber suited for the Aquarian.

With Love from

Caterina and Raphael Mancini

Christmas 2000

I love Butterflies – I feel calm wearing white – and Amber was one of my Birthstones! This gift was very personal and I sensed that a lot of Love had gone into creating it.

* * *

Tue 26th Dec '00

9.30am: Boxing Day. Called Orlando. 'Thanks for my beautiful scarf and sorry for snapping!' I cheerfully greeted. 'Apology accepted! And, Thank You for the Mandala's. I'm going to enjoy colouring them,' he replied.

* * *

Wed 27th Dec '00

7pm: at Orlando's. 'I've been spending more time at your home than mine,' I shared with Orlando. 'Yeah, you've almost moved in – I'm going to start charging you rent!' he joked.

* * *

Sat 30th Dec '00

11.30am: 'Right. I'm leaving before the rent is due! I've been here since Wednesday. My family's going to think I've moved out!' I chuckled. 'Why don't you?' Orlando whispered. I ignored his suggestion – unsure how to answer – and shocked by the idea.

* * *

Sun 31st Dec '00

9.30am: at home. 'What's everyone up to later?' Sidiki asked as we prepared breakfast. 'I'm going to Orlando's. We're going to see the New Year in alone,' I informed.

7.30pm: a car horn blew outside. It was the cab I'd ordered to take me to Orlando's. 'Hope you all see the 'New Year' in as you wish,' I said, kissing each family member – and left.

11.50pm: at Orlando's. 'Will you be a Lifetime Friend and stay with me?' Orlando asked hugging my waist. 'Sounds like a lot of commit-ment to me,' I joked. 'What, more than our commitment to 'Life',' he laughed gazing in my eyes. 'Ummm. I guess not,' I smiled and kissed him. He pulled me closer to him. 'A Lifetime Friend... And stay with you,' I whispered. 'Will you be a Lifetime Friend and stay with me?' I asked with a chuckle. 'Only if you keep washing up,' he laughed. 'And, I'll only be a Lifetime Friend if you keep cooking me delicious meals,' I negotiated with a smile. A chiming clock and cheers by neighbours signified that the 'New Year' had started. 'Yeah! This is exactly how I wanted our 'New Year' to start. 'Me and you in our home and you agreeing to be a Lifetime friend,' he bellowed, lifting me up and spinning me around. 'I haven't agreed to anything!' I contended with shrieks of laughter. 'Oh, yes you have! Because I'm never going to stop cooking you delicious meals!' he declared and placed a CD in the player. Sade's 'I Couldn't Love You More' started playing and he serenaded me...

> *'I wouldn't want to lay or ever love with another*
> *If everyone in the world could give me what I wanted*
> *I wouldn't want for more than I have*
> *I couldn't love you more if I tried.'*

We drank champagne and danced till 3.30am. I felt – Content – Loved – Relaxed. I'd committed myself to 'Love' – I'd committed myself to 'Live' – I'd allowed 'Life to Take Control'.

Afterword

I began a new relationship with Life after experiencing disease and undergoing radical surgery. It became important to understand how my precious Life was placed in jeopardy, because I didn't want it to happen again! I was afraid of the pain and trauma – disease and surgery had put me off for life! So, I began searching for an 'alternative' – namely, Wellbeing. 'Wellbeing'... Living rather than existing.

When I began working in a London 'teaching' hospital, I started listening to peoples' stories regarding illness and disease. I heard accounts from patients and clinicians detailing failures of good health stemming from lifestyle and orthodox medical approaches.

During employment, I participated in a 'Self-Management' (freedom from illness and the ability to maintain community Life) course for people with 'Long-term health conditions'. I wanted to understand how to manage disease – and myself. Throughout the course, we shared coping strategies and adopted different activities that affected our health. Whilst, advice and support from others was useful, we became our most effective Counsellors, Doctors, Exercise Instructors, and Nutritionists, because we carried out the necessary reflection and changes. Appreciating Self-Management, I decided to become a Tutor to facilitate these programmes. Participants continually provided evidence that our diseases were a direct result of our behaviour, our environment, and our mental state. There was no 'chance' in disease or wellbeing – we created them.

It seemed natural to write this book, because my episodes of disease and wellbeing were so vividly recorded in my journals. The writing and reflections lead me to believe they needed revealing. My suffering and wellbeing weren't solely for my benefit – they were also for you!

Our Modern Society isn't always kind to Wellbeing. However, we can use what we have to encourage it. Small changes make a big difference. 'Wellbeing' is a 'Long-term health condition' that needs nurturing! I leave you to continue our experience.

Sam Shakes

Acknowledgements

For Terri Porrett:

The 'Stoma Care Nurse' who went beyond the 'call of duty'. The acknowledgement of dis-ease and assistant in the cure. You wore many hats in order to respond to my unrelenting needs, including that of a Counsellor, Employer, Self-Employment Advisor, Life Coach, and Writers Companion! Eleven years later and you're still responding to my needs and wearing all those hats! Thank you. This contribution is for you, you, you, you, and you!

There is no one person who is more significant than any other in these 'acknowledgements'. So, I've mentioned people in alphabetical order, by surname.

Hakim Adi you were a great Lecturer, and continue to offer guidance and encouragement after University. Thank you for being a great inspiration and helping me realise the 'nonsense!'

Adwoa Asantewaa for over seventeen years, you have made 'difficult' – 'easy', turned 'despair' into 'hope' and 'sadness' into 'joy'. Whenever I have misunderstandings with the way I'm relating in this world – you offer clarification and relief. I have no doubt that you are an Earth Angel. Great Blessings that you chose to guide me – I survive better with you. XX

Carole Barclay a Lifetime Friend met at university. We don't speak or see each other 'often', but then Lifetime Friends don't need to – the heart keeps us connected. Thank you for being one of the great tools when the stoma was winning battle! We continue to met. XX

Samuel Daley I have learnt so much from you. Fundamentally, you shared 'Truth' that 'Life' isn't about 'logic' – but 'Love'. What I've experienced with you is such that is beyond words…

Joan Deitch you answered all my queries regarding publishing, shared contacts and offered encouraging words that motivated.

Gaston Ebua you shared valuable reflections, time, and encouragement. Thank you for responding to my requests (spurred by my inquisitive nature!), and for being honest.

ACKNOWLEDGEMENTS

Bonny Gonsalves you have been with me since the day I was born and assisted at me in significant times throughout my Life. Thus, it's of 'no surprise' that you should have been with me when I was taken through the double doors marked 'Theatre – Only Patients and Staff Beyond This Point'. My Life continues ticking with you. XX.

Caswell Hixon 'Lanks' (departed this physical existence in August 2008) I've missed your response to this contribution! Thank You for supporting me in my past endeavours, and for making me feel useful! I'm glad we met – you remain in my heart.

Nadia Ismail after seven years you spurred me to complete this contribution – how did you do it?! Not only did you motivate me to write – you took part! Reading all Episodes, critiquing, sharing your responses, and encouraging. We Thank You!

Michael Kelly you encouraged and supported me in my first attempts at sharing some of these experiences and ideas. You told me in 2001 that I would one day make a contribution – here it is! Thank you for having faith that it would happen.

Richard Kelly you changed my scrappy manuscript and journal into a book and were so much more that a Designer and Typesetter. You worked as hard as me to make the production of this work 'right'! Thanks for all the sleepless nights and great presentation!

Mary Komur you are always willing to assist and are a fine display of 'how to do Life'. Any woes – you keep going! Giving up doesn't seem to be an option for you! You have inspired me in the past and continue to do so.

Banke Oke you took the time to read, analyse, and assist in making decisions. Without a doubt you were very much part of the driving force behind this contribution. Your passion and support helped keep me going! Thank you for taking the time, your valued support, and for being such a wonderful person. XX

Tycho Photiou your wisdom, generosity, and understanding stimulated invaluable Lifetime changes. You offered support and encouraged me to 'Write' by example!

Sharon Remy you always take an interest in our family adventures and Life. Thank you for years of support and reading this contribution!

Glasford Rock (departed this physical existence in September 2007) you were always encouraging and keen to teach from me from the day I was born! I'm glad we 'chanced the time' for you to read the earlier version this contribution. I'll miss your response to the complete work – as I miss you.

Sharon Rodney you reacted with enthusiasm to this contribution, took the time to read it, and share your thoughts – you are a 'Lifetime Friend'.

David Savo you are one of the few reasons that I'm so glad I studied at Middlesex! Our Friendship began and our trip to Kenya told me that we were going to last forever?! You are a magnificent person – your humility tells me so. Thank you for listening, sharing your wisdom and still being around!

Desreen Shakes you have shared knowledge of relationships that have helped shape the way I relate with world and others. Thank you for listening to parts of this contribution and offering help.

Ensign Shakes you have been the most influential Being in my current existence. I have experienced a range of emotions and many lessons through our relationship that have assisted me to understand this valuable Life – Thank You.

Icina Shakes you shared your ideas and this contribution with others, and never ceased to support in many ways – Thank You.

Marcus Shakes you listened to the draft writings of this story, introduced me to inspiring personalities to promote motivation, and shared my excitement regarding this contribution. Your advice about 'How to do Business' was extremely valuable. XX.

Sadari Shakes you offered crucial feedback that helped inform the way I conveyed 'our' Stories and Experiences in this contribution – Thank You.

Cicily Symmonds (departed this physical existence in September 1998) you were a Friend and Counsellor. I'll miss your thoughts on this contribution (you 'Loved' reading!) – and I miss you.

Fabian Tompsett you assured me that I could produce this without any 'Self-Publishing Business Support'. Thanks for 'saving' me and being a great 'Publishing Advisor!

Anna Tatton your commitment to humanity and caring inspires me. And our Friendship increases my understanding of Love. Thank You.

Emma Triggs we met via our Chronic Diseases! Years later we are still meeting and managing! You have been a great friend, a great advisor and you are a wonderful person – I'm glad we met.

To everyone who found the time to read and share their opinions regarding this story. I Thank All of You for showing me that I wasn't writing for 'writing sake', but for the sake of 'our Lives'.

Inspirational Books

I read the following and found them useful:

Chopra, Deepak, *Ageless Body – Timeless Mind*, Rider, 1993.

Grant, Doris and Joice, Jean, *Food Combining for Health: Don't mix foods that fight*, Thorsons, 1984.

Hay, Louise, *You Can Heal your Life*, Eden Grove Editions, 1984.

Holder, Jackee, *Soul Purpose*, Piatkus, 1999.

Jeffers, Susan, *Feel the Fear and Do It Anyway*, Century Hutchinson Ltd, 1987.

Jensen, Bernard, *Tissue Cleansing through bowel management*, Bernard Jensen Publisher, 1981.

Kloss Jethro, *Back to Eden (58th Edition)*, Back to Eden Publishing Co., 1997.

Kubler-Ross, Elisabeth, *On Death and Dying*, Travistock Publishers, 1970.

Photiou, Tycho, *Inspirational Thoughts, Volume One*, Ocean Books, 1997.

Photiou, Tycho, *You are what you think*, Ocean Books, 1998.

Photiou, Tycho, *You Really Are Responsible*, Ocean Books, 1998.

Redfield, James, *The Celestine Prophecy*, Bantam Books, 1994.

Vanzant, Iyanla, *Acts of Faith: Daily Meditations for People of Color*, Simon and Schuster, 1993.